SCIENCE: MEN, METHODS, GOALS

A Reader: Methods of Physical Science

SCIENCE: MEN, METHODS, GOALS

A Reader: Methods of Physical Science

Edited by
BORUCH A. BRODY
Massachusetts Institute of Technology

NICHOLAS CAPALDI
The City University of New York

W. A. Benjamin, Inc.
New York   1968   Amsterdam

Science: *Men, Methods, Goals*

The final manuscript was put into production on February 23, 1968; this volume was published on September 30, 1968

W.A. BENJAMIN, INC.
New York, New York 10016   12345K321098

PREFACE

Science students are often so preoccupied with technical scientific work that they have little time left for reflection on the nature, methods, and goals of the scientific enterprise. As a result, even very sophisticated students do not always comprehend the ramifications of scientific procedures. The publication of this anthology is an attempt to help correct this situation by making available some of the most important philosophical statements about these issues, and thus enabling science students to deepen their understanding of the enterprise of science.

It is hoped that this material will also be of interest to philosophy students who are just beginning their study of the philosophy of science and to students in science courses for the nonscientist.

Because of the audience for which this book is written, we have avoided technical material that presupposes an extensive background in science, philosophy, or logic. Despite this limitation, we believe that the readings represent many of the major views about the methodology of the physical sciences.

The introductions are more detailed than usual, partly because we feel that the selections still presuppose concepts and information with which the student may not be familiar, and partly because we hope that these introductions will make it possible for the interested student to go through the selections without the aid of a teacher.

The initial version of the first two sections was prepared by Professor Capaldi while the initial version of the last section was prepared by Professor Brody. We are both responsible, however, for the final version of the whole text.

We would like to thank Professor Peter Caws (City University of New York) for encouraging us to proceed with this anthology; Dr. Charles Sherover (Hunter College) and the staff of Educational Resources Corporation for editorial and clerical assistance in producing the manuscript of this book; and the staff of W.A. Benjamin, Inc. for their encouragement and aid. As usual, we are indebted to our wives in more ways than could be mentioned here. Finally, in dedicating this book to our parents, we merely acknowledge, but do not begin to repay, our extensive debts to them.

Boruch A. Brody
Nicholas Capaldi

Cambridge, Massachusetts
New York, New York
June 1968

CONTENTS

Preface   v

I. The Nature of Scientific Theory   1

    Introduction   3

    Reductionism   13
        Mach: The Economy of Physical Theory.   15
        Rankine: Abstractive and Hypothetical Theories . .   23
        Mach: Explanation in Physics   29

    Realism   35
        Eddington: The Nature of the Physical World. . .   37
        Heisenberg: Planck's Quantum Theory and the
            Philosophical Problems of Atomic Physics . . .   45
        Meyerson: Identity and Reality   59

    Instrumentalism   71
        Copernicus: The Role of Hypotheses   73
        Newton: On Hypotheses   76
        Duhem: The Aim and Structure of Physical Theory.   80

II. The Discovery and Justification of Scientific Theories . .   89

    Introduction   91

    The Classical Conception.   97
        Herschel: Scientific Method   99
        Newton: Rules of Reasoning. 115

    Problems of the Classical Conception 121
        Mill: On Induction 123
        Whewell: On Induction 132

Reformulation of the Classical Conception. 141
    Peirce: Retroduction and Genius 143
    Hanson: The Logic of Discovery 150
    Maxwell: The Role of Models in Physics. 163
    Duhem: Experiment in Physics 171
    Popper: Conjectures and Refutations 178

III. Science and Mathematics 201

Introduction 203

Measurement. 223
    Stevens: On the Theory of Scales of Measurement. 225
    Duhem: Quantity and Quality 234

Arithmetic 249
    Mill: Arithmetic as an Empirical Science. 251
    Poincaré: Intuition in Mathematics 266
    Hempel: On the Nature of Mathematical Truth . . . 276

Geometry. 295
    Kant: Geometry as the *A Priori* Science of Space . . 297
    Poincaré: Conventionalism in Geometry 313
    Reichenbach: The Nature of Geometry 325

Suggestions for Further Reading 341

PART I

THE NATURE OF SCIENTIFIC THEORY

INTRODUCTION

Physical science is concerned with the discovery, classification, and explanation of the facts of the physical world. It is an ongoing enterprise, an enterprise with a past, a present, and a future. Hence, any attempt to characterize its specific methodology must take into account at once the history of science and its present practice, as well as the changes that the future may bring. Nevertheless, there are distinguishing characteristics of the methodology of physical science.

One of the most important characteristics of physical science is its concern with laws as opposed to specific items of information. To be sure, scientists will collect individual items of information, such as the boiling point of selected liquids or the specific gravity of solids. But this information is not always discovered and collected haphazardly. As soon as it is collected it is classified. Moreover, the collection and classification are guided by the hope of fitting the individual items of information into the framework of general laws. The general laws, in turn, will explain the individual items of information.

For example, research reveals that individual pieces of copper conduct electricity, that individual pieces of silver conduct electricity, that individual pieces of platinum conduct electricity, and so forth. From these observations, we may generalize that all pieces of copper conduct electricity, and then that all metals conduct electricity. Finally, we may seek to explain in even more general terms why metals conduct electricity. Thus we may conclude that physical science is concerned with general laws.

The distinction between individual items of information such as "this piece of copper conducts electricity" and general laws such as "all metals conduct electricity" is an important one. Let us try to make clear precisely what distinguishes the two kinds of statements. First,

3

although both kinds of statements are taken to be true, one statement refers to a particular thing, this piece of copper, whereas the other statement, the law, refers to every kind of thing named. Laws must be universal statements, statements of the form "all x's are such that . . ." For example, our law is "all x's are such that if x is a metal then x conducts electricity." However, this first distinction is not sufficient. There are universal statements that are not considered to be laws. An example is the statement "all of the books in my library are paperbacks." This second kind of universal statement is considered to be accidental.

What distinguishes an accidental universal from a law or a nonaccidental universal? Accidental universals such as "all of the books in my library are paperbacks" are restricted in both time and space. The statement of the accidental universal is not meant to imply that there are no hardcover books outside of my library (and is therefore restricted in space), nor is it meant to imply that there were not any or that there will not be any (and is therefore restricted in time). Presumably, in the case of a law such as "all metals conduct electricity" there are no limitations of space and time. Metals conduct electricity wherever they are, and the law states that this state of affairs has not and will not change in the course of time. Therefore, laws may be considered to be nonaccidental universal statements.

The foregoing view actually needs a great deal of qualification, because actual scientific usage is a little looser than our definition. Scientists frequently talk about laws that are in fact accidental universals or simply definitions whose practical significance has elevated them to a special status. The term "law" is frequently honorific. There are additional qualifications. However, the definition of "law" that we have given is sufficient in its present form for our purposes.

When we examine the general laws that are actually operative in physical science, we must mark a further distinction. Not all laws are of the same type. We already had an inkling of this distinction when we decided that even the law "all metals conduct electricity" might be explained in terms of something more general.

A further examination of the language of science reveals that many laws are couched in theoretical terms. Thus, laws may use terms, such as "electron" or "field," that do not refer to normally observable things. The same thing is true of dispositional terms, such as "magnetic"; mathematical terms, such as "psi-function"; and expressions referring to idealizations, such as "perfect vacuum."

For these reasons, the laws of physical science may be broadly divided into two classes: laws and theories. A *law,* per se, may be described as an empirical generalization that we accept as true. Each of the nonformal terms in a law, that is, excluding such terms as "and," refers to a single thing, property, process, etc., that is observable under specified experimental conditions. A *theory,* on the other hand, is not an empirical generalization. It contains theoretical terms such as "electron." These theoretical terms do not refer to things, properties, or processes that are directly observable. Theoretical terms, as we shall see later, are correlated with many observations.

The presence of theoretical terms is a crucial difference between theories and laws. It is because of such terms that theories cannot be put to direct tests in the way that laws can. This accounts for the fact that individual laws may survive when one theory is discarded and replaced by another.

Let us exemplify this distinction. The following statement is *Boyle's law:* At a constant temperature, the volume of a given quantity of any gas is inversely proportional to the pressure of the gas. This law is explained in terms of a theory of perfect gases. The *theory of perfect or ideal gases* postulates that an ideal gas would consist of perfectly elastic molecules. Moreover, it is assumed that the volume occupied by the actual molecules and the forces of attraction between them is zero or negligible.

If we examine Boyle's law, we find that the terms refer to what is observable under specified experimental conditions. We can, for example, actually measure and therefore see the pressure of a gas. If we examine the theory of perfect gases, we realize that we cannot isolate a molecule in order to see if it is perfectly elastic. Boyle's law, however, can be directly tested. We could disprove the law by finding a gas that did not behave in the stated way under the appropriate circumstances. No such straightforward test exists for our theory about molecules.

In our discussion of theories, we shall have to refer to three different components. First, we shall note the presence of *observational laws* containing terms that refer directly to empirical or observational phenomena. We might say that the observational laws are not part of the theory but what the theory seeks to explain and predict. Second, there are the *underlying principles,* that is the principles containing theoretical terms that refer to entities or processes postulated by the theory. These entities and processes are not directly observable.

Third, and most important, there are *linking principles,* which serve to relate the theoretical terms in the underlying principles to the observational terms in the observational laws. The linking principles allow a theory to be tested. Other names for linking principles include bridge principles, coordinating definitions, operational definitions, semantic rules, correspondence rules, and rules of interpretation.

These three components may be illustrated with reference to the theory explaining Boyle's law. As you will recall, Boyle's law states that at a constant temperature, the volume of a given quantity of any gas is inversely proportional to the pressure of the gas. The observational terms in the law include "temperature" and "pressure," which refer to what we can observe by means of thermometers and gauges. The underlying principles include the existence of molecules whose random motion is expressible in terms of the laws of probability. The linking principles include two assumptions: (1) that the pressure of the gas is caused by the impact of the molecules; and (2) that the mean kinetic energy of the molecules remains as constant as the temperature.

It is important to note that the relationship of observational terms to theoretical terms is not one-to-one. We do not necessarily have one, and only one, linking principle for each theoretical term. Sometimes there is one; sometimes there are many; sometimes there is none. For example, there is a linking principle for "mean kinetic energy of the totality of molecules," but there is no linking principle for "kinetic energy of an individual molecule."

We might be tempted to ask at this point, why bother to use theories involving theoretical terms if they are so mysterious? Is it not contrary to the purpose of physical science to employ terms and concepts that do not refer to anything we can observe? Are not the things referred to by theoretical terms really mythical? The three views about the nature of theories in the physical sciences, namely, (a) *reductionism,* (b) *realism,* and (c) *instrumentalism,* are alternative answers to these questions.

(a) The thesis of *reductionism* is a thesis about the language of science. One version of this thesis is a claim about translation, namely, that all theoretical terms, such as the term "atom,"and all statements containing theoretical terms can be translated, in principle, into statements that refer only to commonly observable entities. The clearest statement of this thesis is to be found in the selections from Ernst Mach.

The first selection talks about translation into the terminology of everyday experience.

According to this view, theories are convenient summaries for a whole host of data. Instead of using immensely long descriptions, the physical scientist employs a shorthand substitute in the form of a theory. Nevertheless, the reductionist believes that the full description is in principle substitutable for the shorter theory. This function of a theory is exemplified in the second selection from Ernst Mach.

A second version of reductionism is a thesis about replacement. It begins by distinguishing two kinds of theories: the macroscopic and the microscopic. The former are exemplified by Newton's theory of gravitation and classical thermodynamics. These macroscopic theories are descriptions of relations that exist among objects perceived directly by the senses. They are not, strictly speaking, theories; they are merely very general empirical laws. Microscopic theories are exemplified by the molecular theory of gases and atomic theory. These theories are descriptions of relations that exist among hypothetical entities that cannot be perceived directly by the senses.

The distinction between macroscopic and microscopic theories is most clearly articulated in the selection from Rankine, who called the former "abstractive" and the latter "hypothetical" theories. Rankine recognized the instrumental value of hypothetical theories in furthering research. Nevertheless, he viewed them as temporary expedients in the development of abstractive theories, which were preferred because they were free from assumptions about mysterious entities and processes, closer to the world of observation, and more likely to unify the different branches of physics.

The reductionist thesis of Rankine is that science can develop abstractive theories that can replace the hypothetical theories currently used in science, and that when this program is carried through, the language of science will consist solely of observational terms.

There are three major difficulties with reductionism. First, no such translation or replacement has ever been carried out. To date, the thesis of reductionism is an ideal, not an accomplishment. Second, the translation thesis faces the difficulty that a theoretical statement is not correlated or linked with only one observational statement. We have already noted this point in regard to laws and theories. There are an indefinite (possibly infinite) number and variety of observational terms and statements related to any one theoretical statement. How then are we to carry through or complete the translation? The third difficulty with reductionism is that it cannot explain the various other functions performed by theories in the physical sciences, namely, explanation and suggestiveness. It is this third difficulty which leads to the alternative views of theories: realism and instrumentalism.

(b) *Realism* is the oldest of all views on the nature of scientific theories. A realist believes that theories are true or false descriptions of the real world. However, because physical scientists have had conflicting views on what is to be taken as real, there are several varieties of realism.

The first, and most radical, view of what is real holds that what is real is revealed to us only by theoretical terms. What we observe in the everyday world as tables that are "red" and "solid" are mere appearances; only the underlying structure of atoms and electrons is real. Thus, scientific theories present us with a deeper conception of reality and an understanding of how the world really is. This is the view of Arthur S. Eddington.

A second definition of what is real is in many ways more sophisticated. According to this view, the reality of the normally observable world is not denied, and only some theoretical terms are said to stand for something real. Theoretical terms are said to stand for something real if they occur in a highly confirmed law and if they stand for the state of a physical "system." This definition is exemplified in the selection from Werner Heisenberg and is specifically related to quantum theory. In quantum theory, the state of a system is specified in terms of certain abstract mathematical structures. We can then predict, given one state, what other states precede or follow. This state is said to be real. To be real, therefore, is to occupy a special place in the mathematical descriptions of the atomic physicist.

What all of the realists have in common is that they ascribe reality to theoretical entities because they view the purpose of theories in the physical sciences as a way of explaining the world. The great advances in the recent history of science have come with the introduction of microscopic theories, not macroscopic ones. An impressive number of diverse phenomena have been explained by the use of such theories. How could such theories explain the physical world unless theoretical entities were in some sense real? It would seem rather arbitrary to deny outright the reality of at least some theoretical entities. The importance of the explanatory function of theories and the success of theories in fulfilling this function is brought out in the selection from Emile Meyerson.

There are three major objections to the realist's position. First, critics of realism argue that no matter how much evidence the realist adduces for any of his theories, the evidence is always drawn from the world of everyday observation. Atomic theory may explain why a Geiger counter clicks at certain times and places, but all that we ever observe is the clicking of the Geiger counter. So how can we know about these theoretical entities? The second objection is that in the history of science we often find two incompatible theories to explain the same thing. For example, liquids are sometimes treated as if they were composed of separate particles and sometimes as if they were continuous media. Light is sometimes regarded as a wave and sometimes as a particle. If theories are a description of an underlying reality, how is this possible? Finally, if as is commonly agreed, no theory is ever final, does not this support the view that theories in the physical sciences are just useful rules of thumb?

(c) The *instrumentalist* views scientific theories in a twofold way. First, a theory symbolizes but does not describe what we already know from previous scientific investigation. Second, a theory is a technique for suggesting, inferring, or deriving new experiments from what we already know. A theory is thus a method or instrument for acquiring more information.

The first aspect of a theory, namely, its symbolic character, is described by Osiander in the selection from Copernicus. He claims that theories neither explain nor describe hidden realities. The emphasis is on the value of such theories for conveniently and simply ordering what we already know.

The second aspect of a theory, its suggestiveness for further research, is described by Newton. It is still not clear, however, whether Newton was really an instrumentalist. In his now famous discussion of hypotheses, Newton criticized the followers of Descartes who proposed theories (hypotheses) that could not be experimentally tested. Instead only hypotheses (theories) that followed from previous observations and that suggested new observations were to be taken seriously.

The most articulate and comprehensive description of instrumentalism is given in the selection from Pierre Duhem. He proposes that the aim of a theory in the physical sciences "is to become a natural classification, to establish among diverse experimental laws a logical coordination serving as a sort of image and reflection of the true order according to which the realities escaping us are organized. Also, we have said that on this condition theory will be fruitful and will suggest discoveries."

The instrumentalist view of theories avoids the problems of reductionism. Even if it were possible to translate a theory completely into observational language, nothing would be achieved. The actual experimental role of theories would not be influenced. In fact, the trouble with reductionism is that it draws our attention away from this vital role of theories. Second, the instrumentalist view of theories also avoids some of the problems of realism. By denying that theories are either true or false descriptions, the instrumentalist calls attention to the corrigible nature of theories. Theories are frequently discarded for better ones, that is, other theories that are more compact and suggestive. No theory can be accepted as finally true. More important, there is no reason why we cannot use two different theories at the same time.

The major difficulty with the instrumentalist view of theories in the physical sciences is that it fails to account for the explanatory power of theories. Many scientists believe that theories actually explain reality. It is not quite clear how instrumentalists account for this.

We can summarize the three views on the nature and function of scientific theories as follows. According to the translation version of reductionism, a theory is an organized summary of all that we know about normally observable objects and processes. A theory is either true or false. Theoretical terms such as "atom" are abbreviated descriptions of a vast complex of relationships among observable entities. Such terms enable us to describe the world economically.* According to realism, a theory is a description of the physically real world, and as such is either true or false. It is used to explain what is observed. A theory may be accepted as true even though the evidence for it can never be more than highly probable. Theoretical terms referring to such things as atoms may be treated as being on a par with observational

---

*According to the replacement version, a hypothetical theory is temporally useful, but ultimately replaceable by an abstractive theory.

terms referring to such things as tables and chairs, or, as in the case of Eddington, as the only terms referring to real objects. According to instrumentalism, a theory is neither true nor false. It is an instrument for classifying what we already know in the way of experimental laws and for guiding research in the discovery of experimental laws we do not yet know. Theoretical statements have a hypothetical and provisional status, since they are accepted only as long as they are useful for these purposes.

REDUCTIONISM

THE ECONOMY OF PHYSICAL THEORY

*Ernst Mach (1838-1916) was an Austrian physicist best
known for his critique of Newton's views on absolute space
and time. During the first golden age of the philosophy of
science — the last half of the nineteenth century — he was
an oustanding figure in the philosophical analysis of the problems of scientific methodology. Other outstanding figures
of this period include Hertz in Germany, Duhem and Poincaré
in France, Pearson in England, and Peirce in America.*

*The selection is from "The Economical Nature of Physical
Inquiry," a chapter in* Popular Scientific Lectures.*

When the human mind, with its limited powers, attempts to mirror in itself the rich life of the world, of which it is itself only a small
part, and which it can never hope to exhaust, it has every reason for
proceeding economically. Hence that tendency, expressed in the philosophy of all times, to compass by a few organic thoughts the fundamental features of reality.

The belief in occult magic powers of nature has gradually died
away, but in its place a new belief has arisen, the belief in the magical

---

*by Ernst Mach, translated by Thomas J. McCormack (Chicago: Open Court Publ. Co., 1898).
It was originally delivered as an address before the anniversary meeting of the Imperial
Academy of Sciences at Vienna, May 25, 1882.

power of science. Science throws her treasures, not like a capricious fairy into the laps of a favored few, but into the laps of all humanity, with a lavish extravagance that no legend ever dreamt of! Not without apparent justice, therefore, do her distant admirers impute to her the power of opening up unfathomable abysses of nature, to which the senses cannot penetrate. Yet she who came to bring light into the world, can well dispense with the darkness of mystery, and with pompous show, which she needs neither for the justification of her aims nor for the adornment of her plain achievements.

The homely beginnings of science will best reveal to us its simple, unchangeable character. Man acquires his first knowledge of nature half-consciously and automatically, from an instinctive habit of mimicking and forecasting facts in thought, of supplementing sluggish experience with the swift wings of thought, at first only for his material welfare. When he hears a noise in the underbrush he constructs there, just as the animal does, the enemy which he fears; when he sees a certain rind he forms mentally the image of the fruit which he is in search of; just as we mentally associate a certain kind of matter with a certain line in the spectrum or an electric spark with the friction of a piece of glass. A knowledge of causality in this form certainly reaches far below the level of Schopenhauer's pet dog, to whom it was ascribed. It probably exists in the whole animal world, and confirms that great thinker's statement regarding the will which created the intellect for its purposes. These primitive psychical functions are rooted in the economy of our organism and not less firmly than are motion and digestion. Who would deny that we feel in them, too, the elemental power of a long practised logical and physiological activity, bequeathed to us as an heirloom from our forefathers?

Such primitive acts of knowledge constitute to-day the solidest foundation of scientific thought. Our instinctive knowledge, as we shall briefly call it, by virtue of the conviction that we have consciously and intentionally contributed nothing to its formation, confronts us with an authority and logical power which consciously acquired knowledge even from familiar sources and of easily tested fallibility can never possess. All so-called axioms are such instinctive knowledge. Not consciously gained knowledge alone, but powerful intellectual instinct, joined with vast conceptive powers, constitute the great inquirer. The greatest advances of science have always consisted in some successful formulation, in clear, abstract, and communicable terms, of what was instinctively known long before, and of thus making it the permanent property of humanity. By Newton's principle of the equality of pressure and counterpressure, whose truth all before him had felt, but which no predecessor had abstractly formulated, mechanics was placed by a single stroke on a higher level. Our statement might also be historically justified by examples from the scientific labors of Stevinus, S. Carnot, Faraday, J.R. Mayer, and others.

All this, however, is merely the soil from which science starts. The first real beginnings of science appear in society, particularly in the manual arts, where the necessity for the communication of experience arises. Here, where some new discovery is to be described and related, the compulsion is first felt of clearly defining in consciousness the important and essential features of that discovery, as many writers can testify. The aim of instruction is simply the saving of experience; the labor of one man is made to take the place of that of another.

The most wonderful economy of communication is found in language. Words are comparable to type, which spare the repetition of written signs and thus serve a multitude of purposes; or to the few sounds of which our numberless different words are composed. Language, with its helpmate, conceptual thought, by fixing the essential and rejecting the unessential, constructs its rigid pictures of the fluid world on the plan of a mosaic, at a sacrifice of exactness and fidelity but with a saving of tools and labor. Like a piano-player with previously prepared sounds, a speaker excites in his listener thoughts previously prepared, but fitting many cases, which respond to the speaker's summons with alacrity and little effort. . . .

The communication of scientific knowledge always involves description, that is, a mimetic reproduction of facts in thought, the object of which is to replace and save the trouble of new experience. Again, to save the labor of instruction and of acquisition, concise, abridged description is sought. This is really all that natural laws are. Knowing the value of the acceleration of gravity, and Galileo's laws of descent, we possess simple and compendious directions for reproducing in thought all possible motions of falling bodies. A formula of this kind is a complete substitute for a full table of motions of descent, because by means of the formula the data of such a table can be easily constructed at a moment's notice without the least burdening of the memory.

No human mind could comprehend all the individual cases of refraction. But knowing the index of refraction for the two media presented, and the familiar law of the sines, we can easily reproduce or
fill out in thought every conceivable case of refraction. The advantage
here consists in the disburdening of the memory; an end immensely
furthered by the written preservation of the natural constants. More
than this comprehensive and condensed report about facts is not contained in a natural law of this sort. In reality, the law always contains
less than the fact itself, because it does not reproduce the fact as a
whole but only in that aspect of it which is important for us, the rest
being either intentionally or from necessity omitted. Natural laws may
be likened to intellectual type of a higher order, partly movable, partly
stereotyped, which last on new editions of experience may become
downright impediments.

When we look over a province of facts for the first time, it appears to us diversified, irregular, confused, full of contradictions. We
first succeed in grasping only single facts, unrelated with the others.
The province, as we are wont to say, is not *clear*. By and by we discover the simple, permanent elements of the mosaic, out of which we
can mentally construct the whole province. When we have reached a
point where we can discover everywhere the same facts, we no longer
feel lost in this province; we comprehend it without effort; it is *explained* for us.

Let me illustrate this by an example. As soon as we have grasped
the fact of the rectilinear propagation of light, the regular course of
our thoughts stumbles at the phenomena of refraction and diffraction.
As soon as we have cleared matters up by our index of refraction we
discover that a special index is necessary for each color. Soon after we
have accustomed ourselves to the fact that light added to light increases its intensity, we suddenly come across a case of total darkness
produced by this cause. Ultimately, however, we see everywhere in
the overwhelming multifariousness of optical phenomena the fact of
the spatial and temporal periodicity of light, with its velocity of propagation dependent on the medium and the period. This tendency of obtaining a survey of a given province with the least expenditure of thought
and of representing all its facts by some one single mental process, may
be justly termed an economical one.

The greatest perfection of mental economy is attained in that science which has reached the highest formal development, and which is widely employed in physical inquiry, namely, in mathematics. Strange as it may sound, the power of mathematics rests upon its evasion of all unnecessary thought and on its wonderful saving of mental operations. Even those arrangement-signs which we call numbers are a system of marvellous simplicity and economy. When we employ the multiplication-table in multiplying numbers of several places, and so use the results of old operations of counting instead of performing the whole of each operation anew; when we consult our table of logarithms, replacing and saving thus new calculations by old ones already performed, when we employ determinants instead of always beginning afresh the solution of a system of equations; when we resolve new integral expressions into familiar old integrals; we see in this simply a feeble reflexion of the intellectual activity of a Lagrange or a Cauchy, who, with the keen discernment of a great military commander, substituted for new operations whole hosts of old ones. No one will dispute me when I say that the most elementary as well as the highest mathematics are economically-ordered experiences of counting, put in forms ready for use. . . .

Physics is experience, arranged in economical order. By this order not only is a broad and comprehensive view of what we have rendered possible, but also the defects and the needful alterations are made manifest, exactly as in a well-kept household. Physics shares with mathematics the advantages of succinct description and of brief, compendious definition, which precludes confusion, even in ideas where, with no apparent burdening of the brain, hosts of others are contained. . . .

The recognition of the economical character of science will now help us, perhaps, to understand better certain physical notions. . . .

The crude notion of "body" can no more stand the test of analysis than can the art of the Egyptians or that of our little children. The physicist who sees a body flexed, stretched, melted, and vaporized, cuts up this body into smaller permanent parts; the chemist splits it up into elements. Yet even an element is not unalterable. Take sodium. When warmed, the white, silvery mass becomes a liquid, which, when the heat is increased and the air shut out, is transformed into a violet vapor, and on the heat being still more increased glows with a yellow light. If the name sodium is still retained, it is because of the continuous character of the transitions and from a necessary instinct of economy. By condensing the vapor, the white metal may be made to reappear. Indeed, even after the metal is thrown into water and has passed into sodium hydroxide, the vanished properties may by skillful treatment still be made to appear; just as a moving body which has passed behind a column and is lost to view for a moment may make its appearance after a time. It is unquestionably very convenient always to have ready the name and thought for a group of properties wherever that group by any possibility can appear. But more than a compendious economical symbol for these phenomena, that name and thought is not. It would be a mere empty word for one in whom it did not awaken a large group of well-ordered sense-impressions. And the same is true of the molecules and atoms into which the chemical element is still further analysed.

True, it is customary to regard the conservation of weight, or, more precisely, the conservation of mass, as a direct proof of the constancy of matter. But this proof is dissolved, when we go to the bottom of it, into such a multitude of instrumental and intellectual operations, that in a sense it will be found to constitute simply an equation which our ideas in imitating facts have to satisfy. That obscure, mysterious lump which we involuntarily add in thought, we seek for in vain outside the mind. . . .

Let us endeavor now to summarise the results of our survey. In the economical schematism of science lie both its strength and its weakness. Facts are always represented at a sacrifice of completeness and never with greater precision than fits the needs of the moment. The incongruence between thought and experience, therefore, will continue to subsist as long as the two pursue their course side by side; but it will be continually diminished.

In reality, the point involved is always the completion of some partial experience; the derivation of one portion of a phenomenon from some other. In this act our ideas must be based directly upon sensations. We call this measuring.* The condition of science, both in its origin and in its application, is a *great relative stability* of our environment. What it teaches us is interdependence. Absolute forecasts consequently, have no significance in science. With great changes in celestial space we should lose our co-ordinate systems of space and time.

---

*Measurement, in fact, is the definition of one phenomenon by another (standard) phenomenon.

When a geometer wishes to understand the form of a curve, he first resolves it into small rectilinear elements. In doing this, however, he is fully aware that these elements are only provisional and arbitrary devices for comprehending in parts what he cannot comprehend as a whole. When the law of the curve is found he no longer thinks of the elements. Similarly, it would not become physical science to see in its self-created, changeable, economical tools, molecules and atoms, realities behind phenomena, forgetful of the lately acquired sapience of her older sister, philosophy, in substituting a mechanical mythology for the old animistic or metaphysical scheme, and thus creating no end of suppositious problems. The atom must remain a tool for representing phenomena, like the functions of mathematics. Gradually, however, as the intellect, by contract with its subject-matter, grows in discipline, physical science will give up its mosaic play with stones and will seek out the boundaries and forms of the bed in which the living stream of phenomena flows. The goal which it has set itself is the *simplest* and *most economical* abstract expression of facts. . . .

Let us look at the matter without bias. The world consists of colors, sound, temperatures, pressures, spaces, times, and so forth, which now we shall not call sensations, nor phenomena, because in either term an arbitrary, one-sided theory is embodied, but simply *elements*. The fixing of the flux of these elements, whether mediately or immediately, is the real object of physical research. As long as, neglecting our own body, we employ ourselves with the interdependence of those groups of elements which, including men and animals, make up *foreign* bodies, we are physicists. For example, we investigate the change of the red color of a body as produced by a change of illumination. But the moment we consider the special influence on the red of the elements constituting our body, outlined by the well-known perspective with head invisible, we are at work in the domain of physiological psychology. We close our eyes, and the red together with the whole visible world disappears. There exists, thus in the perspective field of every sense a portion which exercises on all the rest a different and more powerful influence than the rest upon one another. With this, however, all is said. In the light of this remark, we call *all* elements, in so far as we regard them as dependent on this special part (our body), *sensations.* That the world is our sensation, in this sense, cannot be questioned. But to make a system of conduct out of this provisional

conception, and to abide its slaves, is as unnecessary for us as would
be a similar course for a mathematician who, in varying a series of variables of a function which were previously assumed to be constant, or
in interchanging the independent variables, finds his method to be the
source of some very surprising ideas for him. . . .

ABSTRACTIVE AND HYPOTHETICAL THEORIES

William John Macquorn Rankine (1820-1872) was a Scottish engineer and physicist. He helped to found the science of energetics, an attempt to establish thermodynamics as the basic natural science.

The following selection is from "Outlines of the Science of Energetics," in Miscellaneous Scientific Papers.*

SECTION I. WHAT CONSTITUTES A PHYSICAL THEORY

An essential distinction exists between two stages in the process of advancing our knowledge of the laws of physical phenomena; the first stage consists in observing the relations of phenomena, whether of such as occur in the ordinary course of nature, or of such as are artificially produced in experimental investigations, and in expressing the relations so observed by propositions called formal laws. The second stage consists in reducing the formal laws of an entire class of phenomena to the form of a science; that is to say, in discovering the most simple system of principles, from which all the formal laws of the class of phenomena can be deduced as consequences.

*London: Charles Griffin & Co., 1881. It was originally read before the Philosophical Society of Glasgow on May 2, 1885, and published in the Proceedings of that Society, Vol. III No. VI.

Such a system of principles, with its consequences methodically deduced, constitutes the PHYSICAL THEORY of a class of phenomena.

A physical theory, like an abstract science, consists of definitions and axioms as first principles, and of propositions, their consequences but with these differences:—First, That in an abstract science, a definition assigns a name to a class of notions derived originally from observation, but not necessarily corresponding to any existing objects of real phenomena; and an axiom states a mutual relation amongst such notions, or the names denoting them: while in a physical science, a definition states properties common to a class of existing objects, or real phenomena; and a physical axiom states a general law as to the relations of phenomena. And, secondly, That in an abstract science, the propositions first discovered are the most simple; whilst in a physical thory, the propositions first discovered are in general numerous and complex, being formal laws, the immediate results of observation and experiment, from which the definitions and axioms are subsequently arrived at by a process of reasoning differing from that whereby one proposition is deduced from another in an abstract science, partly in being more complex and difficult, and partly in being, to a certain extent, *tentative*—that is to say, involving the trail of conjectural principles, and their acceptance or rejection, according as their consequences are found to agree or disagree with formal laws deduced immediately from observation and experiment.

SECTION II. THE ABSTRACTIVE METHOD OF FORMING A PHYSICAL THEORY DISTINGUISHED FROM THE HYPOTHETICAL METHOD

Two methods of framing a physical theory may be distinguished, characterised chiefly by the manner in which classes of phenomena are defined. They may be termed, respectively, the ABSTRACTIVE and the HYPOTHETICAL methods.

According to the ABSTRACTIVE method, a class of objects or phenomena is defined by describing, or otherwise making to be understood, and assigning a name or symbol to, that assemblage of properties which is common to all the objects or phenomena composing the class, as perceived by the senses, without introducing anything hypothetical.

According to the HYPOTHETICAL method, a class of objects or phenomena is defined, according to a conjectural conception of their nature, as being constituted, in a manner not apparent to the senses, by a modification of some other class of objects or phenomena whose laws are already known. Should the consequences of such a hypothetical definition be found to be in accordance with the results of observation and experiment, it serves as the means of deducing the laws of one class of objects or phenomena from those of another.

The conjectural conceptions involved in the hypothetical method may be distinguished into two classes, according as they are adopted as a probable representation of a state of things which may really exist, though imperceptible to the senses, or merely as a convenient means of expressing the laws of phenomena; two kinds of hypotheses, of which the former may be called *objective* and the latter *subjective*. As examples of objective hypotheses may be taken, that of vibrations or oscillations in the theory of light, and that of atoms in chemistry; as an example of a subjective hypothesis, that of magnetic fluids.

SECTION III. THE SCIENCE OF MECHANICS CONSIDERED AS AN ILLUSTRATION OF THE ABSTRACTIVE METHOD

The principles of the science of mechanics, the only example yet existing of a complete physical theory, are altogether formed from the data of experience by the abstractive method. The class of *objects* to which the science of mechanics relates—viz., material bodies— are defined by means of those sensible properties which they all possess— viz., the property of occupying space, and that of resisting change of motion. The two classes of *phenomena* to which the science of mechanics relates are distinguished by two words, *motion* and *force—motion* being a word denoting that which is common to the fall of heavy bodies, the flow of streams, the tides, the winds, the vibrations of sonorous bodies, the revolutions of the stars, and generally, to all phenomena involving change of the portions of space occupied by bodies; and *force* a word denoting that which is common to the mutual attractions and repulsions of bodies, distant or near, and of the parts of bodies, the mutual pressure or stress of bodies in contact, and of the parts of bodies, the muscular exertions of animals, and, generally, to all phenomena tending to produce or to prevent motion.

The laws of the composition and resolution of motions, and of
the composition and resolution of forces, are expressed by propositions
which are the consequences of the definitions of motion and force respectively. The laws of the relations between motion and force are the
consequences of certain axioms, being the most simple and general expressions for all that has been ascertained by experience respecting
those relations.

SECTION IV. MECHANICAL HYPOTHESES IN VARIOUS BRANCHES OF PHYSICS

The fact that the theory of motions and motive forces is the only
complete physical theory, has naturally led to the adoption of *mechanical hypotheses* in the theories of other branches of physics; that is
to say, hypothetical definitions, in which classes of phenomena are
defined conjecturally as being constituted by some kind of motion or
motive force not obvious to the senses (called *molecular* motion or
force), as when light and radiant heat are defined as consisting in molecular vibrations, thermometric heat in molecular vortices, and the
rigidity of solids in molecular attractions and repulsions.

The hypothetical motions and forces are sometimes ascribed to
hypothetical bodies, such as the luminiferous ether; sometimes to
hypothetical parts, whereof tangible bodies are conjecturally defined
to consist, such as atoms, atomic nuclei with elastic atmospheres, and
the like.

A mechanical hypothesis is held to have fulfilled its object, when,
by applying the known axioms of mechanics to the hypothetical motions and forces, results are obtained agreeing with the observed laws
of the classes of phenomena under consideration; and when, by the
aid of such a hypothesis, phenomena previously unobserved are predicted, and laws anticipated, it attains a high degree of probability.

A mechanical hypothesis is the better the more extensive the
range of phenomena whose laws it serves to deduce from the axioms
of mechanics; and the perfection of such a hypothesis would, if
it could, by means of one connected system of suppositions, be made
to form a basis for all branches of molecular physics.

SECTION V. ADVANTAGES AND DISADVANTAGES OF HYPOTHETICAL THEORIES

It is well known that certain hypothetical theories, such as the wave theory of light, have proved extremely useful, by reducing the laws of a various and complicated class of phenomena to a few simple principles, and by anticipating laws afterwards verified by observation.

Such are the results to be expected from well-framed hypotheses in every branch of physics, when used with judgment, and especially with that caution which arises from the consideration, that even those hypotheses whose consequences are most fully confirmed by experiment never can, by any amount of evidence, attain that degree of certainty which belongs to observed facts.

Of mechanical hypotheses in particular, it is to be observed, that their tendency is to combine all branches of physics into one system, by making the axioms of mechanics the first principles of the laws of all phenomena—an object for the attainment of which an earnest wish was expressed by Newton.*

In the mechanical theories of elasticity, light, heat, and electricity, considerable progress has been made toward that end.

The neglect of the caution already referred to, however, has caused some hypotheses to assume, in the minds of the public generally, as well as in those of many scientific men, that authority which belongs to facts alone; and a tendency has, consequently, often evinced itself to explain away, or set aside, facts inconsistent with these hypotheses, which facts rightly appreciated, would have formed the basis of true theories. Thus, the fact of the production of heat by friction, the basis of the true theory of heat, was long neglected, because inconsistent with the hypothesis of caloric; and the fact of the production of cold by electric currents, at certain metallic junctions, the key (as Professor William Thomson recently showed) to the true theory of the phenomena of thermo-electricity, was from inconsistency with prevalent assumptions respecting the so-called "electric fluid," by some regarded as a thing to be explained away, and by others as a delusion.

Such are the evils which arise from the misuse of hypotheses.

---

*Preface to the Mathematical Principles of Natural Philosophy.

SECTION VI. ADVANTAGES OF AN EXTENSION OF THE ABSTRACTIVE METHOD OF FRAMING THEORIES

Besides the perfecting of mechanical hypotheses, another and an entirely distinct method presents itself for combining the physical sciences into one system; and that is, by an *extension of the* ABSTRACTIVE PROCESS in framing theories.

The abstractive method has already been partially applied, and with success, to special branches of molecular physics, such as heat, electricity, and magnetism. We are now to consider in what manner it is to be applied to physics generally, considered as one science.

Instead of supposing the various classes of physical phenomena to be constituted, in an occult way, of modifications of motion and force, let us distinguish the properties which those classes possess in common with each other, and so define more extensive classes denoted by suitable terms. For axioms, to express the laws of those more extensive classes of phenomena, let us frame propositions comprehending as particular cases the laws of the particular classes of phenomena comprehended under the more extensive classes. So shall we arrive at a body of principles, applicable to physical phenomena in general, and which, being framed by induction from facts alone, will be free from the uncertainty which must always attach, even to those mechanical hypotheses whose consequences are most fully confirmed by experiment.

This extension of the abstractive process is not proposed in order to supersede the hypothetical method of theorising; for in almost every branch of molecular physics it may be held, that a hypothetical theory is necessary, as a preliminary step, to reduce the expression of the phenomena to simplicity and order, before it is possible to make any progress in framing an abstractive theory.

MACH

EXPLANATION IN PHYSICS

This second selection from Mach's work is taken from "Mechanical Physics" in History and Root of the Principle of the Conservation of Energy.*

One thing we maintain, and that is, that in the investigation of nature, we have to deal only with knowledge of the connexion of appearances with one another. What we represent to ourselves behind the appearances exists *only* in our understanding, and has for us only the value of a *memoria technica* or formula, whose form, because it is arbitrary and irrelevant, varies very easily with the standpoint of our culture.

If, now, we merely keep our hold on the new laws as to the connexion between heat and work, it does not matter how we think of heat itself; and similarly in all physics. This way of presentation does not alter the facts in the least. But if this way of presentation is so limited and inflexible that it no longer allows us to follow the many-sidedness of phenomena, it should not be used any more as a formula and will begin to be a hindrance to us in the knowledge of phenomena.

This happens, I think, in the mechanical conception of physics. Let us glance at this conception that all physical phenomena reduce to the equilibrium and movement of molecules and atoms.

---

*Translated and annotated by Philip E.B. Jourdain (Chicago: Open Court Publ. Co., 1911). Reprinted by permission.

According to Wundt, all changes of nature are mere changes of place. All causes are motional causes. Any discussion of the philosophical grounds on which Wundt supports his theory would lead us deep into the speculations of the Eleatics and the Herbartians. Change of place, Wundt holds, is the *only* change of a thing in which a thing remains identical with itself. If a thing changed *qualitatively,* we should be obliged to imagine that something was annihilated and something else created in its place, which is not to be reconciled with our idea of the identity of the object observed and of the indestructibility of matter. But we have only to remember that the Eleatics encountered difficulties of exactly the same sort in motion. Can we not also imagine that a thing is destroyed in *one* place and in *another* an exactly similar thing created?

It is a bad sign for the mechanical view of the world that it wishes to support itself on such preposterous things, which are thousands of years old. If the ideas of matter, which were made at a lower stage of culture, are not suitable for dealing with the phenomena accessible to those on a higher plane of knowledge, it follows for the true investigator of nature that these ideas must be given up; not that only those phenomena exist, for which ideas that are out of order and have been outlived are suited.

But let us suppose for a moment that all physical events can be reduced to spatial motions of material particles (molecules). What can we do with that supposition? Thereby we suppose that things which can never be seen or touched and only exist in our imagination and understanding, can have the properties and relations only of things which can be touched. We impose on the creations of though the limitations of the visible and tangible.

Now, there are also other forms of perception of other senses, and these forms are perfectly analogous to space—for example, the tone-series for hearing, which corresponds to a space of one dimension—and we do not allow ourselves a like liberty with them. We do not think of all things as sounding and do not figure to ourselves molecular events musically, in relations of heights of tones, although we are as justified in doing this as in thinking of them spatially.

This, therefore, teaches us what an unnecessary restriction we here impose upon ourselves. There is no more necessity to think of what is merely a product of thought spatially, that is to say, with the relations of the visible and tangible, than there is to think of these things in a definite position in the scale of tones. . . .

Perhaps the reason why, hitherto, people have not succeeded in establishing a satisfactory theory of electricity is because they wished to explain electrical phenomena by means of molecular events in a space of three dimensions.

Herewith I believe that I have shown that one can hold, treasure, and also turn to good account the results of modern natural science without being a supporter of the mechanical conception of nature, that this conception is not necessary for the knowledge of the phenomena and can be replaced just as well by another theory, and that the mechanical conceptions can even be a hindrance to the knowledge of phenomena.

Let me add a view on scientific theories, in general: If all the individual facts—all the individual phenomena, knowledge of which we desire—were immediately accessible to us, a science would never have arisen.

Because of mental power, the memory, of the individual is limited, the material must be arranged. If for example, to every time of falling, we knew the corresponding space fallen through, we could be satisfied with that. Only, what a gigantic memory would be needed to contain the table of the correspondences of s and t. Instead of this we remember the formula $s = \dfrac{gt^2}{2}$, that is to say, the rule of derivation by means of which we find, from a given t, the corresponding s, and this replaces the table just mentioned in a very complete, convenient, and compendious manner.

This rule of derivation, this formula, this "law", has, now, not in the least more real value than the aggregate of the individual facts. Its value for us lies merely in the convenience of its use: it has an economical value. (See note 5, p. 88.)

Besides this collection of as many facts as possible in a synoptical form, natural science has yet another problem which is also economical in nature. It has to resolve the more complicated facts into as few and as simple ones as possible. This we call explaining. These simplest facts, to which we reduce the more complicated ones, are always unintelligible in themselves, that is to say, they are not further resolvable.

An example of this is the fact that one mass imparts an acceleration
to another.

Now, it is only, on the one hand, an economical question, and,
on the other, a question of taste, at what unintelligibilities we stop.
People usually deceive themselves in thinking that they have reduced
the unintelligible. Understanding consists in analysis alone; and people
usually reduce uncommon unintelligibilities to common ones. They
always get, finally, to propositions of the form: if A is, B is, therefore
to propositions which must follow from intuition, and, therefore, are
not further intelligible.

What facts one will allow to rank as fundamental facts, at which
one rests, depends on custom and on history. For the lowest stage of
knowledge there is no more sufficient explanation than pressure and
impact.

The Newtonian theory of gravitation, on its appearance, disturbed
almost all investigators of nature because it was founded on an uncommon unintelligibility. People tried to reduce gravitation to pressure and
impact. At the present day gravitation no longer distrubs anybody: it
has become a *common* unintelligibility.

It is well known that action at a distance has caused difficulties
to very eminent thinkers. "A body can only act where it is"; therefore
there is only pressure and impact, and no action at a distance. But
where is a body? Is it only where we touch it? Let us invert the matter: a body is where it acts. A little space is taken for touching, a
greater for hearing, and a still greater for seeing. How did it come about
that the sense of touch alone dictates to us where a body is? Moreover,
contact-action can be regarded as a special case of action at a distance.

It is the result of a misconception, to believe, as people do at the
present time, that mechanical facts are more intelligible than others,
and that they can provide the foundation for other physical facts.
This belief arises from the fact that the history of mechanics is older
and richer than that of physics, so that we have been on terms of in-
timacy with mechanical facts for a longer time. Who can say that, at
some future time, electrical and thermal phenomena will not appear
to us like that, when we have come to know and to be familiar with
their simplest rules?

In the investigation of nature, we always and alone have to do with
the finding of the best and simplest rules for the derivation of phenomen.

from one another. One fundamental fact is not at all more intelligible than another: the choice of fundamental facts is a matter of convenience, history, and custom.

The ultimate unintelligibilities on which science is founded must be facts, or, if they are hypotheses, must be capable of becoming facts. If the hypotheses are so chosen that their subject *(Gegenstand)* can never appeal to the senses and therefore also can never be tested, as is the case with the mechanical molecular theory, the investigator has done more than science, whose aim is facts, requires of him—and this work of supererogation is an evil.

Perhaps one might think that rules for phenomena, which cannot be perceived in the phenomena themselves, can be discovered by means of the molecular theory. Only that is not so. In a complete theory, to all details of the phenomenon details of the hypothesis must correspond, and all rules for these hypothetical things must also be directly transferable to the phenomenon. But then molecules are merely a valueless image.

Accordingly, we must say with J.R. Mayer: "If a fact is known on all its sides, it is, by that knowledge, explained, and the problem of science is ended."*

---

*Mechanik der Warme, Stuttgart, 1867, p. 239.

REALISM

EDDINGTON

THE NATURE OF THE PHYSICAL WORLD

Arthur S. Eddington (1881-1944) was an outstanding English astronomer whose major scientific achievements were in the fields of astrophysics and relativity theory. He was Einstein's chief assistant on the trip to West Africa in 1919 to observe the solar eclipse. An experiment carried out during that eclipse proved that light from a distant star would be bent as it passed the sun. This experiment helped to confirm the general theory of relativity. Eddington's own work is best represented in his Space, Time, and Gravitation *(1920).*

Eddington's name is well known to the general public because of his attempts to reconcile relativity with more traditional beliefs held by man. The selection represents one such attempt. *

I have settled down to the task of writing these lectures and have drawn up my chairs to my two tables. Two tables! Yes; there are duplicates of every object about me—two tables, two chairs, two pens.

This is not a very profound beginning to a course which ought to reach transcendent levels of scientific philosophy. But we cannot touch bedrock immediately; we must scratch a bit at the surface of things first. And whenever I begin to scratch the first thing I strike is— my two tables.

*From The Nature of the Physical World (New York: Macmillan, 1928), pp. ix-xii, 282-289. By permission of Cambridge University Press.

One of them has been familiar to me from earliest years. It is a commonplace object of that environment which I call the world. How shall I describe it? It has extension; it is comparatively permanent; it is coloured; above all it is *substantial*. By substantial I do not merely mean that it does not collapse when I lean upon it; I mean that it is constituted of "substance" and by that word I am trying to convey to you some conception of its intrinsic nature. It is a *thing;* not like space, which is a mere negation; nor like time, which is—Heaven knows what! But that will not help you to my meaning because it is the distinctive characteristic of a "thing" to have this substantiality, and I do not think substantiality can be described better than by saying that it is the kind of nature exemplified by an ordinary table. And so we go round in circles. After all if you are a plain commonsense man, not too much worried with scientific scruples, you will be confident that you understand the nature of an ordinary table. I have even heard of plain men who had the idea that they could better understand the mystery of their own nature if scientists would discover a way of explaining it in terms of the easily comprehensible nature of a table.

Table No. 2 is my scientific table. It is a more recent acquaintance and I do not feel so familiar with it. It does not belong to the world previously mentioned—that world which spontaneously appears around me when I open my eyes, though how much of it is objective and how much subjective I do not here consider. It is part of a world which in more devious ways has forced itself on my attention. My scientific table is mostly emptiness. Sparsely scattered in that emptiness are numerous electric charges rushing about with great speed; but their combined bulk amounts to less than a billionth of the bulk of the table itself. Notwithstanding its strange construction it turns out to be an entirely efficient table. It supports my writing paper as satisfactorily as table No. 1; for when I lay the paper on it the little electric particles with their headlong speed keep on hitting the underside, so that the paper is maintained in shuttlecock fashion at a nearly steady level. If I lean upon this table I shall not go through; or, to be strictly accurate, the chance of my scientific elbow going through my scientific table is so excessively small that it can be neglected in practical life. Reviewing their properties one by one, there seems to be nothing to choose between the two tables for ordinary purposes; but when abnormal circumstances befall, then my scientific table shows to advantage. If the house catches fire my scientific table will dissolve quite naturally into scientific smoke, whereas my familiar table undergoes a metamorphosis of its substantial nature which I can only regard as miraculous.

There is nothing *substantial* about my second table. It is nearly all empty space—space pervaded, it is true, by fields of force, but these are assigned to the category of "influences", not of "things". Even in the minute part which is not empty we must not transfer the old notion of substance. In dissecting matter into electric charges we have travelled far from that picture of it which first gave rise to the conception of substance, and the meaning of that conception—if it ever had any— has been lost by the way. The whole trend of modern scientific views is to break down the separate categories of "things", "influences", "forms", etc., and to substitute a common background of all experience. Whether we are studying a material object, a magnetic field, a geometrical figure, or a duration of time, our scientific information is summed up in measures; neither the apparatus of measurement nor the mode of using it suggest that there is anything essentially different in these problems. The measures themselves afford no ground for a classification by categories. We feel it necessary to concede some background to the measures—an external world; but the attributes of this world, except in so far as they are reflected in the measures, are outside scientific scrutiny. Science has at last revolted against attaching the exact knowledge contained in these measurements to a traditional picture-gallery of conceptions which convey no authentic information of the background and obtrude irrelevancies into the scheme of knowledge.

I will not here stress further the non-substantiality of electrons, since it is scarcely necessary to the present line of thought. Conceive them as substantially as you will, there is a vast difference between my scientific table with its substance (if any) thinly scattered in specks in a region mostly empty and the table of everyday conception which we regard as the type of solid reality—an incarnate protest against Berkleian subjectivism. It makes all the difference in the world whether the paper before me is poised as it were on a swarm of flies and sustained in shuttlecock fashion by a series of tiny blows from the swarm underneath, or whether it is supported because there is substance below it, it being the intrinsic nature of substance to occupy space to the exclusion of other substance; all the difference in conception at least, but no difference to my practical task of writing on the paper.

I need not tell you that modern physics has by delicate test and remorseless logic assured me that my second scientific table is the only one which is really there—wherever "there" may be. On the other hand I need not tell you that modern physics will never succeed in exercising that first table—strange compound of external nature, mental imagery and inherited prejudice—which lies visible to my eyes and tangible to my grasp. We must bid good-bye to it for the present for we are about to turn from the familiar world to the scientific world revealed by physics. This is, or is intended to be, a wholly external world.

"You speak paradoxically of two worlds. Are they not really two aspects or two interpretations of one and the same world?"

Yes, no doubt they are ultimately to be identified after some fashion. But the process by which the external world of physics is transformed into a world of familiar acquaintance in human consciousness is outside the scope of physics. And so the world studied according to the methods of physics remains detached from the world familiar to consciousness, until after the physicist has finished his labours upon it. . . .

* * *

The Definition of Reality. It is time we came to grips with the loose terms Reality and Existence, which we have been using without any inquiry into what they are meant to convey. I am afraid of this word Reality, not connoting an ordinarily definable characteristic of the things it is applied to but used as though it were some kind of celestial halo. I very much doubt if any one of us has the faintest idea of what is meant by the reality or existence of anything but our own Egos. That is a bold statement, which I must guard against misinterpretation. It is, of course, possible to obtain consistent use of the word "reality" by adopting a conventional definition. My own practice would probably be covered by the definition that a thing may be said to be real if it is the goal of a type of inquiry to which I personally attach importance. But if I insist on no more than this I am whittling down the significance that is generally assumed. In physics we can give a cold scientific defintion of reality which is free from all sentimental mystification. But this is not quite fair play, because the world "reality" is generally used *with the intention of evoking sentiment.* It is a grand word for a peroration. "The right honourable speaker went on to declare that the concord and amity for which he had unceasingly striven had now become a reality (loud cheers)." The conception which it is so troublesome to apprehend is not "reality" but "reality (loud cheers)".

Let us first examine the definition according to the purely scientific usage of the word, although it will not take us far enough. The only subject presented to me for study is the content of my consciousness. You are able to communicate to me part of the content of your consciousness which thereby becomes accessible in my own. For reasons which are generally admitted, though I should not like to have to prove that they are conclusive, I grant your consciousness equal status with my own; and I use this second-hand part of my consciousness to "put myself in your place". Accordingly my subject of study becomes differentiated into the contents of many consciousnesses, each content constituting a *view-point*. There then arises the problem of combining the view-points, and it is through this that the external world of physics arises. Much that is in any one consciousness is individual, much is apparently alterable by volition; but there is a stable element which is common to other consciousnesses. That common element we desire to study, to describe as fully and accurately as possible, and to discover the laws by which it combines now with one view-point, now with another. This common element cannot be placed in one man's consciousness rather than in another's; it must be in neutral ground—an external world.

It is true that I have a strong impression of an external world apart from any communication with other conscious beings. But apart from such communication I should have no reason to trust the impression. Most of our common impressions of substance, world-wide instants, and so on, have turned out to be illusory, and the externality of the world might be equally untrustworthy. The impression of externality is equally strong in the world that comes to me in dreams; the dream-world is less rational, but that might be used as an argument in favour of its externality as showing its dissociation from the internal faculty of reason. So long as we have to deal with one consciousness alone, the hypothesis that there is an external world responsible for part of what appears in it is an idle one. All that can be asserted of this external world is a mere duplication of the knowledge that can be much more confidently asserted of the world appearing in the consciousness. The hypothesis only becomes useful when it is the means of bringing together the worlds of many consciousnesses occupying different view-points.

The external world of physics is thus a symposium of the worlds presented to different view-points. There is general agreement as to the principles on which the symposium should be formed. Statements made about this external world, if they are unambiguous, must be either true or false. This has often been denied by philosophers. It is quite commonly said that scientific theories about the world are neither true nor false but merely convenient or inconvenient. A favourite phrase is that the gauge of value of a scientific theory is that it economises thought than that it is true. But whatever lower standards we may apply in practice we need not give up our ideals; and so long as there is a distinction between true and false theories our aim must be to eliminate the false. For my part I hold that the continual advance of science is not a mere utilitarian progress; it is progress towards ever purer truth. Only let it be understood that the truth we seek in science is the truth about an external world propounded as the theme of study, and is not bound up with any opinion as to the status of that world— whether or not it wears the halo of reality, whether or not it is deserving of "loud cheer".

Assuming that the symposium has been correctly carried out, the external world and all that appears in it are called real without further ado. When we (scientists) assert of anything in the external world that it is real and that it exists, we are expressing our belief that the rules of the symposium have been correctly applied—that it is not a false concept introduced by an error in the process of synthesis, or a hallucination belonging to only one individual consciousness, or an incomplete representation which embraces certain view-points but conflicts with others. We refuse to contemplate the awful contingency that the external world, after all our care in arriving at it, might be disqualified by failing to exist; because we have no idea what the supposed qualification would consist in, nor in what way the prestige of the world would be enhanced if it passed the implied test. The external world is the world that confronts that experience which we have in common, and for us no other world could fill the same role, no matter how high honours it might take in the qualifying examination.

This domestic definition of existence for scientific purposes follows the principle now adopted for all other definitions in science, namely, that a thing must be defined according to the way in which it is in practice recognised and not according to some ulterior significance that we imagine it to possess. Just as matter must shed its conception of substantiality, so existence must shed its halo, before we can admit it into physical science. But clearly if we are to assert or to question the existence of anything not comprised in the external world of physics, we must look beyond the physical definition. The mere questioning of the reality of the physical world implies some higher censorship than the scientific method itself can supply.

The external world of physics has been formulated as an answer to a particular problem encountered in human experience. Officially the scientist regards it as a problem which he just happened across, as he might take up a cross-word problem encountered in a newspaper. His sole business is to see that the problem is correctly solved. But questions may be raised about a problem which play no part and need not be considered in connection with the solving of the problem. The extraneous question naturally raised about the problem of the external world is whether there is some higher justification for embarking on this world solving competition rather than on other problems which our experience might suggest to us. Just what kind of justification the scientist would claim for his quest is not very clear, because it is not within the province of science to formulate such a claim. But certainly he makes claims which do not rest on the aesthetic perfection of the solution or on material benefits derived from scientific research. He would not allow his subject to be shoved aside in a symposium on truth. We can scarcely say anything more definite than that science claims a "halo" for its world.

If we are to find for the atoms and electrons of the external world not merely a conventional reality but "reality (loud cheers)" we must look not to the end but to the beginning of the quest. It is at the beginning that we must find that sanction which raises these entities above the mere products of an arbitrary mental exercise. This involves some kind of assessment of the impulse which sets us forth on the voyage of discovery. How can we make such assessment? Not by any reasoning that I know of. Reasoning would only tell us that the impulse might be judged by the success of the adventure—whether it leads in the end to things which really exist and wear the halo in their own right; it takes us to and fro like a shuttle along the chain of inference in vain search for the elusive halo. But, legitimately or not, the mind is confident that it can distinguish certain quests as sanctioned by indisputable authority.

We may put it in different ways; the impulse to this quest is part of our very nature; it is the expression of a purpose which has possession of us. Is this precisely what we meant when we sought to affirm the reality of the external world? It goes some way towards giving it a meaning but is scarcely the full equivalent. I doubt if we really satisfy the conceptions behind that demand unless we make the bolder hypothesis that the quest and all that is reached by it are of worth in the eyes of an Absolute Valuer.

Whatever justification at the source we accept to vindicate the reality of the external world, it can scarcely fail to admit on the same footing much that is outside physical science. Although no long chains of regularised inference depend from them we recognise that other fibres of our being extend in directions away from sense-impressions. I am not greatly concerned to borrow words like "existence" and "reality" to crown these other departments of the soul's interest. I would rather put it that any raising of the question of reality in its transcendental sense (whether the question emanates from the world of physics or not) leads us to a perspective from which we see man not as a bundle of sensory impressions, but conscious of purpose and responsibilities to which the external world is subordinate.

From this perspective we recognise a spiritual world alongside the physical world. Experience—that is to say, the self *cum* environment—comprises more than can be embraced in the physical world, restricted as it is to a complex of metrical symbols. The physical world is, we have seen, the answer to one definite and urgent problem arising in a survey of experience; and no other problem has been followed up with anything like the same precision and elaboration. Progress towards an understanding of the non-sensory constituents of our nature is not likely to follow similar lines, and indeed is not animated by the same aims. If it is felt that this difference is so wide that the phrase spiritual *world* is a misleading analogy, I will not insist on the term. All I would claim is that those who in the search for truth start from consciousness as a seat of self-knowledge with interests and responsibilities not confined to the material plane, are just as much facing the hard facts of experience as those who start from consciousness as a device for reading the indications of spectroscopes and micrometers.

HEISENBERG

PLANCK'S QUANTUM THEORY AND THE PHILOSOPHICAL PROBLEMS OF ATOMIC PHYSICS

Werner Heisenberg (1901-   ) is best known for his work in quantum theory and as the formulator of the celebrated and controversial principle of indeterminacy. He was awarded the Nobel Prize in Physics in 1932. He is a member of the faculty of the University of Göttingen and the director of the Max Planck Research Institute. His recent research has been mainly concerned with the "unified field theory." Professor Heisenberg has explored the philosophical impli-cations of his work in Physics and Philosophy: The Revolu-tion in Modern Science.

The selection is the text of a lecture delivered in Geneva. It is reprinted from Univeritas, *Vol. 3, No. 2, 1959. by special permission of Prof. Heisenberg.*

Modern physics, and in particular the quantum theory — the most important of Max Planck's discoveries — have posed a series of questions of a very general nature concerning not only specific prob-lems of physics but also the methods used by the exact sciences and the very nature of matter itself. The questions have forced physicists to reconsider philosophical problems which had apparently already been solved once and for all by the strict teachings of classical physics.

There are two cycles of problems in particular which have been brought back to the attention of the scientists by Planck's quantum theory. The first of them is concerned with the nature of matter itself, or, to be more exact, is the old question posed by the Greek philosophers as to how the abundance of material phenomena could be reduced to simple principles and thus made more easily comprehensible. The second of these cycles is concerned with the question — which has been brought up again and again, particularly since Kant directed so much attention to it — as to how far it is possible to objectivize natural science experience, or any kind of material experience, i.e. to draw conclusions as to the nature of an objective process which takes place quite independently of the observer. Kant spoke of the "thing in itself". Later on, philosopher often reproached him because, as they said, the concept of the "thing in itself" was not always consistent in his works. The question concerning the objective background of the phenomena has been brought up again by the quantum theory in a very surprising manner, this time from a different angle. For this reason we can therefore tackle the problem, from the point of view of modern natural science, from a different angle too.

1. First of all, let us look at those problems which arise in natural philosophy when one begins to search for a homogeneous and consistent set of principles by which one can judge material phenomena. The natural philosophers of ancient Greece, in the course of their reflections on the common basis of all visible phenomena, had already stumbled over the question of what constituted the smallest particle of matter. At the end of this glorious epoch in the history of the human intellect, two different schools of thought confronted one another as a result of all this reflection. These two schools have exercised the strongest possible influence on the later development of philosophical thought and have come to be known under the headings of materialism and idealism.

The atomic theory, which was initiated by Leucippos and Democritus, envisaged the smallest particle of matter as existence in its true sense. The smallest particles were considered to be indivisible and unchangeable, they were the eternal and the true basis of all matter and were thus called atoms and therefore did not require — indeed were quite incapable of — any further explanation. The only other properties they were considered to possess were geometrical ones. In the opinion of the philosophers they had a certain form, were separated one from another by empty space and brought about the abundance of phenomena by positioning themselves or moving in different ways in space. They had, however, neither colour, nor taste nor smell, nor did they have temperature or any other physical property known at the time. The properties of the things we can perceive were indirectly the result of the movements or position of the atoms. Just as comedy and tragedy are written with the same letters, so, according to the teachings of Democritus, could very different phenomena in the world be caused by the same atoms. The atoms were therefore the intrinsic, objectively real core of matter and thus of all material phenomena. They were, as already stated above, existence in its true sense, whereas the multitude of different phenomena was merely the indirect result of the behaviour of the atoms. This school of thought is therefore termed materialism.

Plato, on the other hand, considered the smallest particles of matter to be nothing more than geometrical forms. Plato identified the smallest particles of matter with the regular bodies in geometry. Like Empedocles, he believed in the existence of four elements, namely earth, air, fire and water, and envisaged the smallest particle of the earth element as a cube, and the smallest particle of the element water as an icosahedron, whilst the smallest particle of the element fire was considered to be a tetrahedron and the smallest particle of the element air an octohedron. The form was considered to be characteristic for the properties of the element. However, in contrast to Democritus, Plato did not hold these particles to be indestructible and unchangeable. On the contrary, he believed that they could be reduced to triangles and built up again from triangles. For this reason he does not refer to them as atoms. The triangles themselves are no longer matter, since they are not three-dimensional, they do not occupy space. At the lower end of the chain of material structures as seen by Plato we therefore no longer find something material, but simply a mathematical form, or if you like, a purely intellectual entity. The most basic concept comprehensible to man was, in Plato's opinion, mathematical symmetry, form, an idea; and this school of thought is therefore termed idealism.

Strangely enough, this old question of materialism or idealism has been brought up again in a very specific form by modern atomic physics and by the quantum theory of Max Planck in particular. Until the time of the discovery of Planck's action quantum, the exact natural sciences of our time, i.e. physics and chemistry, were materialistically orientated. During the 19th century the chemical atom and its components, which we now call elementary particles, were considered to be the real basis of all matter, and existence in its true sense. The existence of atoms did not seem to require any further explanation or even to be capable of the same.

However, Planck discovered a certain trait of discontinuity in radiation phenomena, which seemed to be related to a surprising extent to the existence of the atom but which could not be explained by this.

This trait of discontinuity, which was discovered through Planck's quantum of action, seemed to indicate that this very characteristic, as well as the existence of the atom, could be common effects of a fundamental natural law, of a mathematical structure within Nature itself, the formulation of which could at the same time open the way for the discovery of those principles governing the structure of matter for which the Greeks had sought so long. Perhaps the existence of the atom was not the final link in the chain after all – perhaps this existence could be traced back, similar to the manner in which Plato had sought to explain the basis of all matter, to the effect of natural laws which could be mathematically formulated, i.e. to the effect of mathematical symmetry.

Planck's law of radiation differed in a very characteristic way from natural laws formulated in earlier times. When earlier natural laws, e.g. Newton's law of mechanics, contained so-called constants, then these constants referred to the properties of things, e.g. their mass, or the strength of a force acting between two bodies or some such similar property. Planck's quantum of action, however, which appears as the characteristic constant in his law of radiation, does not describe the properties of things, but a property of Nature itself. It sets a standard in Nature and at the same time shows that in those regions of Nature where Planck's quantum of action can be considered as a negligible quantity, as in all phenomena of daily life, natural phenomena take a different course to that taken in cases where they are of atomic magnitude, i.e. of the order of Planck's quantum of action. Whereas earlier laws of physics, e.g. Newton's laws of mechanics, apply in exactly the same manner to all orders of magnitude – the rotation of the moon round the earth is supposed to take place according to the same laws as the falling of an apple from a tree or the deflection of an a-particle that flies past the nucleus of an atom – Planck's law of radiation shows for the first time that there are scales and standards in Nature; that phenomena are not simply alike in all orders of magnitude.

Only a few years after Planck's discovery of the quantum of action, a second constant of scale came to be understood in its full importance. Einstein's special theory of relativity made it clear to physicists that the velocity of light did not refer to a property of a special substance known as ether, as had earlier been assumed from a study of electrodynamics, in the belief that this substance was responsible for the propagation of the light, but that we were confronted in this case with a property of time and space, i.e. with a general property of Nature itself, which has nothing to do with specific objects or things in Nature at all. The velocity of light can therefore also be considered to be one of Nature's constants of scale. Our common concepts of time and space can only be used for the description of phenomena in which the velocities occuring are relatively small in comparison with the velocity of light. The well-known paradoxes of the theory of relativity, on the contrary, are due to the fact that phenomena in which the velocities occuring are of more or less the same order as the velocity of light cannot be correctly interpreted with our usual concepts of time and space. I should merely like to quote the well-known paradox of the clock, i.e. the fact that time seems to pass more slowly for the observer who is moving fast than it does for the observer who is standing still. After the mathematical structure of the special theory of relativity had been elucidated, the implications of this mathematical formulation for the interpretation of the phenomena were soon analysed with such thoroughness that the characteristics of Nature associated with the new constant of scale, i.e. the velocity of light, could be completely understood. Admittedly the considerable discussion still going on about the theory of relativity goes to show that our ingrained conceptions still place a number of difficulties in the way of this comprehension, but all doubts could be quickly dispelled.

2. It was, however, much more difficult to comprehend the physical implications of Planck's quantum of action. In one of Einstein's works, dating from the year 1918, it was already shown that the laws of the quantum theory were probably of a statistical nature. The first attempt to state precisely the statistical nature of the quantum theoretical laws was made in 1924 by Bohr, Kramers and Slater. The connection between electromagnetic fields, which had been regarded in classical

physics since the time of Maxwell as responsible for the propagation of
the phenomena of light, and the discontinuous absorption and emission
of light by the atom postulated by Planck were interpreted in the following manner: The electromagnetic field of waves, which is so patently
responsible for the phenomena of interference and diffraction, only
determines the degree of probability with which an atom emits or
absorbs light energy in the form of quanta at the point in space in
question. The electromagnetic field was thus no longer considered
directly as a field of forces which acts on the electrical charges of the
atom and thus causes movement; this action was considered to take
place in a more indirect manner, whereby the field only determines
the degree of probability with which emission or absorption takes
place. This interpretation later on turned out to be not quite correct.
The true connections were still more complicated and were correctly
formulated by Bohr at a later date. However, the work of Bohr, Kramers
and Slater did contain the decisive concept that natural laws do not
determine the occurrence of an event but only the probability of its
occurrence and that this probability must be connected to a field that
conforms to a wave equation that can be formulated mathematically.

Thus a decisive step away from classical physics was taken and
scientists fell back on a formulation which had already played an important role in the philosophy of Aristotle. The probability waves, as
interpreted in the work of Bohr, Kramers and Slater, can be taken as
a quantitative version of the concept of $\delta \upsilon \nu \alpha \mu \iota \varsigma$, of 'possibility', or
(in the later Latin form) of 'potentia' in the philosophy of Aristotle.
The idea that the phenomenon does not take place as a result of some
inescapable coercion but that the possibility or the tendency for some
phenomenon to occur itself possesses a degree of reality — a certain
intermediate kind of reality, which is somewhere between the solid
reality of matter and the mental reality of an idea or concept — plays
a decisive role in the philosophy of Aristotle. It acquires a new form in
the quantum theory inasmuch as this very concept of possibility is
quantitatively formulated as probability and is subjected to mathematically calculable natural laws. Natural laws formulated in the language
of mathematics no longer determine the phenomenon itself, but the
possibility or probability that some phenomenon will take place.

This way of introducing the probability concept corresponded
very accurately at first to the situation found during experimentation

in the course of the study of atomic phenomena. If the physicist determines the strength of radioactive radiation by counting the number of times the radiation sets off the counting tube during the course of a certain interval of time, then he automatically assumes in doing so that the intensity of the radioactive radiation will regulate the probability that the counting tube will register. The exact intervals between the pulses do not really interest the physicist at all — they are, as he would say, "statistically distributed". The only factor of interest to the scientist is the average frequency of the pulses. It has already been established by numerous tests that this statistical interpretation reproduces the experimental situation very precisely. In cases where quantum mechanics permits quantitative statements to be made, as concerning the wavelengths of spectral lines or the binding energies of molecules, they have also been confirmed by the experiments. In short, there was no reason to doubt the validity of this theory. However, the question as to how the statistical interpretation would agree with the wealth of experience embodied in classical physics was rather more difficult. All experiments are based on the fact that there is a definite connection between observation and the physical phenomenon. If, for example, we measure a spectral line of a certain frequency with a diffraction grating, we automatically assume that the atoms of the radiating substance must have emitted light of just this frequency. Or again, if a photographic plate is darkened, then we automatically assume that rays or particles of matter have fallen on it at this point. Physics therefore makes use of the causal determination of phenomena in order to gather experimental experience and thus becomes apparently contrasted to the experimental situation in the atomic field and to the quantum theory where such a causal determination of the phenomenon does frequently not exist.

The inner contradiction which appears to occur here is removed in modern physics by establishing that the phenomena are only determined in so far as they can be described with the concepts of classical physics. The use of these concepts is, on the other hand, limited by the so-called indeterminacy relations. These contain quantitative information concerning the limits of the use of classical concepts. The physicist therefore knows which phenomena he can consider as determined and which he must consider as undetermined, and he can thus use a method which is free from all contradictions in observing them and interpreting their

physical behaviour. Admittedly the question arises as to why it should
be necessary here to keep to the concepts of classical physics, instead
of converting the entire description of the physical behaviour to a new
system of concepts based on the quantum theory.

First of all one must stress, as von Weizsacker has done, that the
concepts of classical physics play a similar part in the interpretation
of the quantum theory to that played by the a priori forms of perception used by Kant in his philosophy. Just as Kant explained the concepts of space and time or causality as a priori, since they formed the
preconditions for all forms of experience and could not therefore be
considered as the result of experience, so are the concepts of classical
physics an a priori basis for all experience obtained about atomic
phenomena, as we can only carry out experiments in the atomic field
with the aid of these classical concepts.

Admittedly, Kant's "a priori" loses a certain claim to be absolute,
a claim which it certainly made in his philosophy, as a result of such an
interpretation. Whereas Kant was still able to assume that our a priori
forms of perception, i.e. space and time, would form the basis of
physics for all time, we now know that this is by no means the case.
For example, the complete independence of space and time which we
take for granted in our perception does not in fact exist in Nature if we
observe very accurately. Our forms of perception, although they are
a priori, do not agree with the results to be obtained only with the aid
of the most sensitive technical equipment about processes or phenomena
which take place at a velocity close to that of light. Our statements
about space and time must therefore vary, according to whether we
mean the a priori forms of perception inherent in our human nature or
the pattern of order which exists in Nature, quite independent of all
human observation, and in which all the objective phenomena of the
world appear to be spread out. In a similar manner, classical physics
forms the a priori basis for atomic physics and quantum theory, but it
does not apply everywhere with equal validity, i.e. there are many different types of phenomena which cannot be described in detail using
the concepts of classical physics.

In these fields of atomic physics, of course, much of the old conventional physics becomes lost. Not only the applicability of the concepts and laws of such physics, but also the entire concept of reality
on which the exact natural sciences right down to our modern atomic

physics were based. The term concept of reality is here meant to denote the idea that there are objective phenomena which take place in
time and space in a certain manner, irrespective of whether they are
observed or not. In atomic physics observations can no longer be ob-
jectivized in this simple manner, i.e. they can no longer be traced back
to an objective and describable course of events in time and space.
Here we find a consequence of the fact that natural science is not concerned with Nature itself, but with Nature as man describes and under-
stands it. This does not mean that an element of subjectivity is introduced into natural science — no one claims that the processes and phenomena that take place in the world are dependent on our observation —
but attention is brought to the fact that natural science stands between
man and Nature and that we cannot dispense with the aid of perceptual
concepts or other concepts inherent in the nature of man. This characteristic of quantum theory makes it difficult to accept the system laid
down in the philosophy of materialism and to consider the smallest
particles of matter, the elementary particles, as existence in the true
sense. For these elementary particles are, if quantum theory is correct,
no longer real in the same sense as are things of our everyday life, such
as the trees and stones. They rather appear to be abstractions taken from
the observation material, which is real in the true sense. However, if it
were impossible to attribute existence in the true sense to the elementary particles, it would also be difficult to consider matter as existence
in the true sense. It is for this reason that doubts concerning the
present-day interpretation of the quantum theory have been raised on
various occasions during the last few years in the camp of dialectic
materialism.

However, even this camp has been unable to bring forward any
fundamentally new interpretation of the quantum theory. I should just
like to mention one attempt at a new interpretation. An attempt was
made to say that the fact that a thing, e.g. an electron, belongs to an
assembly of electrons, is an objective fact that has nothing to do with
whether the object is being observed or not, i.e. is completely independent of the observer. A formulation of this nature would, however,
only be justified if the assembly existed in reality. However, in actual
fact one is generally concerned with only the one object in question,
such as one electron, whereas the assembly merely exists in our imagination, inasmuch as we imagine that the experiment with this one object

could be repeated as often as we like. However, it hardly seems possible
for us to describe the fact that something belongs to an assembly that
only exists in our mind as an objective fact. We cannot therefore escape
the conclusion that our earlier concept of reality is no longer valid in
the field of atomic physics and that we will become entangled in complicated abstractions if we regard the atom as existence in the true
sense. The concept of existence in the true sense has really been dis-
credited by modern physics and the fundamental teaching of materialistic philosophy must be modified at this point.

3. In the meanwhile, during the last two decades, the developments
in atomic physics have led even further away from the fundamental concepts of materialistic philosophy in the ancient sense. Experiments
have shown that the structures that we must beyond doubt regard as
the smallest particles of matter, namely the elementary particles, are
not constant and unchangeable as Democritus had assumed, but can be
changed one into another. First of all we must explain why we are
permitted to consider the elementary particles as the smallest particles
of matter. It could otherwise be argued that the elementary particles
were composed of other, even smaller structures which were in actual
fact constant and unchangeable. How can the physicist exclude the
possibility that the elementary particles consist of smaller structures
which for some reason have managed to escape observation?

I should like to explain in full the answer provided by modern
physics, as it shows very clearly the rather abstract nature of modern
atomic physics. If one wishes to establish experimentally whether an
elementary particle is elementary or is composed of other, even smaller
structures, then one must evidently attempt to break it up by the
strongest means available. As there are naturally no knives or tools
with which one can set about an elementary particle, the only possibility
is to let elementary particles collide with great force and watch whether
they break up in the process. The enormous accelerating machines in
use or under construction in various parts of the world today serve
this purpose. One of the largest machines of this type is just being
built by the European organization CERN in Geneva. With the aid of
these machines it is possible to accelerate elementary particles — these
are generally protons — to the highest possible velocity, to let them
collide with other elementary particles, namely the smallest particles
of any substance used as a target, and then to study the effect carefully.

Although a great deal of experimental material has still to be collected concerning the details of such collisions before one can hope to clear away all the problems existing in this field of physics, it is already possible to explain reasonably accurately how such a process takes place. It has transpired beyond doubt that a breakup of the elementary particle can take place, and that in many cases quite a number of particles are created in the process, but — and this is the paradoxical and surprising feature — the particles which are created during the collision are not smaller than the elementary particles which were broken up, but are elementary particles themselves. This paradox is explained by the fact that according to the theory of relativity, energy can be converted into mass. The elementary particles, which have been given an enormous kinetic energy during the process of acceleration, are able with the aid of this energy, which can be converted into mass, to create new elementary particles. These elementary particles are therefore in actual fact the last in the chain of units of matter, the smallest units into which matter can be broken down if extreme force is applied.

This state of affairs can also be described as follows: all elementary particles are made of the same material i.e. energy. They are the various forms which energy must take in order to become matter. Here we meet the concepts of "content and form" or "substance and form" used in the philosophy of Artistotle. Energy is not merely the force which keeps everything in a state of perpetual motion — it is, like fire in the philosophy of Heraclitus — the fundamental substance of which the world consists. Matter is created when the substance energy takes on the form of the elementary particle. As we know today there are various forms of this nature — we can now distinguish about 25 different sorts of elementary particles — and we have good reason to believe that all these forms are the expression or the consequence of certain fundamental mathematical structures i.e. the results of a fundamental law which can be expressed in mathematical terms and from which the elementary particles follow as a solution in the same way as the various energy states of the hydrogen atom are obtained as a solution of Schrodinger's differential equation. The elementary particles are therefore fundamental forms which the substance energy must take on in order to become matter and these fundamental forms must be determined in some manner by a natural law, by a fundamental law which can be expressed in mathematical terms.

This fundamental law which modern physics is searching for must fulfil two conditions, both of which are directly deduced from experimental experience. In the course of research into the elementary particles, particularly in research for which large accelerating machines were used, so-called selection rules have resulted for transitions which take place during impact processes or radioactive disintegration of particles. These selection rules, which can be mathematically formulated by means of suitably chosen quantum numbers, are the direct expression of symmetry properties which belong to the fundamental equation of matter or its solutions. The fundamental law must therefore contain these symmetries in some form or other, and must represent them mathematically. Secondly, the fundamental equation of matter — if we may assume that such a simple formulation exists — must, in addition to the two constants of the speed of light and Planck's quantum of action, contain at least one other constant of scale of a similar type, since the masses of the elementary particles can only follow from the fundamental equation, by reason of their size, if one third constant of scale, apart from those already mentioned above, is introduced. Observations of atomic nuclei and elementary particles seem to suggest that this third constant of scale should be represented as a universal length of the order of 10^{-13}.

In the basic natural law which determines the forms of matter, i.e. the elementary particles, three constants of scale should occur, although the numerical value of the three constants of scale no longer contains any information of a physical nature. The numerical value is rather a statement concerning the scales with which we intend to measure the processes which occur in Nature. However, the mathematical symmetry properties must form the actual conceptual core of the fundamental law, since they are represented by this law. The most important symmetry properties of the fundamental equation for which we are still seeking are already known from experience. I should like to list them briefly: First of all the so-called Lorentz group must certainly be included in the fundamental law as this can be considered to represent the properties of space and time required by the theory of relativity. In addition, the fundamental equation must also be approximately invariant under a group of transformations which can be mathematically designated as the group of the unitary transformations of two complex variables. The physical reason for this transformation property is a quantum number which was deduced from observations over twenty years ago and distinguishes neutrons and protons from one another. It is now generally known as isospin. Research by Pauli and Gursey during the last few years has shown that this quantum number can be represented by the above-mentioned mathematical transformation property. In addition to this there are a few other group properties, reflection symmetries in time and space, but we shall not go into these details at this point.

So far one suggestion has been made for the fundamental equation of matter which fulfils the above-mentioned conditions and is, moreover, very simple. The simplest and most symmetrical non-linear wave equation for a field operator conceived as a spinor fulfils all the conditions. However, whether it represents the correct formulation of the natural law will not be known until the highly complicated mathematical analysis is completed in the course of the next few years. I should like to point out here that there are also a number of physicists who are not so optimistic about the mathematical form of the fundamental laws and their simplicity. In view of the complicated system of the elementary particles observed they are more inclined to assume that a number of different basic field operators must exist — some mention at least four, others at least six of these field quantities — and that a correspondingly complicated system of mathematical relations exists between them. The question as to how complicated or how simple the formulation of this fundamental law will be is therefore not yet decided and one can hope that the observation material that will be collected in the course of the next few years with the aid of the large accelerating plants will soon provide a firm foundation for the solution of this question.

Quite independent of the final result of this research we are already in a position to say that the final result will be nearer to the philosophical conception as represented for instance in Plato's dialogue Timaios [Timaeus] than to the conception of the ancient materialists. This should not be taken as an easy way of rejecting the views of the modern materialists of the 19th century, who produced many interesting ideas that were lacking in the natural philosophy of the ancients, since they were able to draw on the natural sciences of the 17th and 18th centuries. In spite of this, however, one cannot dispute that the elementary particles of modern physics are more closely related to Plato's regular bodies than Democritus' atoms.

The elementary particles of modern physics are determined by mathematical symmetry requirements, rather like the regular bodies mentioned in Plato's philosophy, they are not constant and unchanging and can therefore scarcely be considered as real in the usual sense of the word. They are rather to be considered as simple representations of the fundamental mathematical structures at which we arrive if we attempt to divide up matter into sections of ever decreasing size, and which form the content of the fundamental natural laws. We therefore see that in modern natural science it is not the thing but the form, the mathematical symmetry, that is the beginning of all things. And since the mathematical structure is in the end nothing but an intellectual content, one could well say, in the words of Goethe's Faust "At the beginning was the concept." To recognize this concept, in so far as it concerns the fundamental structure of matter, in all its details and perfectly clearly is the task of modern atomic physics and of its apparatus, which is unfortunately all too complicated. It seems fascinating to me to think that at the present time, in all parts of the world, and with all the technical means at our disposal, man is struggling to solve problems which were formulated by the Greek philosophers two and a half thousand years ago and that we shall know the answers in the course of the next few years, or at least during the next two decades.

IDENTITY AND REALITY

Emile Meyerson (1859-1933) was a well-known French philos-
sopher of science and a chevalier of the Légion d'Honneur.
The selection is from Identity and Reality.*

From the preceding pages this conclusion, it seems, stands out: it is not true that the sole end of science is action, nor that it is solely governed by the desire for economy in this action. Science also wishes to make us *understand* nature. It tends, indeed, according to Le Roy's expression, toward the "progressive rationalization of reality."[1]

Science has, in truth, been established with the almost complete certainty that nature is regulated, but also with the tenacious hope that it will manifest itself as intelligible. In every chapter of science these two principles have been applied simultaneously and continue to be so applied. Their action is irrevocably entangled, because they pass and repass their acquisitions to each other; not only, as has been said, do empirical facts serve to establish theories which bring about the discovery of new facts, but also considerations of conservation, of identity, intervene at every step in empirical science, which is, in spite of appearances, saturated with these *a priori* elements.

Science is not *positive* and does not even contain positive data in the precise meaning which Auguste Comte and his adherents have given to this term—that is, data "stripped of all ontology." Ontology is of a piece with science itself and cannot be separated from it. Those who

---

*Translated by Kate Loewenberg (London: George Allen & Unwin, Ltd.; New York: Humanities Press, Inc., 1930) pp. 384-395. Reprinted by permission of the publishers.

pretend to separate them are unconsciously using a current metaphysical system, a common sense more or less transformed by science of the past, which is familiar to them. The positivist plan is, therefore, truly chimerical. Not only does it correspond neither to modern science nor to any which humanity has known at any epoch of evolution, but it implies and demands such a modification, such an unsettling of our habits of thought, that we have infinite difficulty in conceiving it and especially in measuring all of its consequences. Indeed, the only means of doing away with every ontology would consist in accomplishing that operation at the very beginning of physics, by dissolving the object and returning to the immediate data of Bergson, in order to try afterwards to establish direct relations between these data, without passing through the hypothesis of an objective existence. Is such a science possible? Malebranche expressly denied it. He attempted to show that in no case could one pretend to measure sensations directly by one another, as subjective phenomena; and that all comparison of these presupposes a preliminary reduction to objective causes, and therefore a subjection of them to fixation in time and space. This seems to be an impregnable deduction. We saw that a purely qualitative science, which was still substantialistic, though capable of setting up *scales,* could no longer *measure.* With still greater reason would this be so in the science that is truly phenomenalistic, from which the very quality itself, viewed as substratum, would be excluded. And yet must the possibility of a science of this kind be radically denied, and its entire uselessness from the point of view of prevision be asserted? What makes one hesitate before this absolute negation is precisely the novelty, the unknown factor in the proposed method. Without further attempt to go to the bottom of this question, which would be too great a digression from the subject of this book, let us observe, once again, how greatly science thus constituted, supposing even that it were possible, would depart from all that we know. It would certainly no longer be physics, but rather a sort of psycho-physics pushed to the extreme; it would, indeed be infinitely more than all we know under this name, removed from physics, since modern psycho-physics, it is easily understood, presupposes physics as a basis, and consequently the whole ontological world of common sense and of science.— The ontological character of scientific explanation is ineffaceable. Doubtless, through the unity of matter it finally ends in uniform and empty space. But here there is destruction of reality, of the whole external world; and in this destruction, it goes without saying, law also has been abolished, for there being no longer any diversity either in time or in space, there is no longer any phenomenon, and therefore nothing which law may rule. Therefore, and contrary

to what is sometimes supposed believable, there is not, there cannot
be, in the natural evolution of scientific theories, any phase where
ontological reality would disappear, and at the same time the concept
of conformity to law remain standing. Their disappearance is certainly
simultaneous, and if we take the world of scientific theory at the
moment, so to speak, when it is going to evolve into non-entity, we
shall find it as ontological as that of the reality of common sense; the
singular points of the ether, in so far as we differentiate them from
our medium by any means whatsover, will be just as real, just as
much *objects,* and even more fundamentally independent of us and
our sensation than anything in our perception. Explanatory science,
indeed, rejoins absolute idealism or solipsism, but it is only in complete
acosmism that these two ways encounter each other. Between these two
parallel lines, along which science and philosophy, each one by itself, tend to destroy reality, one cannot imagine any point in common
except one situated in infinity.

This explains a peculiar characteristic of physicists' research into
the constitution of matter, a characteristic which is certainly of a
nature to strike the attention of the philosopher—to wit, the unconscious certainty, one might almost say the alacrity, which the scientist
shows in this domain, whereas to the philosopher, his conclusions
appear formidable, extravagant in the literal sense of the word, completely departing from the ordinary plan of experimental research.
How does it happen, then, that the physicist does not possess this
feeling at all, that he has, on the contrary, the very distinct impression
of being in his own domain and of following his customary methods?
It is because, starting from a conception of the world such as our
naive perception offers, he has never transformed it except by putting
into play the very rules according to which this conception was constituted. He has continually substituted the invisible for the visible,
but what he has created is of the same order as what he has destroyed.
He simply treats the atom as the biologist treats the microbe, the first
is compared to a billiard ball as the second is compared to an animal.

With all the more reason the scientist feels himself protected from
doubt in less extreme, less exposed parts of his domain; and it is not
astonishing that this security has at times been envied by the philosopher. This is why frequently renewed attempts have been made to
extract a real philosophy from science with the help of processes of

extrapolation and generalization. The progress and ultimate end of this kind of enterprise may be traced in advance to a certain extent. Indeed, in creating science, man has constantly obeyed his casual instinct; starting from sensation, he has unceasingly tried to explain it, to make it yield to the exigencies of his reason. Therefore, what will be most general in science will necessarily be also a form of these exigencies, and, consequently, a conception saturated with the *a priori:* a casual hypothesis such as that of the persistence of qualities and especially the atomic or mechanical theory. And so it is that believing to generalize the results of experience we succeed paradoxically in liberating our conceptions, prior to experience, from the restrictions imposed by experience.

It goes without saying that in pressing his thought into the ontological mould, in giving to it the form of an hypothesis about the reality of things, the scientist, just like the commonsense man, acts in an entirely unconscious manner. It is not astonishing, therefore, to see him unacquainted with the process which he is applying—nay, even with the metaphysical tendency which is pushing him on. No more than any other man does the scientist see himself thinking. Doubtless if he has peculiarly powerful gifts, he may succeed, by a slow and patient analysis, in sometimes recognizing the true path which his thought has followed; but the fact of being a scientist, nay, even a great scientist, has nothing to do with it. Indeed, the distinctive quality of a great scientist is a powerful scientific instinct, a sort of divination which allows him to touch the high places only. The discovery, it has often been noticed, comes to him suddenly—after long labour, of course; it is a flash, a revelation: is it astonishing that he has not been able to trace its genesis? And so it follows that we must not look to the scientist for the principles which have really guided his thought; we must not even believe him on his word when he tries to state them. He may have discovered these principles in almost any other way than by a patient analysis of his own thought. He has most often found them already fashioned in some book; they penetrated him without his knowledge, because they pervaded the intellectual atmosphere surrounding him.

This explains how one can go astray in searching for the principles of science, even on the supposition that one is following closely the scientist; their methodical ways are cheerfully accepted, without

questioning whether the aforesaid methods had ever really been applied by the scientists themselves. It is this error, we think, which is
at the bottom of the affirmation according to which, as a very eminent
contemporary philosopher says, "Mathematical physics turns aside
from the essence of things and their inner substantiality in order to
turn toward their numerical order and connection, and their functional
and mathematical structure."[2]

Declarations of this sort may certainly be found in the creators
of modern physical science—in Kepler, in Newton, even in Descartes,
in Boyle, and in Boscovich. But if, on the other hand, we consider
without prejudice and on its merits their work as scientists, we easily
perceive that it offers a quite different picture. Thus Boscovich seems,
indeed, according to the title of his *Theoria,* to reduce the concept of
force to that of law. But it is clear, when one reaches the heart of the
work, that he considers this force to be, on the contrary, a real being,
a *thing,* the true essence of nature, which he has sought for and found;
his argumentation against the corpuscular theory would have no meaning if this were not so. Boyle, we have seen, was one of the strictest
atomists known to the history of science at any time; he invented the
term "corpuscular" for the particular form of the theory which he
adopted and which he constantly used. His foregone conclusion from
this point of view greatly impressed his contemporaries, such as
Spinoza and Leibniz; and it is clear that in attempting to reduce a
change of colour to the displacement of molecules, as he did many
times, he was not concerned simply with the rule of a phenomenon,
but with its true nature, its essence, and its cause. And as to Descartes,
it is certain that he sought for the essence of things as eagerly as the
scholastics, but unlike these latter, he found it in space; surely no
one has been more affirmative, more apodictic than he is this respect.
In spite of appearances the situation was the same with Kepler and
with Newton. Kepler, while seeking for the laws of planetary attraction, sought at the same time for its cause, and formulated a whole
theory on this subject. Newton, in spite of the *hypotheses non fingo,*
based his *Opticks* on the theory of emission. His famous definition of
mass by density can only be explained as Rosenberger has justly
shown, [3] by strongly entrenched atomistic convictions. And it is
reasonable to doubt whether, in eliminating every real hypothesis, he
ever conceived the action of gravitation as a pure and simple law; on

the contrary, he openly accepted in the first place the partly theological
hypothesis of More, attempting to give it a more scientific appearance
by the assumption of a particular medium, and afterward allowed
Cotes, in the preface to the second edition of *Principia,* to speak of
force acting at a distance as of a real being.

This situation is so apparent that, in building up anti-substantialis-
tic conceptions of science, it could not be entirely ignored. The difficulty has generally been avoided by treating the works and the attempts
in question as simple digressions, by pretending to believe that it was
a question of parts which were not essential to the whole of the work
and which could be easily detached. Now it is certain that, on the contrary, such an operation would be extremely difficult, even for Newton,
whose *Opticks* and *Principia* would be deprived of some of their most
essential chapters. And if one tried to do it for Descartes, all his *Principia*
would have to be effaced. Evidently the scientific work of these great
scientists holds together and is ordered in quite a different sense from
the statements of method which are cited.

We saw at the beginning of this book[4] that the primitive source of
what might be called the positivist error lies in the confusion between
law and cause, in the misunderstanding of the truth, that in explaining
a phenomenon by a law we are only using a synecdoche. The fact,
however, that many scientists have made statements condemning all
search for essence and for cause is susceptible, we believe, of more direct psychological explanations. It must be noted that it is a very simple
principle, which can be expressed under a precise form like that finally
given it by the scientist's pride, since it makes his chosen field appear
to be in a manner sovereign, and entirely independent of the other
pursuits of human thought. It is conceivable that it was on these last
grounds that positivism conquered the nineteenth century, an epoch
distinguished for the fruitfulness of experimental research. But it is
not at all astonishing that this conception in a way surreptitiously se-
duced many minds before that time. One should rather be astonished
at the contrary, and, indeed, if this conception did not appear sooner,
if when sometimes formulated very distinctly (as it was, for instance,
by Berkeley) it again disappeared, immediately forgotten, it is not, as
has frequently been said, because of a kind of vicious propensity of the
human mind toward ontology, but rather because it is entirely contrary
to the real advance of the intellect as much in the individual thinker as

in the whole evolution of science. What would have happened in the
past if humanity, seeking the impossible, had adopted Berkeley's or
Comte's point of view and considered that there is no cause beyond
law or that it ought not to be sought for? The great idealistic philosopher prudently abstained from applying his principle. But Auguste
Comte expressed himself with greater precision. Thus he praised
Fourier for having dealt with heat without trying to know whether it
was matter or movement.[5] He denied that the undulatory theory of
any other could ever possess "any real usefulness in guiding our minds
in the effective study of optics";[6] he considered that the "pretended
optical interferences or the analogous crossings in acoustics" were
"essentially subjective phenomena," the contrary opinion of physicists
being "a serious illusion";[7] he affirmed that all comparison between light,
sound, or motion will always be "an arbitrary assumption";[8] he condemned in general as due "to the prolonged preponderance of the old
philosophical mind" all tendencies attempting to establish relations between what to-day we call the different forms of energy.[9] Moreover,
it is easy to ascertain that these errors of the founder of positivism are
in no way accidental. Starting from the utilitarian concept of science,
as we saw in Chapter I, one can justify explicative hypotheses, if
necessary. However, it becomes difficult to explain the physicist's pre-
dilection for atomic conceptions; and we see that Comte's anathema
against the undulatory theory, etc., is really a part of his doctrine.

Principles of positivism, or, at any rate, analogous principles,
have since been adopted, at least in appearance, by many scientists,
who have often felt bound to protest, like Comte, against atomic
theories; but, as a matter of fact, and in spite of the aid given to this
tendency by the great and legitimate authority of Mach, it remains
to-day, as it did during the nineteenth century, without the least influence on the progress of science. The scientists of the beginning of
the twentieth century continue to build up atomic theories just as
their predecessors have done. All, doubtless, do not believe in the truth
of the theories which they imagine or which they follow; but all believe
in their utility. All see in them, for want of something better, an instrument of research of great value, "working hypotheses." These play
an extremely important role. Bacon believed that one could arrive at
scientific discoveries by mechanical processes of induction, so to speak;
he went to great lengths in elaborating detailed plans the use of which

would leave little to be attributed "to the penetration and vigour of minds," making them, on the contrary, "all nearly equal."[10] It is incontestable that certain rules stated by Bacon (such as, for example, those of concomitant variations) are useful in scientific reasoning. But his table or schemes, one may boldly affirm, have never been employed in a constant manner by a scientist worthy of that name; at any rate, no scientific discovery, great or small, is due to their application.[11] It would seem that one cannot better refute Bacon's opinions than by citing those of three eminent men, counted amongst the creators of that especially experimental science, the chemistry of the end of the eighteenth century and the first half of the nineteenth. "To attempt an experiment," says Berthollet, "one must have an end, be guided by an hypothesis."[12] Humphry Davy affirms that "it is only in forming theories and in comparing them with facts that we can hope to discover the true system of nature."[13] And Liebig, after having declared that between experiments in Bacon's sense and true scientific research "there is the same relation as between the noise a child produces by striking on a drum and music,"[14] shows that, on the contrary, it is the scientific imagination which plays the most important role is discoveries, and that experiment, like the calculus, only aids in the process of thought.

Among our contemporaries, Poincare, in his Report to the *Congres International de Physique de 1900,* stated that to wish to experiment without preconceived ideas would be to render all experiment sterile, and more over, that it is impossible to free oneself from ideas of this kind; and Duhem showed the close dependence of experiments upon scientific theories[15] and made clear the impossibility of the famous *experimentum crucis,* which plays such an important part in the Baconian theory.[16]

As to the working hypotheses," the only point of view which directly interests the scientist is their fertility, their aptitude for making him discover relations between phenomena which he had not suspected. What assumptions have ever equalled from this point of view the utility of mechanical hypotheses? In the entire domain of science, which they fill, they have produced, and are producing, a prodigious harvest of discoveries of the highest value. Where scientists in the first place have thought there was only a quite superficial similitude, subsequent research has sometimes brought to light in a most unexpected manner a more profound analogy. Let us recall how sceptical people were at first, about Kekule's hypothesis concerning the structure of the components of carbon and the position of atoms in the molecule; and even when it was proved that this description explained admirably an immense series of phenomena, which, until then, constituted a kind of impenetrable jungle, to many it still seemed grossly inadequate. And yet what an astonishing extension and verification of these theories were Le Bel's and van't Hoff's discoveries about the asymmetric atom of carbon! Who does not marvel at the role of the atomic hypotheses in the recent progress of electricity and at the alliance of chemistry with it through the efforts of Svante Arrhenius? And is it not surprising to notice that the greater part of irreversible phenomena, which by their nature seem to elude causal explanations, appear traced, so to speak, to a mechanical phenomenon, viz. friction, to the point that physicists are now convinced that it is more than a simple analogy— something which reveals the intimate nature of things.[17] We have cited only recent, almost contemporary, examples, but there were just as many in the past, as, for instance, only to mention one illustrious example, the so brilliantly realized previsions which were deduced from Fresnel's theorem.[18]

So also the history of sciences shows us that, thanks to atomic conceptions, humanity has really foreseen to some extent certain important scientific truths, and developed a kind of prescience. When the Greek atomists affirmed that air, like any other substance, must be composed of discrete parts, it was a pure a *priori* conception. No fact was known at that time to confirm this opinion; on the contrary, everything seemed to show that air is a continuum. But we can now prove experimentally that this last opinion is untenable, that the gases really have a structure, are discontinuous. So also the chemists of the nineteenth century, by attaching a tenacious hope to the hypothesis of the unity of matter, were in opposition to the best established experimental facts which formed the very basis of their own doctrine. And yet phenomena relating to cathode rays, to radiant matter, etc., are tending to furnish an experimental foundation to this hypothesis. What is taking place as regards the reversibility of chemical reactions is of the same order. It is certain (Berthollet's ideas on this having had almost no influence on the progress of science) that this notion was absolutely foreign to the mind of a

chemist in the middle of the nineteenth century; and nothing was
less justifiable from this point of view than the use of the sign of
equality to unite the two terms of what is called a "chemical equation."
This sign, a palpable manifestation of the causal tendency, expressed
a postulate or, if you will, a hope, which in the light of the then prevailing theories, was unrealizable or rather absurd, since it was understood that the two sides of the equation indicated, one the initial
state and the other the final state of the phenomenon, which always
had to take place in the same direction, without hope of return. It is
all the more astonishing to state that this almost chimerical hope has,
in a certain measure, been realized: chemical reactions appear to us
to-day as generally reversible and we can, in fact, replace the equation
sign (the meaning of which was distorted), by van't Hoff's two arrows.

But the most striking, the most marvellous phenomenon of this
order, is the existence of the principles of conservation. In virtue of
the causal tendency, humanity had a presentiment of them; it had
formed the concept of the atom-substance long before any experiment
on the conservation of matter, and it vaguely conceived mechanical
systems as implying the persistence of motion before inertia and the
conservation of energy. So if, on the one hand, these principles seem
simply to formulate a knowledge that humanity had always possessed,
on the other hand, they surpass, so to speak, the very limits of the
hope it had a right to conceive. Thus heat and light might well have
been movements, conforming to the postulate of universal mechanism,
without any possibility of converting these movements of particles
into movements of mass, or vice versa. This was approximately the
conception of Leibniz and Huygens, and, in general, of most mechanis-
tic physicists before the establishment of the conservation of energy.
This last discovery is a quite unexpected confirmation. In the same
way the most determined mechanist would never have dared to hope
in the nineteenth century, before the work of Gouy, that the agitation
of molecules could ever be made directly visible by its most immediate
mechanical effects. These surprising agreements attracted the attention
of thinkers. We saw (Chapter II, p. 91) that Cournot, in stating the
perennial character of atomic theories, had concluded that it was
possible that its inventors had "immediately fallen on the very key of
natural phenomena." At other times he thought that he could infer
from the conservation of the weight of matter that the idea of sub-

stance is not merely a logical abstraction, but that it has "its founda-tion in the essence of bodies."[19] Many remarks of contemporary physicists may be cited in which they express their astonishment at the agreement between the conceptions of the mind and the results of experimental research. Poincare's observation on irreversible phenom-ena, which we have noted earlier, belongs to this region of ideas. At another time this eminent theorist marvels rightly at the surprising analogy between electric oscillation and the motion of the pendulum.[20] Boltzmann states that "all the consequences of the mechanical theory of heat, even those belonging to the most incongruous domains, have been confirmed by experiment; it may even be said that they agree most strangely, even in their finest shades, with the pulse of nature."[21] Hertz, in the beginning of his mechanics, declares that in a general man-ner, in order that we may form images of things, the logical consequence of these images must indeed be images of the consequences which things really produce in nature. There must, therefore, be agreement between nature and our minds.[22]

It was consequently wrong to have called, as we did, causal hypo-theses, simple instruments of research, "working" hypotheses. They are more than the scaffolding destined to disappear when the building is constructed. They have their own value; they correspond certainly to something very profound and very essential in nature itself.

And so, and this is very important to notice, the agreement between the postulates of our mind and phenomena goes beyond pure confor-mity to law. Nature not only shows itself to be ordered, but, even to a certain point, really intelligible.

1. E. LeRoy, Science et Philosophie, Revue de métaphysique, vii, 1899, p. 534.

2. Cassirer, Das Erkenntnisproblem in der Philosophie und Wissenschaft der neueren Zeit; Berlin, 1906-1907, Vol. II, p. 530. See the article, Revue de metaphysique, January, 1911, p. 122.

3 F. Rosenberger, Isaak Newton, Leipzig, 1895, pp. 173, 192. The same author points out the contradiction between the title Philosophiae naturalis principia mathematica and the content of the writing, which, in fact, constitutes only an exposition of the principles of mechanics (p. 172); but this is because Newton, like Descartes and like Leibniz, had the firm conviction that everything in physics should be reduced to mechanics.

4. Identity and Reality, Chapter I, pp. 18, 39.

5. A. Comte, Cours de philosophie positive, 4th ed., Paris, 1877, Vol. I, p.18.

6. Ibid., Vol. II, p. 453.

7. A. Comte, Politique positive, Vol. I, p. 531. The date at which he expresses this opinion (1851) only renders it the more curious.

8. A. Comte, Cours de philosophie positive, Vol. II, p. 445.

9. Ibid., Vol. III, pp. 152 ff.

10. F. Bacon, Novum Organon, Book I, Aph. 61. It is very curious to observe that, just like Comte and evidently for analogous reasons, Bacon was strangely mistaken in his judgment about the great conquests of science. Thus he severely blamed Copernicus (Glom. inst., Chap. VI); and Gilbert, whose works on electricity are a veritable monument to the purest scientific thought, was his pet aversion (Novum Org., I, 54; II, Aph. 48). Naturally, we in no wise mean to attribute to Comte, on this question, opinions analogous to those of Bacon. On the contrary, Comte constantly insisted upon the necessity of hypothesis; absolute empiricism, according to him, is "not only entirely sterile, but even radically impossible for our understanding" (Cours, Vol. VI, p. 471). He only protested against hypotheses characterized by him as "metaphysical." But this attitude, although less absolute than that of Bacon, was enough to lead him into errors of the same kind.

11. F. Rosenberger, Geschichte, II, p. 191, remarks on Bacon's little real influence on the progress of science. Boyle seems to have allowed himself to be tempted to apply, not, indeed, Bacon's schemes (that would probably have been impossible), but certain of his principles. Rosenberger thinks that this circumstance was the reason why, having in hand all the experimental data of Mariotti's law (Boyle's law), it slipped from him in the end.

12. C.L. Berthollet, Essai de statique chimique, Paris, 1803, p. 5.

13. Encyclopaedia Britannica, 9th ed., "Davy", p. 847.

14. J. von Liebig, Reden und Abhandlungen, Leipzig, 1874, p. 249.

15. P. Duhem, La théorie physique, p. 300 (see Identity and Reality, p. 368).

16. Ibid., p. 308.

17. H. Poincaré, La science et l'hypothèse, p. 208.

18. See P. Duhem, La théorie physique, p. 43.

19. A. Cournot, Traité de L'enchaînement, Paris, 1861, p. 157.

20. H. Poincaré, La science et l'hypothèse, p. 191.

21. L. Boltzmann, Über die Unentbehrlichkeit der Atomistik, Wiedemann's Annalen, Vol. LX, 1897, p. 243.

22. H. Hertz, Gesammelte Werke, Leipzig, 1895, Vol. I, p. 1.

INSTRUMENTALISM

COPERNICUS

THE ROLE OF HYPOTHESES

*Nicholas Copernicus (1473-1543) is, of course, the famous
Polish-German astronomer who revived the heliocentric theory
of the solar system.*

Copernicus' major work De Revolutionibus Orbium
Coelestium *(On the Revolutions of the Celestial Spheres)**
*appeared in 1543. Fearing possible repercussions, his editor,
Osiander, added an unsigned preface in which he stated that
the notion of the heliocentric solar system was a mere hypothesis entertained for speculative purposes and not meant to
be taken literally. It was not until years later that Johannes
Kepler exposed Osiander as the author of the preface.*

*Whether it was meant to be serious or not, the preface is
considered one of the earliest articulations of the view of instrumentalism. The selection is taken from the Introduction
and is an address to the reader.*

Since the newness of the hypotheses of this work—which sets the
earth in motion and puts an immovable sun at the centre of the universe—has already received a great deal of publicity, I have no doubt
that certain of the savants have taken great offense and think it wrong

---

*The selection appeared originally in Vol. 16 of <u>Great Books of the Western World,</u> pp. 505-506,
translated by Charles Glenn Wallis (Chicago: Encyclopaedia Britannica, 1952). Used by permission.

to raise any disturbance among liberal disciplines which have had the right set-up for a long time now. If, however, they are willing to weigh the matter scrupulously, they will find that the author of this work has done nothing which merits blame. For it is the job of the astronomer to use painstaking and skilled observation in gathering together the history of the celestial movements, and then—since he cannot by any line of reasoning reach the true causes of these movements—to think up or construct whatever causes or hypotheses he pleases such that, by the assumption of these causes, those same movements can be calculated from the principles of geometry for the past and for the future too. This artist is markedly outstanding in both of these respects; for it is not necessary that these hypotheses should be true, or even probably; but it is enough if they provide a calculus which fits the observations— unless by some chance there is anyone so ignorant of geometry and optics as to hold the epicycle of Venus as probable and to believe this to be a cause why Venus alternately precedes and follows the sun at an angular distance of up to 40° or more. For who does not see that it necessarily follows from this assumption that the diameter of the planet in its perigee should appear more than four times greater, and the body of the planet more than sixteen times greater, than in its apogee? Nevertheless the one experience of all the ages is opposed to that. There are also other things in this discipline which are just as absurd, but it is not necessary to examine them right now. For it is sufficiently clear that this art is absolutely and profoundly ignorant of the causes of the apparent irregular movements. And if it constructs and thinks up causes—and it has certainly thought up a good many— nevertheless it does not think them up in order to persuade anyone of their truth but only in order that they may provide a correct basis for calculation. But since for one and the same movement varying hypotheses are proposed from time to time, as eccentricity or epicycle for the movement of the sun, the astronomer much prefers to take the one which is easiest to (ii^a) grasp. Maybe the philosopher demands probability instead; but neither of them will grasp anything certain or hand it on, unless it has been divinely revealed to him. Therefore let us permit these new hypotheses to make a public appearance among old ones which are themselves no more probable, especially since they are wonderful and easy and bring with them a vast storehouse of learned observations. And as far as hypotheses go, let no one expect anything in the way of certainty from astronomy, since astronomy can offer us nothing certain, lest, if anyone take as true that which has been constructed for another use, he go away from this discipline a bigger fool than when he came to it. Farewell.

NEWTON

ON HYPOTHESES

*Isaac Newton (1642-1727) was not only one of the founders
of modern science but he was the first scientist to capture
the public's admiration. His early scientific work was in the
field of optics; he formulated the law for the composition of
light. In mathematics he formulated the binomial theorem
and the differential calculus. A suggestion by the famous
astronomer, Halley, led Newton to formulate his famous
theory of universal gravitation.*

*Newton's career also comprised theological speculation,
a post at the royal mint, and membership in the British
Parliament.*

His most famous work was Philosophiae Naturalis Principia
Mathematica *(Mathematical Principles of Natural Philosophy),
1687. In it, he presented the mathematical foundations of
astronomy and dynamics. Newton's work also became the
model for scientific method in the eighteenth and early nineteenth centuries.*

*The selection is from the Preface to the first edition of
the* Principia *and from the General Scholium of the same
work.* *

Since the ancients (as we are told by *Pappus*), made great account
of the science of mechanics in the investigation of natural things; and
the moderns, laying aside substantial forms and occult qualities, have
endeavoured to subject the phænomena of nature to the laws of mathematics, I have in this treatise cultivated mathematics so far as it regards philosophy. The ancients considered mechanics in a twofold respect; as rational, which proceeds accurately by demonstration; and

---

*Translated from the Latin by Andrew Motte

practical. To practical mechanics all the manual arts belong, from which mechanics took its name. But as artificers do not work with perfect accuracy, it comes to pass that mechanics is so distinguished from geometry, that what is perfectly accurate is called geometrical; what is less so, is called mechanical. But the errors are not in the art, but in the artificers. He that works with less accuracy is an imperfect mechanic; and if any could work with perfect accuracy, he would be the most perfect mechanic of all;for the description of right lines and circles, upon which geometry is founded, belongs to mechanics. Geometry does not teach us to draw these lines, but requires them to be drawn; for it requires that the learner should first be taught to describe these accurately, before he enters upon geometry; then it shows how by these operations problems may be solved. To describe right lines and circles are problems, but not geometrical problems. The solution of these problems is required from mechanics; and by geometry the use of them, when so solved, is shown; and it is the glory of geometry that from those few principles, brought from without, it is able to produce so many things. Therefore geometry is founded in mechanical practice, and is nothing but that part of universal mechanics which accurately proposes and demonstrates the art of measuring. But since the manual arts are chiefly conversant in the moving of bodies, it comes to pass that geometry is commonly referred to their magnitudes, and mechanics to their motion. In this sense rational mechanics will be the science of motions resulting from any forces whatsoever, and of the forces required to produce any motions, accurately proposed and demonstrated. This part of mechanics was cultivated by the ancients in the five powers which relate to manual arts, who considered gravity (it not being a manual power), no otherwise than as it moved weights by those powers. Our design not respecting arts, but philosophy, and our subject not manual but natural powers, we consider chiefly those things which relate to gravity, levity, elastic force, the resistance of fluids, and the like forces, whether attractive or impulsive; and therefore we offer this work as the mathematical principles of philosophy; for all the difficulty of philosophy seems to consist in this — from the phenomena of motions to investigate the forces of nature, and then from these forces to demonstrate the other phænomena; and to this end the general propositions in the first and second book are directed. In the third book we give an example of this in the explication of the

System of the World; for by the propositions mathematically demonstrated in the former books, we in the third derive from the celestial
phænomena the forces of gravity with which bodies tend to the sun
and the several planets. Then from these forces, by other propositions
which are also mathematical, we deduce the motions of the planets,
the comets, the moon, and the sea. I wish we could derive the rest of
the phænomena of nature by the same kind of reasoning from mechanical principles; for I am induced by many reasons to suspect that
they may all depend upon certain forces by which the particles of
bodies, by some causes hitherto unknown, are either mutually impelled
towards each other, and cohere in regular figures, or are repelled and
recede from each other; which forces being unknown, philosophers
have hitherto attempted the search of nature in vain; but I hope the
principles here laid down will afford some light either to this or some
truer method of philosophy. . . .

*   *   *

Hitherto we have explained the phænomena of the heavens and
of our sea by the power of gravity, but have not yet assigned the cause
of this power. This is certain, that it must proceed from a cause that
penetrates to the very centres of the sun and planets, without suffering
the least diminution of its force; that operates not according to the
quantity of the surfaces of the particles upon which it acts (as mechanical causes use to do), but according to the quantity of the solid matter which they contain, and propagates its virtue on all sides to immense distances, decreasing always in the duplicate proportion of the
distances. Gravitation towards the sun is made up out of the gravita-
tions towards the several particles of which the body of the sun is
composed; and in receding from the sun decreases accurately in the
duplicate proportion of the distances as far as the orb of Saturn, as
evidently appears from the quiescence of the aphelions of the planets;
nay, and even to the remotest aphelions of the comets, if those aphelions are also quiescent. But hitherto I have not been able to discover
the cause of those properties of gravity from phænomena, and I frame
no hypotheses; for whatever is not deduced from the phænomena is to
be called an hypothesis; and hypotheses, whether metaphysical or
physical, whether of occult qualities or mechanical, have no place in

experimental philosophy. In this philosophy particular propositions are inferred from the phænomena, and afterwards rendered general by induction. Thus it was that the impenetrability, the mobility, and the impulsive force of bodies, and the laws of motion and of gravitation, were discovered. And to us it is enough that gravity does really exist, and act according to the laws which we have explained, and abundantly serves to account for all the motions of the celestial bodies, and of our sea. . . .

THE AIM AND STRUCTURE OF PHYSICAL THEORY

Pierre Duhem (1861-1916) was an outstanding French physicist, philosopher, and historian of science. In the history of his subject, he was mainly concerned with the period from Plato to Copernicus. He was responsible for the revival of interest in, and respect for, the great scientific advances of the middle ages.

His major work was La Theorie Physique: Son Objet, Sa Structure *(The Aim and Structure of Physical Theory), 1906. The book originally appeared as a series of articles in 1904 and 1905 in* Revue de philosophie.

The following selection is from Part I, Chapter II, "Physical Theory and Natural Classification," of The Aim and Structure of Physical Theory.*

1. WHAT IS THE TRUE NATURE OF A PHYSICAL THEORY AND THE OPERATIONS CONSTITUTING IT?

While we regard a physical theory as a hypothetical explanation of material reality, we make it dependent on metaphysics. In that way, far from giving it a form to which the greatest number of minds can give their assent, we limit its acceptance to those who acknowledge the philosophy it insists on. But even they cannot be entirely satisfied

---

*Translated by Philip P. Wiener (Princeton: Princeton University Press, 1954). pp. 19-21, 23-24, 27-30. Used by permission of Princeton University Press.

with this theory since it does not draw all its principles from the metaphysical doctrine from which it is claimed to be derived.

These thoughts, discussed in the preceding chapter, lead us quite naturally to ask the following two questions:

Could we not assign an aim to physical theory that would render it *autonomous?* Based on principles which do not arise from any metaphysical doctrine, physical theory might be judged in its own terms without including the opinions of physicists who depend on the philosophical schools to which they may belong.

Could we not conceive a method which might be *sufficient* for the construction of a physical theory? Consistent with its own definition the theory would employ no principle and have no recourse to any procedure which it could not legitimately use.

We intend to concentrate on this aim and this method, and to study both.

Let us posit right now a definition of physical theory; the sequel of this book will clarify it and will develop its complete content: A physical theory is not an explanation. It is a system of mathematical propositions, deduced from a small number of principles, which aim to represent as simply, as completely, and as exactly as possible a set of experimental laws.

In order to start making this definition somewhat more precise, let us characterize the four successive operations through which a physical theory is formed:

1. Among the physical properties which we set ourselves to represent we select those we regard as simple properties, so that the others will supposedly be groupings or combinations of them. We make them correspond to a certain group of mathematical symbols, numbers, and magnitudes, through appropriate methods of measurement. These mathematical symbols have no connection of an intrinsic nature with the properties they represent; they bear to the latter only the relation of sign to thing signified. Through methods of measurement we can make each state of a physical property correspond to a value of the representative symbol, and vice versa.

2. We connect the different sorts of magnitudes, thus introduced, by means of a small number of propositions which will serve as principles in our deductions. These principles may be called "hypotheses" in the etymological sense of the word for they are truly the grounds on

which the theory will be built; but they do not claim in any manner to state real relations among the real properties of bodies. These hypotheses may then be formulated in an arbitrary way. The only absolutely impassable barrier which limits this arbitrariness is logical contradiction either among the terms of the same hypothesis or among the various hypotheses of the same theory.

3. The diverse principles or hypotheses of a theory are combined together according to the rules of mathematical analysis. The requirements of algebraic logic are the only ones which the theorist has to satisfy in the course of this development. The magnitudes on which his calculations bear are not claimed to be physical realities, and the prinicples he employs in his deductions are not given as stating real relations among those relatities; therefore it matters little whether the operations he performs do or do not correspond to real or conceivable physical transformations. All that one has the right to demand of him is that his syllogisms be valid and his calculations accurate.

4. The various consequences thus drawn from the hypotheses may be translated into as many judgments bearing on the physical properties of the bodies. The methods appropriate for defining and measuring these physical properties are like the vocabulary and key permitting one to make this translation. These judgments are compared with the experimental laws which the theory is intended to represent. If they agree with these laws to the degree of approximation corresponding to the measuring procedures employed, the theory has attained its goal, and is said to be a good theory; if not, it is a bad theory, and it must be modified or rejected.

Thus a true theory is not a theory which gives an explanation of physical appearances in conformity with reality; it is a theory which represents in a satisfactory manner a group of experimental laws. A false theory is not an attempt at an explanation based on assumptions contrary to reality; it is a group of propositions which do not agree with the experimental laws.

Agreement with experiment is the sole criterion of truth for a physical theory.

The definition we have just outlined distinguishes four fundamenta operations in a physical theory: (1) the definition and measurement of physical magnitudes; (2) the selection of hypotheses; (3) the mathematical development of the theory; (4) the comparison of the theory with experiment.

Each one of these operations will occupy us in detail as we proceed with this book, for each of them presents difficulties calling for minute analysis. But right now it is possible for us to answer a few questions and to refute a few objections raised by the present definition of physical theory.

2. WHAT IS THE UTILITY OF A PHYSICAL THEORY? THEORY CONSIDERED AS AN ECONOMY OF THOUGHT

And first, of what use is such a theory?

Concerning the very nature of things, or the realities hidden under the phenomena we are studying, a theory conceived on the plan we have just drawn teaches us absolutely nothing, and does not claim to teach us anything. Of what use is it, then? What do physicists gain by replacing the laws which experimental method furnishes directly with a system of mathematical propositions representing those laws?

First of all, instead of a great number of laws offering themselves as independent of one another, each having to be learnt and remembered on its own account, physical theory substitutes a very small number of propositions, viz., fundamental hypotheses. The hypotheses once known, mathematical deduction permits us with complete confidence to call to mind all the physical laws without omission or repetition. Such condensing of a multitude of laws into a small number of principles affords enormous relief to the human mind, which might not be able without such an artifice to store up the new wealth it acquires daily.

The reduction of physical laws to theories thus contributes to that "intellectual economy" in which Ernst Mach sees the goal and directing principle of science.* . . .

3. THEORY CONSIDERED AS CLASSIFICATION

Theory is not solely an economical representation of experimental laws; it is also a *classification* of these laws.

Experimental physics supplies us with laws all lumped together and, so to speak, on the same plane, without partitioning them into

---

*E. Mach, "Die okonomische Natur der physikalischen Forschung," Popular-wissenschaftliche Vorlesungen (3rd ed.; Leipzig, 1903), Chapter XIII, p. 215.

groups of laws united by a kind of family tie. Very often quite accidental causes or rather superficial analogies have led observers in their
research to bring together different laws. Newton put into the same
work the laws of the dispersion of light crossing a prism and the laws
of the colors adorning a soap bubble, simply because of the colors
that strike the eye in these two sorts of phenomena.

On the other hand, theory, by developing the numerous ramifications of the deductive reasoning which connects principles to experimental laws, establishes an order and a classification among these laws.
It brings some laws together, closely arranged in the same group; it
separates some of the others by placing them in two groups very far
apart. Theory gives, so to speak, the table of contents and the chapter
headings under which the science to be studied will be methodically
divided, and it indicates the laws which are to be arranged under each
of these chapters.

Thus, alongside the laws which govern the spectrum formed by
a prism it arranges the laws governing the colors of the rainbow; but
the laws according to which the colors of Newton's rings are ordered
go elsewhere to join the laws of fringes discovered by Young and
Fresnel; still in another category, the elegant coloration analyzed by
Grimaldi is considered related to the diffraction spectra produced by
Fraunhofer. The laws of all these phenomena, whose striking colors
lead to their confusion in the eyes of the simple observer, are, thanks
to the efforts of the theorist, classified and ordered.

These classifications make knowledge convenient to use and safe
to apply. Consider those utility cabinets where tools for the same purpose lie side by side, and where partitions logically separate instruments
not designed for the same task: the worker's hand quickly grasps, without fumbling or mistake, the tool needed. Thanks to theory, the physicist finds with certitude, and without omitting anything useful or using
anything superfluous, the laws which may help him solve a given problem.

Order, wherever it reigns, brings beauty with it. Theory not only
renders the group of physical laws it represents easier to handle, more
convenient, and more useful, but also more beautiful.

It is impossible to follow the march of one of the great theories
of physics, to see it unroll majestically its regular deductions starting
from initial hypotheses, to see its consequences represent a multitude

of experimental laws down to the smallest detail, without being charmed by the beauty of such a construction, without feeling keenly that such a creation of the human mind is truly a work of art. . . .

4. A THEORY TENDS TO BE TRANSFORMED INTO A NATURAL CLASSIFICATION

The physicist cannot take account of this conviction. The method at his disposal is limited to the data of observation. It therefore cannot prove that the order established among experimental laws reflects an order transcending experience; which is all the more reason why his method cannot suspect the nature of the real relations corresponding to the relations established by theory.

But while the physicist is powerless to justify this conviction, he is nonetheless powerless to rid his reason of it. In vain is he filled with the idea that his theories have no power to grasp reality, and that they serve only to give experimental laws a summary and classificatory representation. He cannot compel himself to believe that a system capable of ordering so simply and so easily a vast number of laws, so disparate at first encounter, should be a purely artificial system. Yielding to an intuition which Pascal would have recognized as one of those reasons of the heart "that reason does not know," he asserts his faith in a real order reflected in his theories more clearly and more faithfully as time goes on.

Thus the analysis of the methods by which physical theories are constructed proves to us with complete evidence that these theories cannot be offered as explanations of experimental laws; and, on the other hand, an act of faith, as incapable of being justified by this analysis as of being frustrated by it, assures us that these theories are not a purely artificial system, but a natural classification. And so, we may here apply that profound thought of Pascal: "We have an impotence to prove, which cannot be conquered by any dogmatism; we have an idea of truth which cannot be conquered by any Pyrrhonian skepticism."

5. THEORY ANTICIPATING EXPERIMENT

There is one circumstance which shows with particular clarity our belief in the natural character of a theoretical classification; this circumstance is present when we ask of a theory that it tell us the results of an experiment before it has occurred, when we give it the bold injunction: "Be a prophet for us."

A considerable group of experimental laws had been established by investigators; the theorist has proposed to condense the laws into a very small number of hypotheses, and has succeeded in doing so; each one of the experimental laws is correctly represented by a consequence of these hypotheses.

But the consequences that can be drawn from these hypotheses are unlimited in number; we can, then, draw some consequences which do not correspond to any of the experimental laws previously known, and which simply represent possible experimental laws.

Among these consequences, some refer to circumstances realizable in practice, and these are particularly interesting, for they can be submitted to test by facts. If they represent exactly the experimental laws governing these facts, the value of the theory will be augmented, and the domain governed by the theory will annex new laws. If, on the contrary, there is among these consequences one which is sharply in disagreement with the facts whose law was to be represented by the theory the latter will have to be more or less modified, or perhaps completely rejected.

Now, on the occasion when we confront the predictions of the theory with reality, suppose we have to bet for or against the theory; on which side shall we lay our wager?

If the theory is a purely artificial system, if we see in the hypothese on which it rests statements skillfully worked out so that they represent the experimental laws already known, but if the theory fails to hint at any reflection of the real relations among the invisible realities, we shall think that such a theory will fail to confirm a new law. That, in the space left free among the drawers adjusted for other laws, the hitherto unknown law should find a drawer already made into which it may be fitted exactly would be a marvelous feat of chance. It would be folly for us to risk a bet on this sort of expectation.

If on the contrary, we recognize in the theory a natural classification, if we feel that its principles express profound and real relations among things, we shall not be surprised to see its consequences anticipating experience and stimulating the discovery of new laws; we shall bet fearlessly in its favor.

The highest test, therefore, of our holding a classification as a natural one is to ask it to indicate in advance things which the future alone will reveal. And when the experiment is made and confirms the predictions obtained from our theory, we feel strengthened in our conviction that the relations established by our reason among abstract notions truly correspond to relations among things.

Thus, modern chemical symbolism, by making use of developed formulas, establishes a classification in which diverse compounds are ordered. The wonderful order this classification brings about in the tremendous arsenal of chemistry already assures us that the classification is not a purely artificial system. The relations of analogy and derivation by substitution it establishes among diverse compounds have meaning only in our mind; yet, we are convinced that they correspond to kindred relations among substances themselves, whose nature remains deeply hidden but whose reality does not seem doubtful. Nevertheless, for this conviction to change into overwhelming certainty, we must see the theory write in advance the formulas of a multitude of bodies and, yielding to these indications, synthesis must bring to light a large number of substances whose composition and several properties we should know even before they exist.

Just as the syntheses announced in advance sanction chemical notation as a natural classification, so physical theory will prove that it is the reflection of a real order by anticipating observation.

Now the history of physics provides us with many examples of this clairvoyant guesswork; many a time has a theory forecast laws not yet observed, even laws which appear improbable, stimulating the experimenter to discover them and guiding him toward that discovery.

The Academie des Sciences had set, as the subject for the physics prize that was to be awarded in the public meeting of March 1819, the general examination of the phenomena of the diffraction of light. Two memoirs were presented, and one by Fresnel was awarded the prize, the commission of judges consisting of Biot, Arago, Laplace, Gay-Lussac, and Poisson.

From the principles put forward by Fresnel, Poisson deduced through an elegant analysis the following strange consequence; If a small, opaque, and circular screen intercepts the rays emitted by a point source of light, there should exist behind the screen, on the very axis of this screen, points which are not only bright, but which shine exactly as though the screen were not interposed between them and the source of light.

Such a corollary, so contrary, it seems, to the most obvious experimental certainties, appeared to be a very good ground for rejecting the theory of diffraction proposed by Fresnel. Arago had confidence in the natural character arising from the clairvoyance of this theory. He tested it, and observation gave results which agreed absolutely with the improbable predictions from calculation.*

Thus physical theory, as we have defined it, gives to a vast group of experimental laws a condensed representation, favorable to intellectual economy.

It classifies these laws and, by classifying, renders them more easily and safely utilizable. At the same time, putting order into the whole, it adds to their beauty.

It assumes, while being completed, the characteristics of a natural classification. The groups it establishes permit hints as to the real affinities of things.

This characteristic of natural classification is marked, above all, by the fruitfulness of the theory which anticipates experimental laws not yet observed, and promotes their discovery.

That sufficiently justifies the search for physical theories, which cannot be called a vain and idle task even though it does not pursue the explanation of phenomena.

*Oeuvres completes d'Augustin Fresnel, 3 vols. (Paris, 1866-1870), I, 236, 365, 368.

PART II

THE DISCOVERY AND JUSTIFICATION OF SCIENTIFIC THEORIES

INTRODUCTION

The scientist is interested in laws and theories, not in particular facts. At the same time, he uses particular facts as evidence for or against laws and theories. How is this possible? We can divide this question into two problems. First, how does the scientist arrive at theories from an examination of particular facts? This is the problem of discovery. Second, how does the scientist justify his theory from an examination of particular facts? This is the problem of justification or confirmation.

We shall begin with a description of the classical conception of the scientific method. It consists of four parts: (1) the initial collection of all relevant facts; (2) the formulation of a generalization that abstracts the common element from the facts collected; (3) a deduction of particular consequences from the generalization; and (4) the testing of the particular consequences.

The classical conception of scientific method is developed in a clear and sophisticated fashion in the writings of Sir John Herschel. Herschel points out that the development and confirmation of scientific theories is possible only because scientists construct hypotheses not already found in the data. But, as he points out, we must check the data, and additional data to be obtained by experimentation, to see if the consequences of the hypotheses in question acutally hold.

Herschel makes two important points about the testing of a hypothesis: (1) There are many cases in which the consequences deduced from one hypothesis differ from those deduced from a different hypothesis. If we see which consequences actually hold, then we can use those observations to eliminate one hypothesis and to confirm the other. (2) We must always consider the possibility that an error in the data may lead us astray. Consequently, the experiment must be rerun often enough to make the possibility of error so improbable that it can be disregarded. These two points raise important issues whose significance is developed in the selection from Pierre Duhem that is discussed below.

Isaac Newton's contribution to the classical conception of the scientific method consisted of four rules designed to aid in the actual construction of a theory or hypothesis as well as in the choice between two competing theories. These rules may be viewed more as instructions of what not to do than as positive instructions about what to do.

Rule one is reminiscent of the traditional rule of economy formulated in the middle ages and called "Ockham's razor." In it, Newton advises us to be economical in inventing theoretical constructs and terms. Rule Two is the principle of analogy. Where we can think of alternative explanations, the one that is most like what we already know is to be preferred. Rule Three contains Newton's views on what is to be considered "basic" or real, and thus capable of explaining other less basic properties. In Rule Four, Newton warns us to accept only hypotheses that are clearly related to observation.

We can summarize the discussion of the classical conception of the scientific method by noting its three main components: *hypothesis, deduction,* and *test.* A hypothesis (theory) is formulated to account for the observed facts; from this general hypothesis we deduce a particular conclusion or an as yet unobserved (inferred) fact; the particular conclusion is then tested, and if the inferred fact is observed, the hypothesis is said to be confirmed.

This idealized classical conception of the scientific method may be exemplified with reference to astronomy. For centuries, ancient astronomers had observed and plotted the movements of the heavenly bodies. Various hypotheses had been suggested to explain these observations. As early as the fourth century B.C., Aristarchus had suggested that the earth revolves around the sun. However, the Ptolemaic theory, which posited the movement of the sun around the earth, was the accepted theory. Nicholas Copernicus reintroduced the hypothesis of Aristarchus. Despite its shortcomings, Copernicus' hypothesis had distinct advantages over the Ptolemaic one in terms of simplicity and greater explanatory power. The next stage involved the further observations of Tycho Brahe, observations that disclosed discrepencies in Copernicus' hypothesis. The observed facts were not the same as what could be deduced from Copernicus' hypothesis. These additional observations led Johannes Kepler to reformulate the Copernican hypothesis and to view the motions of heavenly bodies around the sun as ellipses instead of circles.

From the revised Copernican hypothesis, it was deduced that the fixed stars were at immense distances from the earth. This deduction was confirmed by Galileo, who observed "new" stars with his telescope. Obviously, their great distance from the earth made them unobservable to the unaided eye. Newton was finally able to measure the distance of these stars from the earth, and he confirmed what Copernicus had predicted and what Galileo had seen. Moreover, Newton's theory (hypothesis) of gravitation was able to explain not only the motions of heavenly bodies but the motion of objects on the earth as well. Newton's hypothesis itself has led to further deductions that have been tested, and so it goes.

In the nineteenth century, John Stuart Mill and William Whewell engaged in a great debate over the classical conception of confirmation. The debate was specifically related to the scientific work of Kepler. According to Mill, Kepler was simply giving a summary description of the observations of Tycho Brahe. Mill thus viewed Kepler's work in terms of a simple model: We observe phenomena in certain cases and we suppose that it will be that way in other cases.

William Whewell disagreed with Mill. Whewell argued that induction was "a conception supplied by the mind and superimposed upon the facts." Induction as the formulation of a hypothesis is not a mere generalization from observation, nor is it an additional observation. It is a creation of the mind. Once the mind supplies this hypothesis, the hypothesis can be tested. According to Whewell, Kepler was able to formulate a hypothesis about the orbit of Mars that fit all of the known facts at that time, suggested new facts, and was eventually confirmed by experimental tests.

It would seem that Whewell was correct and Mill wrong in the account of what Kepler did. Kepler did not simply generalize from the observed elliptical orbits of the planets. He had to "see" those orbits in the data. But although the data suggested this idea to Kepler they did not logically imply what Kepler saw. Others had not seen the ellipses, and neither did Kepler at first.

As we have defined it, the classical conception of the scientific method involves three stages: hypothesis, deduction, and test. The debate about this conception has led to the recognition of difficulties within it and to reformulations of that method. To begin with, the classical conception might seem perfectly clear as long as we confine ourselves to empirical laws. For example, having observed that the known planets move in elliptical orbits, we may generalize (hypothesis) that all planets move in elliptical orbits. From this generalization we infer (deduction) that any newly discovered planets will move in elliptical orbits. As new planets are discovered, the generalization is confirmed (test).

Even at this level, however, problems arise about the formation of the hypothesis. We do not really observe the elliptical orbit. How do we (that is, Kepler) hit upon this idea?

The problems become even more apparent when we turn to hypotheses involving theoretical statements and terms. Theoretical terms, as you will recall, have no direct referent in observation. How can we possibly arrive at a hypothesis about unseen or unseeable entities? This is the problem of *discovery*. Even if we are reductionists in our view of the status of scientific theories, and we believe that ultimately all theoretical terms will disappear from our formulations, we still cannot explain how the original formulator of the theory (hypothesis) arrives at the hypothesis, or how the original observations suggests it.

For a long time, this problem was ignored. It was assumed that some scientists were very clever, and as such they simply had bright ideas from time to time. These bright ideas occurred under conditions so diverse that no one seemed able to duplicate them. So discovery was attributed solely to cleverness. There are, however, historically important cases of more than one scientist discovering the same thing at the same time. An example is the discovery of the principle of the conservation of energy which was made by many people at the same time. Are these simultaneous discoveries mere coincidences or is there a special process of invention that allows for them?

Various recent philosophers of science have attempted to supplement the classical conception of scientific method by evolving a theory of the discovery of hypotheses. Charles Sanders Peirce describes what he calls "retroduction"(also called "abduction") as that mental movement from the observation of particular facts to a scientific theory or hypothesis. Reason supplies these "spontaneous conjectures" because human reason is in some way attuned to nature. From among all the things of which we might think, we are somehow guided most often to think of the right ones.

A more careful study of the history of science, such as that made by Thomas Kuhn and reported in his book *The Structure of Scientific Revolutions,* reveals that there are many different kinds of discovery, at least two of which are noteworthy. First, there are discoveries that occur within previously established scientific conventions of what problems are important and what standards are relevant to their solution. Second, there are discoveries involving a major reorientation in scientific convention, a reorientation that amounts to a revolution.

Recently, Norwood Russell Hanson has argued for a logic of scientific discovery. In the selection from Hanson, two points are especially noteworthy. First, discovery cannot be attributed to genius or cleverness. Second, the reasons that suggest a discovery and the reasons for adopting a hypothesis are distinct. Hanson claims that the former are worthy of serious attention from philosophers of science.

A rarely discussed issue is the problem that arises in connection with the second stage, the actual deduction of the consequences. How does a scientist think of experimental implications that can be deduced from the theory and can be used to test it? Although there does not seem to be any set pattern, James Clerk Maxwell suggests, in his discussion of Faraday, that scientists often develop a theory on the analogy of another theory that is already accepted. The accepted theory is said to serve as a *model* for the one to be tested. The model helps not only in the formulation of the theory but in its testing and application as well. Needless to add, the model may suggest fruitless as well as fruitful analogies. Maxwell's discussion, like that of Whewell and Hanson, is important because it, too, emphasizes that the hypothesis stage is not always clearly separable from the later stages of deduction and testing of a theory.

Perhaps the most serious problem for the classical conception arises when we consider what happens because of the actual tests carried out. The classical conception views the results of experimental testing as data capable of being used to confirm or disconfirm a theory. That is, a large number of favorable tests in terms of both quantity and variety supposedly leads us to accept a theory, whereas even relatively few unfavorable tests lead us to reject a theory. Is this the case?

A traditional objection to the confirmation theory was expressed by David Hume, who argued that no matter how many tests confirm a hypothesis, it might still be wrong. A more recent objection is that of Pierre Duhem, who maintained that there is no such thing as a *crucial experiment*. No matter how unfavorable the tests might be, the hypothesis might be preserved by either adding assumptions or surrendering one of the accepted assumptions. An individual hypothesis can never be tested in isolation from a whole group of other theories.

One attempt to solve this problem of confirmation is that introduced by Karl Popper. The selection from Popper deals with his notions of *falsification* and simplicity. Popper argues that theories are not confirmed or proven true; rather they are disconfirmed or proven false. Those theories are preferable that lend themselves to the most testing and therefore to the greatest possibility of falsification. Moreover, it is the *simpler* theory that is easier to falsify if it is false. (One theory is simpler than another, according to Popper, if it has greater empirical content than the other; its greater empirical content makes it more testable, and hence more readily falsifiable.)

For example, consider two theories of planetary orbits; t_1, in which it is asserted that orbits are circular; and t_2, in which it is asserted that orbits are elliptical. Theory t_1 is simpler than theory t_2 because we can falsify the former more readily. This follows from the fact that t_1 can be falsified by finding four points of its orbit that do not form a circle. As you will recall from your study of geometry, any three points can always be constructed into a circle. In order to falsify theory t_2 we would need six points of the orbit. Theory t_1 was falsified. Even before it was falsified it was preferable to theory t_2 because of the former's greater simplicity.

There is no widespread agreement among either scientists or philosophers of science about how the problems of discovery, deduction, or confirmation are to be solved. Much work remains to be done in these areas. You should therefore read the selections dealing with the reformulation of the classical conception as pioneering effort at clarification rather than as definitive studies and answers.

THE CLASSICAL CONCEPTION

SCIENTIFIC METHOD

*Sir John Frederick William Herschel (1792-1871) is primarily
known as an astronomer. His catalogue of the stars became
the standard point of departure for observational astronomy
throughout the nineteenth century. He is also known for
his famous work on scientific methodology,* Preliminary
Discourse on the Study of Natural Philosophy *(London,
1842). The selection is from Chapter 7 of Part II of that
book.*

(202) The immediate object we propose to ourselves in physical
theories is the analysis of phenomena, and the knowledge of the hidden processes of nature in their production, so far as they can be
traced by us. An important part of this knowledge consists in a discovery of the actual structure or mechanism of the universe and its
parts, through which, and by which, those processes are executed;
and of the agents which are concerned in their performance. Now,
the mechanism of nature is for the most part either on too large or
too small a scale to be immediately cognizable by our senses; and
her agents in like manner elude direct observation, and become
known to us only by their effects. It is in vain therefore that we
desire to become witnesses to the processes carried on with such
means, and to be admitted into the secret recesses and laboratories
where they are effected. Microscopes have been constructed which

magnify more than a thousand times in *linear* dimension, so that the smallest visible grain of sand may be enlarged to the appearance of one a thousand million times more bulky; yet the only impression we receive by viewing it through such a magnifier is, that it reminds us of some vast fragment of a rock, while the intimate structure on which depend its color, its hardness, and its chemical properties, remains still concealed: . . .

(207) Now, nothing is more common in physics than to find two, or even many, theories maintained as to the origin of a natural phenomenon. For instance, in the case of heat itself, one considers it as a really existing material fluid, of such exceeding subtlety as to penetrate all bodies, and even to be capable of combining with them chemically; while another regards it as nothing but a rapid vibratory or rotatory motion in the ultimate particles of the bodies heated; and produces a singularly ingenious train of mechanical reasoning to show, that there is nothing contradictory to sound dynamical principles in such a doctrine. Thus, again, with light: one considers it as consisting in actual particles darted forth from luminous bodies, and acted upon in their progress by forces of extreme intensity residing in the substances on which they strike; another in the vibratory motion of the particles of luminous bodies, communicated to a peculiar subtle and highly elastic ethereal medium, filling all space, and conveyed through it into our eyes, as sounds are to our ears, by the undulations of the air.

(208) Now, are we to be deterred from framing hypotheses and constructing theories, because we meet with such dilemmas, and find ourselves frequently beyond our depth? Undoubtedly not. *Est quodam prodire tenus si non datur ultra.* Hypotheses, with respect to theories, are what presumed proximate causes are with respect to particular inductions: they afford us motives for searching into analogies; ground of citation to bring before us all the cases which seem to bear upon them, for examination. A well imagined hypothesis, if it has been suggested by a fair inductive consideration of general laws, can hardly fail at least of enabling us to generalize a step farther, and group together several such laws under a more universal expression. But this is taking a very limited view of the value and importance of hypothesis: it may happen (and it has happened in the case of the undulatory doctrine of light) that such a weight of analogy and probability may

become accumulated on the side of an hypothesis, that we are compelled to admit one of two things; either that it is an actual statement
of what really passes in nature, or that the reality, whatever it be,
must run so close a parallel with it, as to admit of some mode of expression common to both, at least in so far as the phenomena actually
known are concerned. Now, this is a very great step, not only for its
own sake, as leading us to a high point in philosophical speculation,
but for its applications; because whatever conclusions we deduce from
an hypothesis so supported must have at least a strong presumption in
their favor: and we may be thus led to the trial of many curious experiments, and to the imagining of many useful and important contrivances,
which we should never otherwise have thought of, and which, at all
events, *if* verified in practice, are real additions to our stock of knowledge and to the arts of life.

(209) In framing a theory which shall render a rational account
of any natural phenomenon, we have *first* to consider the agents on
which it depends, or the causes to which we regard it as ultimately
referable. These agents are not to be arbitrarily assumed; they must
be such as we have good inductive grounds to believe do exist in nature,
and do perform a part in phenomena analogous to those we would
render an account of; or such, whose presence in the actual case can
be demonstrated by unequivocal signs. They must be *vera causa,* in
short, which we can not only show to exist and to act, but the laws
of whose action we can derive independently, by direct induction,
from experiments purposely instituted; or at least make such suppositions respecting them as shall not be contrary to our experience, and
which will remain to be verified by the coincidence of the conclusions
we shall deduce from them, with facts. For example, in the theory of
gravitation, we suppose an agent—*viz.* force, or mechanical power—to
act on *any* material body which is placed in the presence of *any* other,
and to urge the two mutually towards each other. This is a *vera causa;*
for heavy bodies (that is, all bodies, but some more, some less) tend
to, or endeavor to reach, the earth, and require the exertion of force
to counteract this endeavor, or to keep them up. Now, that which
opposes and neutralizes force *is* force. And again, a plumb-line, which
when allowed to hang freely, always hangs perpendicularly, is found to
hang observably aside from the perpendicular when in the neighborhood
of a considerable mountain, thereby proving that a force is exerted upon

it, which draws it towards the mountain. Moreover, since it is a fact that the moon does circulate about the earth, it must be drawn towards the earth by a force; for if there were no force acting upon it, it would go on in a straight line without turning aside to circulate in an orbit, and would, therefore, soon go away and be lost in space. This force, then, which we call the *force* of gravity, is a real cause.

(210) We have next to consider the laws which regulate the action of these our primary agents; and these we can only arrive at in three ways: 1st, By inductive reasoning; that is, by examining all the cases in which we know them to be exercised, inferring, as well as circumstances will permit, its amount or intensity in each particular case, and then piecing together, as it were, these *disjecta membra,* generalizing from them, and so arriving at the laws desired; 2dly, By forming at once a bold hypothesis, particularizing the law, and trying the truth of it by following out its consequences, and comparing them with facts; or, 3dly, By a process partaking of both these, and combining the advantages of both without their defects, viz. by assuming indeed the laws we would discover, but so generally expressed, that they shall include an unlimited variety of particular laws;—following out the consequences of this assumption, by the application of such general principles as the case admits;—comparing them in succession with all the particular cases within our knowledge; and, lastly, *on this comparison,* so modifying and restricting the general enunciation of our laws as to *make the results agree.*

(211) All these three processes for the discovery of those general elementary laws on which the higher theories are grounded, are applicable with different advantage in different circumstances. We might exemplify their successive application to the case of gravitation; but as this would rather lead into a disquisition too particular for the objects of this discourse, and carry us too much into the domain of technical mathematics, we shall content ourselves with remarking, that the method last mentioned is that which mathematicians (especially such as have a considerable command of those general modes of representing and reasoning on quantity, which constitute the higher analysis) find the most universally applicable, and the most efficacious; and that it is applicable with especial advantage in cases where subordinate inductions of the kind described in the last section have already led to laws of a certain generality admitting of mathematical

expression. Such a case, for instance, is the elliptic motion of a planet, which is a general proposition including the statement of an infinite number of particular *places,* in which the laws of its motion allow it to be some time or other found, and for which, of course, the law of force must be so assumed as to account.

(212) With regard to the first process of the three above enumerated, it is in fact an induction of the kind described in § 185.; and all the remarks we there made on that kind of induction apply to it in this stage. The direct assumption of a particular hypothesis has been occasionally practised very successfully. As examples, we may mention Coulomb's and Poisson's theories of electricity and magnetism, in both which, phenomena of a very complicated and interesting nature are referred to the actions of attractive and repulsive forces, following a law similar in its expression to the law of gravitation. But the difficulty and labor, which, in the greater theories, always attend the pursuit of a fundamental law into its remote consequences, effectually precludes this method from being commonly resorted to as a means of discovery, unless we have some good reason, from analogy or otherwise, for believing that the attempt will prove successful, or have been first led by partial inductions to particular laws which naturally point it out for trial.

(213) In this case, the law assumes all the characters of a general phenomenon resulting from an induction of particulars, but not yet verified by comparison with *all* the particulars, nor extended to all that it is capable of including. It is the verification of such inductions which constitutes theory in its largest sense, and which embraces an estimation of the influence of all such circumstances as may modify the effect of the cause whose laws of action we have arrived at and would verify. To return to our example: particular inductions drawn from the motions of the several planets about the sun, and of the satellites round their primaries, &c., having led us to the general conception of an attractive force exerted by every particle of matter in the universe on every other, according to the law to which we attach the name of gravitation; when we would verify this induction, we must set out with assuming this law, considering the whole system as subjected to its influence, and implicitly obeying it, and nothing interfering with its action; we then, for the first time, perceive a train of modifying circumstances which had not occurred to us when

reasoning upwards from particulars to obtain the fundamental law; we perceive that *all the planets* must attract *each other,* must therefore draw each other out of the orbits which they would have if acted on only by the sun; and as this was never contemplated in the inductive process, its validity becomes a question, which can only be determined by ascertaining precisely how great a deviation this new class of mutual actions will produce. To do this is no easy task, or rather it is the most difficult task which the genius of man has every yet accomplished: still it *has* been accomplished by the mere application of the general laws of dynamics; and the result (undoubtedly a most beautiful and satisfactory one) is, that all those observed deviations in the motions of our system which stood out as exceptions or were noticed as residual phenomena, and reserved for further inquiry in that imperfect view of the subject which we got in the subordinate process by which we rose to our general conclusion, prove to be the immediate consequences of the above-mentioned mutual actions. As such, they are neither exceptions nor residual facts, but fulfilments of general rules, and essential features in the statement of the case, *without* which our induction would be invalid, and the law of gravitation positively untrue.

(214) In the theory of gravitation, the law is all in all, applying itself at once to the materials, and directly producing the result (A). But in many other cases we have to consider not merely the laws which regulate the actions of our ultimate causes, but a system of mechanism, or a structure of parts through the intervention of which their effects become sensible to us. Thus, in the delicate and curious electro-dynamic theory of Ampere, the mutual attraction or repulsion of two magnets is referred to a more universal phenomenon, the mutual action of electric currents, according to a certain fundamental law. But in order to bring the case of a magnet within the range of this law, he is obliged to make a supposition of a peculiar structure or mechanism, which constitutes a body a magnet, viz. that around each particle of the body there shall be constantly circulating, in a certain stated direction, a small current of electric fluid.

(215) This, we may say, is too complex; it is artificial, and cannot be granted: yet, if the admission of this or any other structure tenfold more artificial and complicated will enable any one to present in a general point of view a great number of particular facts,—to make them a part of one system, and enable us to reason from the known

to the unknown, and actually to *predict facts before trial,*—we would ask, why should it *not* be granted? When we examine those instances of nature's workmanship which we can take to pieces and understand, we find them in the highest degree artifical in our own sense of the word. Take, for example, the structure of an eye, or of the skeleton of an animal,—what complexity and what artifice! In the one, a *pellucid muscle;* a lens formed with elliptical surfaces; a circular aperture capable of enlargement or contraction without loss of form: in the other, a framework of the most curious carpentry; in which occurs not a single straight line, nor any known geometrical curve, yet all evidently systematic, and constructed by rules which defy our research. Or examine a crystallized mineral, which we can in some measure dissect, and thus obtain direct evidence of an internal structure. Neither artifice nor complication are here wanting; and though it is easy to assert that these appearances are, after all, produced by something which would be very simple, it we did but know it, it is plain that the same might be *said* of a steam-engine executing the most complicated movements previous to any investigation of its nature, or any knowledge of the source of its power.

(216) In estimating, however, the value of a theory, we are not to look, *in the first instance,* to the question, whether it establishes satisfactorily, or not, a particular process or mechanism; for of this, after all, we can never obtain more than that indirect evidence which consists in its leading to the same results. What, in the actual state of science, is far more important for us to know, is whether our theory truly represent *all* the facts, and include *all* the laws, to which observation and induction lead. A theory which did this would, no doubt, go a great way to establish any hypothesis of mechanism or structure, which might form an essential part of it: but this is very far from being the case, except in a few limited instances; and, till it is so, to lay any great stress on hypotheses of the kind, except in as much as they serve to scaffold, for the erection of general laws, is to "quite mistake the scaffold for the pile." Regarded in this light, hypotheses have often an eminent use; and a facility in framing them, if attended with an equal facility in laying them aside when they have served their turn, is one of the most valuable qualities a philosopher can possess; while, on the other hand, a bigoted adherence to them, or indeed to peculiar views of any kind, in opposition to the tenor of facts as they arise, is the bane of all philosophy.

(217) There is no doubt, however, that the safest course, when it can be followed, is to rise by inductions carried on among laws, among facts, from law to law, perceiving, as we go on, how laws which we have looked upon as unconnected become particular cases either one of the other, or all of one still more general, and, at length, blend altogether in the point of view from which we learn to regard them. An example will illustrate what we mean. It is a general law that all hot bodies throw out or *radiate* heat in all directions (by which we mean, not that heat is an actual substance darted out from hot bodies, but only that the laws of the transmission of heat to distant objects are similar to those which would regulate the distribution of particles thrown forth in all directions), and that other colder bodies placed in their neighborhood become hot, *as if* they received the heat so radiated. Again, all solid bodies which become heated in one part *conduct,* or diffuse, the heat from that part through their whole substance. Here we have two modes of communicating heat,—by radiation, and by conduction; and both these have their peculiar, and, to all appearance, very different laws. Now, let us bring a hot and a cold body (of the same substance) gradually nearer and nearer together,— as they approach, the heat will be communicated from the hot to the cold one by the *laws of radiation;* and from the nearer to the farther part of the colder one, as it gradually grows warm, by *those of conduction.* Let their distance be diminished till they just lightly touch. How does the heat *now* pass from one to the other? Doubtless, by radiation; for it may be proved, that in such a contact there is yet an interval. Let them then be *forced* together, and it will seem clear that it must now be by *conduction.* Yet their *interval* must diminish gradually, as the force by which they are pressed together increases, till they actually cohere, and form one. The law of continuity, then, of which we have before spoken, forbids us to suppose that the intimate nature of the process of communication is changed in this transition from light to violent contact, and from that to actual union. If so, we might ask, At what point does the change happen? Especially since it is also demonstrable, that the particles of the most solid body are not really in contact. *Therefore* the laws of conduction and radiation have a mutual dependence, and the former are only extreme cases of the latter. If, then, we would rightly understand what passes, or what is the process of nature in the slow communication of heat through

the substance of a solid, we must ground our inquiries upon what takes place at a distance, and then urge the laws to which we have arrived, up to their extreme case.

(218) When two theories run parallel to each other, and each explains a great many facts in common with the other, any experiment which affords a crucial instance to decide between them, or by which one or other must fall, is of great importance. In thus verifying theories, since they are grounded on general laws, we may appeal, not merely to particular cases, but to whole classes of facts; and we therefore have a great range among the individuals of these for the selection of some particular effect which ought to take place oppositely in the event of one of the two suppositions at issue being right and the other wrong. A curious example is given by M. Fresnel, as decisive, in his mind, of the question between the two great opinions on the nature of light, which, since the time of Newton and Huyghens, have divided philosophers. (See § 207.) When two very clean glasses are laid one on the other, if they be not perfectly flat, but one or both in an almost imperceptible degree convex or prominent, beautiful and vivid colors will be seen between them; and if these be viewed through a red glass, their appearance will be that of alternate dark and bright stripes. These stripes are formed *between* the two surfaces in apparent contact, as any one may satisfy himself by using, instead of a flat *plate* of glass for the upper one, a triangular-shaped piece, called a prism, like a three-cornered stick, and looking through the inclined side of it next to the eye by which arrangement the reflection of light from the upper surface is prevented from intermixing with that from the surfaces in contact. Now, the colored stripes thus produced are explicable on both theories, and are appealed to by both as strong confirmatory facts; but there is a difference in one circumstance according as one or the other theory is employed to explain them. In the case of the Huyghenian doctrine, the intervals between the bright stripes ought to appear *absolutely black;* in the other, *half bright,* when so viewed through a prism. This curious case of difference was tried as soon as the opposing consequences of the two theories were noted by M. Fresnel, and the result is stated by him to be decisive in favor of that theory which makes light to consist in the vibrations of an elastic medium.

(219) Theories are best arrived at by the consideration of general laws; but most securely verified by comparing them with particular

facts, because this serves as a verification of the whole train of induction from the lowest term to the highest. But, then, the comparison must be made with facts purposely selected, so as to include every variety of case, not omitting extreme ones, and in sufficient number to afford every reasonable probability of detecting error. A single numerical co-incidence in a final conclusion, however striking the coincidence or important the subject, is not sufficient. Newton's theory of sound, for example, leads to a numerical expression for the actual velocity of sound, differing but little from that afforded by the correct theory afterwards explained by La Grange, and (when certain considerations not contemplated by him are allowed for) agreeing with fact; yet this coincidence is no verification of Newton's view of the general subject of sound, which is defective in an essential point, as the great geometer last named has very satisfactorily shown. This example is sufficient to inspire cautionin resting the verification of theories upon any thing but a very extensive comparison with a great mass of observed facts.

(220) But, on the other hand, when a theory will bear the test of such extensive comparison, it matters little how it has been originally framed. However strange, and, at first sight, inadmissible, its postulates may appear, or however singular it may seem that such postulates should have been fixed upon,—if they only lead us, by legitimate reasonings, to conclusions in exact accordance with numerous observations purposely made, under such a variety of circumstances as fairly embrace the whole range of the phenomena which the theory is intended to account for,—we cannot refuse to admit them; or if we still hesitate to regard them as demonstrated truths, we cannot, at least, object to receive them as temporary substitutes for such truths, until the latter shall be-come known. If they suffice to explain all the phenomena known, it becomes highly improbable that they will not explain more; and if all their conclusions we have tried have proved correct, it is probable that others yet untried will be found so too; so that in rejecting them al-together, we should reject all the discoveries to which they may lead.

(221) In all theories which profess to give a true account of the process of nature in the production of any class of phenomena, by re-ferring them to general laws, or to the action of general causes, through a train of modifying circumstances; before we can apply those laws or trace the action of those causes in any assigned case, we require to know the circumstances: we must have data whereon to ground their applicati

Now, these can be learned only from observation; and it may seem to be arguing in a vicious circle to have recourse to observation for any part of those theoretical conclusions, by whose comparison with fact the theory itself is to be tried. The consideration of an example will enable us to remove this difficulty. The most general law which has yet been discovered in chemistry is this, that all the elementary substances in nature are susceptible of entering into combination with each other only in fixed or *definite proportions* by weight, and not arbitrarily; so that when any two substances are put together with a view to unite them, if their weights are not in some certain determinate proportion, a complete combination will not take place, but some part of one or the other ingredient will remain over and above, and uncombined. Suppose, now, we have found a substance having all the outward characters of a homogeneous or unmixed body, but which, on analysis, we discover to consist of sulphur and lead in the proportion of 20 parts of the former to 130 of the latter ingredient; and we would know whether this is to be regarded as a verification of the law of definite proportions or an exception to it. The question is reduced to this, whether the proportion 20 to 130 be or be not *that* fixed and definite proportion (or one of the, if there be more than one proportion possible), in which, according to the law in question, sulphur and lead can combine; now, this can never be decided by merely looking at the law in all its generality. It is clear, that, when particularized by restricting its expression to sulphur and lead, the law should state *what are* those particular fixed proportions in which these bodies can combine.That is to say, there must be certain data or numbers,by which these are distinguished from all other bodies in nature, and which require to be known before we can apply the general law to the particular case. To determine such data, observation must be consulted; and if we were to have recourse to that of the combination of the two substances in question with each other, no doubt there would be ground for the logical objection of a vicious circle: but this is not done; the determination of these numerical data is derived from experiments purposely made on a great variety of different combinations, among which that under consideration does not of necessity occur, and all these being found, independently of each other, to agree in giving the same results, they are therefore safely assumed as part of the system. Thus the law of definite proportions, when applied to the actual state of nature, requires two separate statements, the one announcing the general law of combination, the other particularizing the numbers appropriate to the several elements of which natural bodies consist, or the data of nature. Among these data, if arranged in a list, there will be found opposite to the element sulphur the number 16, and opposite to lead, 104, and since 20 is to 130 in the exact proportion of 16 to 104, it appears that the combination in question affords a satisfactory verification of the law.

(222) The great importance of physical data of this description, and the advantage of having them well determined, will be obvious, if we consider, that a list of them, when taken in combination with the general law, affords the means of determining at once the exact proportion of the ingredients of all natural compounds, if we only know the place they hold in the system. In chemistry, the number of admitted elements is between fifty and sixty, and new ones are added continually as the science advances. Now, the moment the number corresponding to any new substance added to the list is determined, we have, in fact, ascertained all the proportions in which it can enter into combination with all the others, so that a careful experiment made with the object of determining this number is, in fact, equivalent to as many different experiments as there are binary, ternary, or yet more complicated combinations capable of existing, into which the new substance may enter, as an ingredient.

(223) The importance of obtaining exact physical data can scarcely be too much insisted on, for without them the most elaborate theories are little better than mere inapplicable forms of words. It would be of little consequence to be informed, abstractedly, that the sun and planets attract each other, with forces proportional to their masses, and inversely as the squares of their distances: but, as soon as we know the data of our system, as soon as we have an accurate statement (no matter how obtained) of the distances, masses, and actual motions of the several bodies which compose it, we need no more to enable us to predict all the movements of its several parts, and the changes that will happen in it for thousands of years to come; and even to extend our views backwards into time, and recover from the past, phenomena, which no observation has noted, and no history recorded, and which yet (it is possible) may have left indelible traces of their existence in their influence on the state of nature in our own globe, and those of the other planets.

(224) The proof, too, that our data *are* correctly assumed, is

involved in the general verification of the whole theory, of which, when once assumed, they form a part; and the same comparison with observation which enables us to decide on the truth of the abstract principle, enables us, at the same time, to ascertain whether we have fixed the values of our data in accordance with the actual state of nature. If not, it becomes an important question, whether the assumed values can be corrected, so as to bring the results of theory to agree with facts? Thus it happens, that as theories approach to their perfection, a more and more exact determination of data becomes requisite. Deviations from observed fact, which, in a first or approximative verification, may be disregarded as trifling, become important when a high degree of precision is obtained. A difference between the calculated and observed places of a planet, which would have been disregarded by Kepler in his verification of the law of elliptic motion, would now be considered fatal to the theory of gravity, unless it could be shown to arise from an erroneous assumption of some of the numerical data of our system.

(225) The observations most appropriate for the ready and exact determination of physical data are, therefore, those which it is most necessary to have performed with exactness and perseverance. Hence it is, that their performance, in many cases, becomes a national concern, and observatories are erected and maintained, and expeditions dispatched to distant regions, at an expense which, to a superficial view, would appear most disproportioned to their objects. But it may very reasonably be asked why the direct assistance afforded by governments to the execution of continued series of observations adapted to this especial end should continue to be, as it has hitherto almost exclusively been, confined to astronomy.

(226) Physical data intended to be employed as elements of calculation in extensive theories, require to be known with a much greater degree of exactness than any single observation possesses, not only on account of their dignity and importance, as affording the means of representing an indefinite multitude of facts; but because, in the variety of combinations that may arise, or in the changes that circumstances may undergo, cases will occur when any trifling error in one of the data may become enormously magnified in the final result to be compared with observation. Thus, in the case of an eclipse of the sun, when the moon enters very obliquely upon the sun's disc, a trifling error in the diameter of either the sun or moon may make a great one in the

time when the eclipse shall be announced to commence. It ought to be remarked, that these are, of all others, the conjunctures where observations are most available for the determination of data; for, by the same rule that a small change in the data will, in such cases, produce a great one in the thing to be observed; so, *vice versa,* any moderate amount of error committed in an observation undertaken for ascertaining its value, can produce but a very trifling one in the *reverse* calcluation from which the data come to be determined by observation. This remark extends to every description of physical data in every department of science, and is never to be overlooked when the object in view is the determination of data with the last degree of precision.

(227) But how, it may be asked, are we to ascertain *by* observation, data more precise than observation itself? How are we to conclude the value of that which we do not see, with greater certainty than that of quantities which we actually see and measure? It is the number of observations which may be brought to bear on the determination of data that enables us to do this. Whatever error we may commit in a single determination, it is highly improbable that we should always err the same way, so that, when we come to take an average of a great number of determinations (unless there be some constant cause which gives a bias one way or the other), we cannot fail, at length, to obtain a very near approximation to the truth, and even allowing a bias, to come much nearer to it than can fairly be expected from any single observation, liable to be influenced by the same bias.

(228) This useful and valuable property of the average of a great many observations, that it brings us nearer to the truth than any single observation can be relied on as doing, renders it the most constant resource in all physical inquiries where accuracy is desired. And it is surprising what a rapid effect, in equalizing fluctuations and destroying deviations, a moderate multiplication of individual observations has. A better example can hardly be taken than the average height of the quicksilver in the common barometer, which measures the pressure of the air, and whose fluctuations are proverbial. Nevertheless, if we only observe it regularly every day, and, at the end of each month, take an average of the observed heights, we shall find the fluctuations surprisingly diminished in amount: and if we go on for a whole year, or for many years in succession, the annual averages will be found to agree with still greater exactness. This equalizing power of averages,

by destorying all such fluctuations as are irregular or accidental,
frequently enables us to obtain evidence of fluctuations really
regular, periodic in their recurrence, and so much smaller in their
amount than the accidental ones, that, but for this mode of proceeding,
they never would have become apparent. Thus, if the height of the
barometer be observed four times a day, constantly, for a few months,
and the averages taken, it will be seen that a regular *daily* fluctuation,
of very small amount, takes place, the quicksilver rising and falling
twice in the four-and-twenty hours. It is by such observations that we
are enabled to ascertain—what no single measure (unless by a fortunate
coincidence) could give us any idea, and never any certain knowledge
of—the true *sea level* at any part of the coast, or the height at which
the water of the ocean would stand, if perfectly undisturbed by winds,
waves, or tides; a subject of very great importance, and upon which it
would be highly desirable to possess an extensive series of observations,
at a great many points on the coasts of the principal continents and
islands over the whole globe.

(229) In all cases where there is a direct and simple relation between the phenomenon observed and a single *datum* on which it depends, every single observation will give a value of this quantity, and
the average of all (under certain restrictions) will be its exact value. We
say, under certain restrictions; for, if the circumstances under which
the observations are made be not alike, they may not all be equally
favorable to exactness, and it would be doing injustice to those most
advantageous, to class them with the rest. In such cases as these, as
well as in cases where the *data* are numerous and complicated together
so as not to admit of single, separate determination (a thing of continual occurrence), we have to enter into very nice, and often not a little
intricate, considerations respecting the *probable* accuracy of our results, or the limits of error within which it is *probable* they lie. In so
doing we are obliged to have recourse to a refined and curious branch
of mathematical inquiry called the doctrine of probabilities, the object of which (as its name imports) is to reduce our estimation of the
probability of any conclusion to calculation, so as to be able to give
more than a mere guess at the degree of reliance which ought to be
placed in it.

To give some general idea of the considerations which such com-
putations involve, let us imagine a person firing with a pistol at a wafer

on a wall ten yards distant: we might, in a general way, take it for granted, that he would hit the wall, but not the wafer, at the first shot: but if we would form any thing like a probable conjecture of *how near* he would come to it, we must first have an idea of his skill. No better way of judging could be devised than by letting him fire a hundred shots at it, and marking where they all struck. Suppose this done,—suppose the wafer has been hit once or twice, that a certain number between one and two inches, and so on, and that one or two have been some feet wide of the mark. Still the question arises, what estimate are we thence to form of his skill? How *near* (or nearer) may we after this experience, safely, or at least not unfairly, bet that he will come to the mark the next subsequent shot? This the laws of probability enable us on such data to say. Again, suppose, *before* we were allowed to measure the distances, the wafer were to have been taken away, and we were called upon, on the mere evidence of the marks on the wall, to say where it had been placed; it is clear that no reasoning would enable any one to say with certainty; yet there is assuredly one place which we may fix on with greater probability of being right than any other. Now, this is a very similar case to that of an observer—an astronomer for example—who would determine the exact place of a heavenly body. He points to it his telescope, and obtains a series of results disagreeing among themselves, but yet all agreeing within certain limits, and only a comparatively small number of them deviating considerably from the mean of all; and from these he is called upon to say, definitively, what he shall consider to have been the most probable place of his star at the moment. Just so in the calculation of physical *data*; where no two results agree exactly, and where all come within limits, some wide, some close, what have we to guide us when we would make up our minds what to conclude respecting them? It is evident that any system of calculation that can be shown to lead of necessity to the most probable conclusion where certainty is not to be had must be valuable. However, as this doctrine is one of the most difficult and delicate among the applications of mathematics to natural philosophy, this slight mention of it must suffice at present.

NEWTON

RULES OF REASONING

This second group of selections from the writings of Sir Isaac Newton are taken from Book III of the Principia, *the first four "Rules of Reasoning in Philosophy," and from Newton's correspondence with Oldenberg and Cotes.*

RULE I.

We are to admit no more causes of natural things than such as are both true and sufficient to explain their appearances.
To this purpose the philosophers say that Nature does nothing in vain, and more is in vain when less will serve; for Nature is pleased with simplicity, and affects not the pomp of superfluous causes.

RULE II.

Therefore to the same natural effects we must, as far as possible, assign the same causes.
As to respiration in a man and in a beast; the descent of stones in *Europe* and in *America;* the light of our culinary fire and of the sun; the reflection of light in the earth, and in the planets.

RULE III.

The qualities of bodies, which admit neither intension nor remission of degrees, and which are found to belong to all bodies with the

reach of our experiments, are to be esteemed the universal
qualities of all bodies whatsoever.

For since the qualities of bodies are only known to us by experiments, we are to hold for universal all such as universally agree with experiments; and such as are not liable to diminuition can never be quite taken away. We are certainly not to relinquish the evidence of experiments for the sake of dreams and vain fictions of our own devising; nor are we to recede from the analogy of Nature, which uses to be simple, and always consonant to itself. We no other way know the extension of bodies than by our senses, nor do these reach it in all bodies; but because we perceive extension in all that are sensible, therefore we ascribe it universally to all others also. That abundance of bodies are hard, we learn by experince; and because the hardness of the whole arises from the hardness of the parts, we therefore justly infer the hardness of the undivided particles not only of the bodies we feel but of all others. That all bodies are impenetrable, we gather not from reason, but from sensation. The bodies which we handle we find impenetrable, and thence conclude impenetrability to be an universal property of all bodies whatsoever. That all bodies are moveable, and endowed with certain powers (which we call the *vires inertia*) of persevering in their motion, or in their rest, we only infer from the like properties observed in the bodies which we have seen. The extension, hardness, impenetrability, mobility, and *vis inertiæ* of the whole, result from the extension, hardness, impenetrability, mobility, and *vires inertiæ* of the parts; and thence we conclude the least particles of all bodies to be also all extended, and hard, and impenetrable, and moveable, and endowed with their proper *vires inertiæ*. And this is the foundation of all philosophy. Moreover, that the divided but contiguous particles of bodies may be separated from one another, is matter of observation; and, in the particles that remain undivided, our minds are able to distinguish yet lesser parts, as is mathematically demonstrated. But whether the parts so distinguished, and not yet divided, may, by the powers of Nature, be actually divided and separated from one another, we cannot certainly determine. Yet, had we the proof of but one experiment that any undivided particle, in breaking a hard and solid body, suffered a division, we might by virtue of this rule conclude that the undivided as well as the divided particles may be divided and actually separated to infinity.

Lastly, if it universally appears, by experiments and astronomical observations, that all bodies about the earth gravitate towards the earth, and that in proportion to the quantity of matter which they severally contain; that the moon likewise, according to the quantity of its matter, gravitates towards the earth; that, on the other hand, our sea gravitates toward the moon; and all the planets mutually one towards another; and the comets in like manner towards the sun; we must, in consequence of this rule, universally allow that all bodies whatsoever are endowed with a principle of mutual gravitation. For the argument from the appearances concludes with more force for the universal gravitation of all bodies than for their impenetrability; of which, among those in the celestial regions, we have no experiments, nor any manner of observation. [Not that I affirm gravity to be essential to bodies: by their *vis insita* I mean nothing but their *vis inertiæ*. This is immutable. Their gravity is diminished as they recede from the earth.] *

RULE IV.

In experimental philosophy we are to look upon propositions collected by general induction from phænomena as accurately or very nearly true, notwithstanding any contrary hypotheses that may be imagined, till such time as other phænomena occur, by which they may either be made more accurate, or liable to exceptions.

This rule we must follow, that the argument of induction may not be evaded by hypotheses. . .

. . . For the best and safest method of philosophizing seems to be, first, to inquire diligently into the properties of things and to establish those properties by experiments, and to proceed later to hypotheses for the explanation of things themselves. For hypotheses ought to be applied only in the explanation of the properties of things, and not made use of in determining them; except in so far as they may furnish experiments. And if anyone offers conjectures about the truth of things from the mere possiblitiy of hypotheses, I do not see by what stipulation anything certain can be determined in any science; since one or another set of hypotheses may always be devised which will appear to supply

---

*Added by Newton, third edition, 1726.

new difficulties. Hence I judged that one should abstain from contemplating hypotheses, as from improper argumentation. . .

* * * * *

The difficulty. . .which lies in these words, "since every attraction is mutual," is removed by considering that, as in geometry, the word 'hypotheses' is not taken in so large a sense as to include the axioms and postulates; so, in experimental philosophy, it is not to be taken in so large a sense as to include the first principles or axioms, which I call the laws of motion. These principles are deduced from phenomena and made general by induction, which is the highest evidence that a proposition can have in this philosophy. And the word 'hypothesis' is here used by me to signify only such a proposition as is not a phenomenon nor deduced from any phenomena, but assumed or supposed— without any experimental proof. Now the mutual and mutually equal attraction of bodies is a branch of the third law of motion, and how this branch is deduced from phenomena you may see at the end of the corollaries of the laws of motion. . . .

. . . And for preventing exceptions against the use of the word 'hypothesis,' I desire you to conclude the next paragraph in this manner: "For anything which is not deduced from phenomena ought to be called a hypothesis, and hypotheses of this kind, whether metaphysical or physical, whether of occult qualities or mechanical, have no place in experimental philosophy. In this philosophy, propositions are deduced from phenomena, and afterward made general by induction.". . .

. . . I cannot think it effectual for determining truth to examine the several ways by which phenomena may be explained, unless where there can be a perfect enumeration of all those ways. You know, the proper method for inquiring after the properties of things is to deduce them from experiments. And I told you that the theory which I propounded was evinced to me, not be inferring *'tis thus because not otherwise,* that is, not by deducing it only from a confutation of contrary suppositions, but by deriving it from experiments concluding positively and directly. The way therefore to examine it is by considering whether the experiments which I propound do prove those parts of the theory to which they are applied, or by prosecuting other experiments which the theory may suggest for its examination.

To determine by these and such like queries seems the most proper and direct way to a conclusion. And therefore I could wish all objections were suspended from hypotheses or any other heads than these two: of showing the insufficiency of experiments to determine these queries, or prove any other parts of my theory, by assigning the flaws and defects in my conclusions drawn from them; or of producing other experiments which directly contradict me, if any such may seem to occur. For if the experiments which I urge be defective, it cannot be difficult to show the defects; but if valid, then by proving the theory, they must render all objections invalid.

PROBLEMS OF THE CLASSICAL CONCEPTION

ON INDUCTION

*John Stuart Mill (1806-1873), the famous English liberal,
is best known today for his ethical writings,* Utilitarianism
(1863), and his political writings, On Liberty *(1859). Mill,
however, sought to ground his ethical and political views
on a clear theory of the scientific method and the social
sciences. To this end he devoted much study to the method
of science. The result was* A System of Logic *(1843), the
famous textbook of the last half of the nineteenth century.*
    The selection is taken from A System of Logic, *Book
III, Chapters I, II, and III.**

CHAPTER I
PRELIMINARY OBSERVATIONS ON
INDUCTION IN GENERAL

§2. For the purposes of the present inquiry, Induction may be
defined, the operation of discovering and proving general propositions.
It is true that (as already shown) the process of indirectly ascertaining
individual facts is as truly inductive as that by which we establish general truths. But it is not a different kind of induction; it is a form of
the very same process: since, on the one hand, generals are but collections of particulars, definite in kind but indefinite in number; and on

---

*London: Longman's Green & Co., 1893.

the other hand, whenever the evidence which we derive from observation of known cases justifies us in drawing an inference respecting even one unknown case, we should on the same evidence be justified in drawing a similar inference with respect to a whole class of cases. The inference either does not hold at all, or it holds in all cases of a certain description; in all cases which, in certain definable respects, resemble those we have observed.

CHAPTER II
OF INDUCTIONS IMPROPERLY SO CALLED

§3. There remains one improper use of the term Induction, which it is of real importance to clear up, because the theory of Induction has been, in no ordinary degree, confused by it, and because the confusion is exemplified in the most recent and elaborate treatise on the inductive philosophy which exists in our language. The error in question is that of confounding a mere description, by general terms, of a set of observed phenomena, with an induction from them.

Suppose that a phenomenon consists of parts, and that these parts are only capable of being observed separately, and as it were piecemeal. When the observations have been made, there is a convenience (amounting for many purposes to a necessity) in obtaining a representation of the phenomenon as a whole, by combining, or, as we may say, piecing these detached fragments together. A navigator sailing in the midst of the ocean discovers land: he cannot at first, or by any one observation, determine whether it is a continent or an island; but he coasts along it, and after a few days finds himself to have sailed completely round it: he then pronounces it an island. Now there was no particular time or place of observation at which he could perceive that this land was entirely surrounded by water; he ascertained the fact by a succession of partial observations, and then selected a general expression which summed up in two or three words the whole of what he so observed. But is there anything of the nature of an induction in this process? Did he infer anything that had not been observed, from something else which had? Certainly not. He had observed the whole of what the proposition asserts. That the land in question is an island is not an inference from the partial facts which the navigator saw in the course of his circumnavigation; it is the facts themselves; it is a summary of those facts; the description of a complex fact, to which those simpler ones are as the parts of a whole.

Now there is, I conceive, no difference in kind between this simple operation, and that by which Kepler ascertained the nature of the planetary orbits; and Kepler's operation, all at least that was characteristic in it, was not more an inductive act than that of our supposed navigator.

The object of Kepler was to determine the real path described by each of the planets, or let us say by the planet Mars (since it was of that body that he first established the two of his three laws which did not require a comparison of planets). To do this there was no other mode than that of direct observation; and all which observation could do was to ascertain a great number of the successive places of the planet, or rather, of its apparent places. That the planet occupied successively all these positions or at all events, positions which produced the same impressions on the eye, and that it passed from one of these to another insensibly, and without any apparent breach of continuity; thus much the senses, with the aid of the proper instruments, could ascertain. What Kepler did more than this, was to find what sort of a curve these different points would make, supposing them to be all joined together. He expressed the whole series of the observed places of Mars by what Dr. Whewell calls the general conception of an ellipse. This operation was far from being as easy as that of the navigator who expressed the series of his observations on successive points of the coast by the general conception of an island. But it is the very same sort of operation; and if the one is not an induction but a description, this must also be true of the other.

The only real induction concerned in the case consisted in inferring that because the observed places of Mars were correctly represented by points in an imaginary ellipse, therefore Mars would continue to revolve in that same ellipse; and in concluding (before the gap had been filled up by further observations) that the positions of the planet during the time which intervened between two observations, must have coincided with the intermediate points of the curve. For these were facts which had not been directly observed. They were inferences from the observations; facts inferred, as distinguished from facts seen. But these inferences were so far from being a part of Kepler's philosophical operation, that they had been drawn long before he was born. Astronomers had long known that the planets periodically returned to the same places. When this had been ascertained, there was no induction left for Kepler to make, nor did he make any further induction. He merely applied his new conception to the facts inferred, as he did to the facts observed. Knowing already that the planets continued to move in the same paths; when he found that an ellipse correctly represented the past path he knew that it would represent the future path. In finding a compendious expression for the one set of facts, he found one for the other: but he found the expression only, not the inference; nor did he (which is the true test of a general truth) add anything to the power of prediction already possessed.

§4. The descriptive operation which enables a number of details to be summed up in a single proposition, Dr. Whewell, by an aptly chosen expression, has termed the Colligation of Facts. In most of his observations concerning that mental process I fully agree, and would gladly transfer all that portion of his book into my own pages. I only think him mistaken in setting up this kind of operation, which, according to the old and received meaning of the term, is not induction at all, as the type of induction generally; and laying down, throughout his work, as principles of induction, the principles of mere colligation.

Dr. Whewell maintains that the general proposition which binds together the particular facts, and makes them, as it were, one fact, is not the mere sum of those facts, but something more, since there is introduced a conception of the mind, which did not exist in the facts themselves. "The particular facts," says he,* "are not merely brought together, but there is a new element added to the combination by the very act of thought by which they are combined. . . .When the Greeks, after long observing the motions of the planets, saw that these motions might be rightly considered as produced by the motion of one wheel revolving in the inside of another wheel, these wheels were creations of their minds, added to the facts which they perceived by sense. And even if the wheels were no longer supposed to be material, but were reduced to mere geometrical spheres or circles, they were not the less products of the mind alone,—something additional to the facts observed. The same is the case in all other discoveries. The facts are known, but they are insulated and unconnected, till the discoverer supplies from his own store a principle of connection. The pearls are there, but they will not hang together till someone provides the string."

*Novum Organum Renovatum, pp. 72, 73.

Let me first remark that Dr. Whewell, in this passage, blends together, indiscriminately, examples of both the processes which I am endeavouring to distinguish from one another. When the Greeks abandoned the supposition that the planetary motions were produced by the revolutions of material wheels, and fell back upon the idea of "mere geometrical spheres or circles" there was more in this change of opinion than the mere substitution of an ideal curve for a physical one. There was the abandonment of a theory, and the replacement of it by a mere description. No one would think of calling the doctrine of material wheels a mere description. That doctrine was an attempt to point out the force by which the planets were acted upon, and compelled to move in their orbits. But when, by a great step in philosophy, the materiality of the wheels was discarded, and the geometrical forms alone retained, the attempt to account for the motions was given up, and what was left of the theory was a mere description of the orbits. The assertion that the planets were carried round by wheels revolving in the inside of other wheels, gave place to the proposition that they moved in the same lines which would be traced by bodies so carried; which was a mere mode of representing the sum of the observed facts; as Kepler's was another and a better mode of representing the same observations.

It is true that for these simply descriptive operations, as well as for the erroneous inductive one, a conception of the mind was required. The conception of an ellipse must have presented itself to Kepler's mind before he could identify the planetary orbits with it. According to Dr. Whewell, the conception was something added to the facts. He expressed himself as if Kepler had put something into the facts by his mode of conceiving them. But Kepler did no such thing. The ellipse was in the facts before Kepler recognised it; just as the island was an island before it had been sailed round. Kepler did not *put* what he had conceived into the facts, but *saw* it in them. A conception implies, and corresponds to, something conceived: and though the conception itself is not in the facts, but in our mind, yet if it is to convey any knowledge relating to them it must be a conception *of* something which really is in the facts, some property which they actually possess, and which they could manifest to our senses if our senses were able to take cognisance of it. If, for instance, the planet left behind it in space a visible track, and if the observer were in a fixed position at such a distance from the plane of the orbit as would enable him to see the whole of it at once, he would see it to be an ellipse; and if gifted with appropriate instruments and powers of locomotion, he would prove it to be such by measuring its different dimensions. Nay, further: if the track were visible, and he were so placed that he could see all parts of it in succession, but not all of them at once, he might be able, by piecing together his successive observations, to discover both that it was an ellipse and that the planet moved in it. The case would then exactly resemble that of the navigator who discovers the land to be an island by sailing round it. If the path was visible, no one I think would dispute that to identify it with an ellipse is to describe it: and I cannot see why any difference should be made by its not being directly an object of sense, when every point in it is as exactly ascertained as if it were so.

Subject to the indispensable condition which has just been stated, I do not conceive that the part which conceptions have in the operation of studying facts has ever been overlooked or undervalued. No one ever disputed that in order to reason about anything we must have a conception of it; or that when we include a multitude of things under a general expression, there is implied in the expression a conception of something common to those things. But it by no means follows that the conception is necessarily pre-existent, or constructed by the mind out of its own materials. If the facts are rightly classed under the conception, it is because there is in the facts themselves something of which the conception is itself a copy; and which if we cannot directly perceive, it is because of the limited power of our organs, and not because the thing itself is not there. The conception itself is often obtained by abstraction from the very facts which, in Dr. Whewell's language, it is afterwards called in to connect. This he himself admits, when he observes, (which he does on several occasions), how great a service would be rendere to the science of physiology by the philosopher "who should establish a precise, tenable, and consistent conception of life.* Such a conception can only be abstracted from the phenomena of life itself; from the very facts which it is put in requisition to connect. In other cases, no doubt, instead of collecting the conception from the very phenomena which we are attempting to colligate, we select it from among those which have been pre viously collected by abstraction from other facts. In the instance of Kepl Kepler's laws, the latter was the case. The facts being out of the reach of being observed in any such manner as would have enabled the senses to

---

*Ibid, p. 32.

identify directly the path of the planet, the conception requisite for
framing a general description of that path could not be collected by
abstraction from the observations themselves; the mind had to supply
hypothetically, from among the conceptions it had obtained from other
portions of its experience, some one which would correctly represent
the series of the observed facts. It had to frame a supposition respecting
the general course of the phenomenon, and ask itself, If this be the
general description, what will the details be? and then compare these
with the details actually observed. If they agreed, the hypothesis would
serve for a description of the phenomenon: if not, it was necessarily
abandoned, and another tried. It is such a case as this which gives rise
to the doctrine that the mind, in framing the descriptions, adds something of its own which it does not find in the facts.

Yet it is a fact surely that the planet does describe an ellipse; and
a fact which we could see if we had adequate visual organs and a suitable position. Not having these advantages, but possessing the conception of an ellipse, or (to express the meaning in less technical language)
knowing what an ellipse was, Kepler tried whether the observed places
of the planet were consistent with such a path. He found they were so;
and he, consequently, asserted as a fact that the planet moved in an
ellipse. But this fact, which Kepler did not add to, but found in, the
motions of the planet, namely, that it occupied in succession the various
points in the circumference of a given ellipse, was the very fact the
separate parts of which had been separately observed; it was the sum
of the different observations.

Having stated this fundamental difference between my opinion
and that of Dr. Whewell, I must add, that his account of the manner in
which a conception is selected suitable to express the facts appears to
me perfectly just. The experience of all thinkers will, I believe, testify
that the process is tentative; that it consists of a succession of guesses;
many being rejected, until one at last occurs fit to be chosen. We know
from Kepler himself that before hitting upon the "conception" of an
ellipse, he tried nineteen other imaginary paths, which, finding them inconsistent with the observations, he was obliged to reject. But, as Dr.
Whewell truly says, the successful hypothesis, though a guess, ought
generally to be called, not a lucky, but a skillful guess. The guesses which
serve to give mental unity and wholeness to a chaos of scattered particulars are accidents which rarely occur to any minds but those abounding
in knowledge and disciplined in intellectual combinations. . . .

It can scarcely be contended that Kepler's operation was an Induction in this sense of the term. The statement that Mars moves in an elliptical orbit was no generalisation from individual cases to a class of cases. Neither was it an extension to all time of what had been found true at some particular time. The whole amount of generalisation which the case admitted of was already completed, or might have been so. Long before the elliptic theory was thought of, it had been ascertained that the planets returned periodically to the same apparent places; the series of these places was, or might have been completely determined, and the apparent course of each planet marked out on the celestial globe in an uninterrupted line. Kepler did not extend an observed truth to other cases than those in which it had been observed: he did not widen the *subject* of the proposition which expressed the observed facts. The alteration he made was in the predicate. Instead of saying, the successive places of Mars are so and so, he summed them up in the statement that the successive places of Mars are points in an ellipse. It is true this statement, as Dr. Whewell says, was not the sum of the observations *merely;* it was the sum of the observations *seen under a new point of view.* But it was not the sum of *more* than the observations, as a real induction is. It took in no cases but those which had been actually observed, or which could have been inferred from the observations before the new point of view presented itself. There was not that transition from known cases to unknown which constitutes Induction in the original and acknowledged meaning of the term.

Old definitions, it is true, cannot prevail against new knowledge: and if the Keplerian operation, as a logical process, be really identical with what takes place in acknowledged induction, the definition of induction ought to be so widened as to take it in; since scientific language ought to adapt itself to the true relations which subsist between the things it is employed to designate. Here then it is that I am at issue with Dr. Whewell. He does think the operations identical. He allows of no logical process in any case of induction other than what there was in Kepler's case, namely, guessing until a guess is found which tallies with the facts; and accordingly, as we shall see hereafter, he rejects all canons of induction, because it is not by means of them that we guess. Dr. Whewell's theory of the logic of science would be very perfect if it did not pass over altogether the question of Proof. But in my apprehension there is such a thing as proof, and inductions differ altogether from descriptions in their relation to that element. Induction is proof; it is inferring something unobserved from something observed: it requires, therefore, an appropriate test of proof; and to provide that test is the special purpose of inductive logic. When, on the contrary, we merely collate known observations, and, in Dr. Whewell's phraseology, connect them by means of a new conception; if the conception does serve to connect the observations, we have all we want. As the proposition in which it is embodied pretends to no other truth than what it may share with many other modes of representing the same facts, to be consistent with the facts is all it requires: it neither needs nor admits of proof; though it may serve to prove other things, inasmuch as, by placing the facts, in mental connection with other facts not previously seen to resemble them, it assimilates the case to another class of phenomena, concerning which real Inductions have already been made. Thus Kepler's so-called law brought the orbit of Mars into the class ellipse, and by doing so, proved all the properties of an ellipse to be true of the orbit: but in this proof Kepler's law supplied the minor premise, and not (as is the case with real Inductions) the major.

Dr. Whewell calls nothing Induction where there is not a new mental conception introduced, and everything induction where there is. But this is to confound two very different things, Invention and Proof. The introduction of a new conception belongs to Invention: and invention may be required in any operation, but is the essence of none. A new conception may be introduced for descriptive purposes, and so it may for inductive purposes. But it is so far from constituting induction, that induction does not necessarily stand in need of it. Most inductions require no conception but what was present in every one of the particular instances on which the induction is grounded. That all men are mortal is surely an inductive conclusion; yet no new conception is introduced by it. Whoever knows that any man has died, has all the conceptions involved in the inductive generalisation. But Dr. Whewell considers the process of invention, which consists in framing a new conception consistent with the facts, to be not merely a necessary part of all induction, but the whole of it. . . .

ON INDUCTION

*William Whewell (1794-1866) was an English mathematician
strongly influenced by the Prussian philosopher and scientist
Immanuel Kant.* His most famous work was A History of
Scientific Ideas *(1858).* In Part II of this work, entitled
Novum organon renovatum, *he engages in a critique of the
views of Sir Francis Bacon.*
  The selection is taken from Of Induction,* *in which
Whewell defends his views against the criticism of John
Stuart Mill.*

4. Confining myself, then, to the material sciences, I shall proceed
to offer my remarks on Induction with especial reference to Mr. Mill's
work. And in order that we may, as I have said, proceed as intelligibly
as possible, let us begin by considering what we mean by *Induction,* as
a mode of obtaining truth; and let us note whether there is any difference between Mr. Mill and me on this subject.

"For the purposes of the present inquiry," Mr. Mill says (i. 347**),
"Induction may be defined the operation of discovering and forming
general propositions:" meaning, as appears by the context, the discovery of them from particular facts. He elsewhere (i, 370) terms it
"generalization from experience:" and again he speaks of it with greater

---

*London: Parker, 1849
**My references are throughout (except when otherwise expressed) to the volume and the
page of Mr. Mill's first edition of his logic.

precision as the inference of a more general proposition from less general ones.

5 Now to these definitions and descriptions I assent as far as they go; though, as I shall have to remark, they appear to me to leave unnoticed a feature which is very important, and which occurs in all cases of Induction, so far as we are concerned with it. Science then, consists of general propositions, inferred from particular facts, or from less general propositions, by Induction; and it is our object to discern the nature and laws of *Induction* in this sense. That the propositions are general, or are more general than the facts from which they are inferred, is an indispensable part of the notion of Induction, and is essential to any discussion of the process, as the mode of arriving at Science, that is, at a body of general truths.

6 I am obliged therefore to dissent from Mr. Mill when he includes in his notion of Induction, the process by which we arrive at *individual facts* from other facts *of the same order of particularity.*

Such inference is, at any rate, not Induction *alone;* if it be Induction at all, it is Induction applied to an example.

For instance, it is a general law, obtained by Induction from particular facts, that a body falling downwards from rest, describes spaces proportional to the squares of the times. But that a particular body will fall through 16 feet in one second and 64 feet in two seconds, is not an induction simply, it is a result obtained by applying the inductive law to a particular case.

But farther, such a process is often not induction *at all.* That a ball striking another ball directly will communicate to it as much momentum as the striking ball itself loses, is a law established by induction: but if, from habit or practical skill, I make one billiard-ball strike another, so as to produce the velocity which I wish, without knowing or thinking of the general law, the term *Induction* cannot then be rightly applied. If I *know the law* and act upon it, I have in my mind both the general induction and its particular application. But if I act by the ordinary billiard-player's skill, without thinking of momentum or law, there is no Induction in the case.

7 This distinction becomes of importance, in reference to Mr. Mill's doctrine, because he has extended his use of the term *Induction,* not only to the cases in which the general induction is consciously applied to a particular instance; but to the cases in which the particular

instance is dealt with by means of experience, in that rude sense in which *experience* can be asserted of brutes; and in which, of course, we can in no way imagine that the law is possessed or understood, as a general proposition. He has thus, as I conceive, overlooked the broad and essential difference between speculative knowledge and practical action; and has introduced cases which are quite foreign to the idea of science, alongside with cases from which we may hope to obtain some views of the nature of science and the processes by which it must be formed. . . .

18 In the cases hitherto noticed, Mr. Mill extends the term *Induction,* as I think, too widely, and applies it to cases to which it is not rightly applicable. I have now to notice a case of an opposite kind, in which he does not apply it where I do, and condemns me for using it in such a case. I had spoken of Kepler's discovery of the Law, that the planets move round the sun in ellipses, as an example of Induction. The separate facts of any planet (Mars, for instance,) being in certain places at certain times, are all included in the general proposition which Kepler discovered, that Mars describes an ellipse of a certain form and position. This appears to me a very simple but a very distinct example of the operation of discovering general propositions; general, that is, with reference to particular facts; which operation Mr. Mill, as well as myself, says is Induction. But Mr. Mill denies this operation in this case to be Induction at all (i. 357). I should not have been prepared for this denial by the previous parts of Mr. Mill's book, for he had said just before (i. 350), "Such facts as the magnitudes of the bodies of the solar system, their distances from each other, the figure of the earth and its rotation. . . are proved indirectly, by the aid of inductions founded on other facts which we can more easily reach." If the figure of the earth and its rotation are proved by Induction, it seems very strange, and is to me quite incomprehensible, how the figure of the earth's orbit and its revolution (and of course, of the figure of Mars's orbit and its revolution in like manner,) are not also proved by Induction. No, says Mr. Mill, Kepler, in putting together a number of places of the planet into one figure, only performed an act of *description.* "This descriptive operation," he adds (i. 359), "Mr. Whewell, by an aptly chosen expression, has termed Colligation of Facts." He goes on to commend my observations concerning this process, but says that according to the old and received meaning of the term, it is not Induction.

19 Now I have already shown that Mr. Mill himself, a few pages earlier, had applied the term *Induction* to cases undistinguishable from this in any essential circumstance. And even in this case, he allows that Kepler did really perform an act of Induction (i. 358), "namely, in concluding that, because the observed places of Mars were correctly represented by points in an imaginary ellipse, therefore Mars would continue to revolve in that same ellipse; and even in concluding that the position of the planet during the time which had intervened between the two observations must have coincided with the intermediate points of the curve." Of course, in Kepler's Induction, of which I speak, I include all this; all this is included in speaking of the *orbit* of Mars: a continuous line, a periodical motion, are implied in the term *orbit*. I am unable to see what would remain of Kepler's discovery, if we take from it these conditions. It would not only not be an induction, but it would not be a description, for it would not recognise that Mars moved in an orbit. Are particular positions to be conceived as points in a curve, without thinking of the intermediate positions as belonging to the same curve? If so, there is no law at all, and the facts are not bound together by any intelligible tie.

In another place (ii, 209) Mr. Mill returns to his distinction of Description and Induction; but without throwing any additional light upon it, so far as I can see.

20 The only meaning which I can discover in this attempted distinction of Description and Induction is, that when particular facts are bound together by their relation in *space*, Mr. Mill calls the discovery of the connection *Description*, but when they are connected by other general relations, as time, cause and the like, Mr. Mill terms the discovery of the connection *Induction*. And this way of making a distinction, would fall in with the doctrine of other parts of Mr. Mill's book, in which he ascribes very peculiar attributes to space and its relations, in comparison with other Ideas, (as I should call them). But I cannot see any ground for this distinction, of connection according to space and other connections of facts.

To stand upon such a distinction, appears to me to be the way to miss the general laws of the formation of science. For example: The ancients discovered that the planets revolved in recurring periods, and thus connected the observations of their motions according to the Idea of *Time*. Kepler discovered that they revolved in ellipses, and thus connected the observations according to the Idea of *Space*. Newton discovered that they revolved in virtue of the Sun's attraction, and thus connected the motions according to the Idea of *Force*. The first and third of these discoveries are recognised on all hands as processes of Induction. Why is the second to be called by a different name? or what but confusion and perplexity can arise from refusing to class it with the other two? It is, you say, Description. But such Description is a kind of Induction, and must be spoken of as Induction, if we are to speak of Induction as the process by which Science is formed: for the three steps are all, the second in the same sense as the first and third, in co-ordination with them, steps in the formation of astronomical science.

21 But, says Mr. Mill, (i. 363) "it is a fact surely that the planet does describe an ellipse, and a fact which we could see if we had adequate visual organs and a suitable position." To this I should reply: "Let it be so; and it is a fact, surely, that the planet does move periodically: it is a fact, surely, that the planet is attracted by the sun. Still, therefore, the asserted distinction fails to find a ground." Perhaps Mr. Mill would remind us that the elliptical form of the orbit is a fact which we could see if we had adequate visual organs and a suitable position: but that force is a thing which we cannot see. But this distinction also will not bear handling. Can we not see a tree blown down by a storm, or a rock blown up by gunpowder? Do we not here see force:—see it, that is, by its effects, the only way in which we need to see it in the case of a planet, for the purposes of our argument? Are not such operations of force, Facts which may be the objects of sense? and is not the operation of the sun's Force a Fact of the same kind, just as much as the elliptical form of orbit which results from the action? If the latter be "surely a Fact," the former is a Fact no less surely.

22 In truth, as I have repeatedly had occasion to remark, all attempt to frame an argument by the exclusive or emphatic appropriation of the term *Fact* to particular cases, are necessarily illusory and inconclusive. There is no definite and stable distinction between Facts and Theories; Facts and Laws; Facts and Inductions. Laws, Theories, which are true, *are* Facts. Facts involve Inductions. It is a Fact that the moon is attracted by the earth, just as much as it is a Fact that an apple falls from a tree. That the former fact is collected by a more distinct and conscious

Induction, does not make it the less a Fact. That the orbit of Mars is a Fact—a true Description of the path—does not make it the less a case of Induction. . . .

27 There is a difference between Mr. Mill and me in our view of the essential elements of this Induction of Kepler, which affects all other cases of Induction, and which is, I think, the most extensive and important of the differences between us. I must therefore venture to dwell upon it a little in detail.

I conceive that Kepler, in discovering the law of Mars's motion, and in asserting that the planet moved in an ellipse, did this;—he bound together particular observations of separate places of Mars by the notion or, as I have called it the *conception*, of an *ellipse*, which was supplied by his own mind. Other persons, and he, before he made this discovery, had present to their minds the facts of such separate successive positions of the planet; but could not bind them together rightly, because they did not apply to them this conception of an *ellipse*. To supply this conception, required a special preparation, and a special activity in the mind of the discoverer. He, and others before him, tried other ways of connecting the special facts, none of which fully succeeded. To discover such a connection, the mind must be conversant with certain relations of space, and with certain kinds of figures. To discover the right figure was a matter requiring research, invention, resource. To hit upon the right conception is a difficult step; and when this step is once made, the facts assume a different aspect from what they had before: that done, they are seen in a new point of view; and the catching this point of view is a special mental operation, requiring special endowments and habits of thought. Before this, the facts are seen as detached, separate, lawless; afterwards, they are seen as connected, simple, regular; as parts of one general fact, and thereby possessing innumerable new relations before unseen. Kepler, then, I say, bound together the facts by superinducing upon them the *conception* of an *ellipse,* and this was an essential element in his Induction.

28 And there is the same essential element in all Inductive discoveries. In all cases, facts, before detached and lawless, are bound together by a new thought. They are reduced to law, by being seen in a new point of view. To catch this new point of view, is an act of the mind, springing from its previous preparation and habits. The facts, in other discoveries, are brought together according to other relations,

or, as I have called them, *Ideas;*–the Ideas of Time, of Force, of Number, of Resemblance, of Elementary Composition, of Polarity, and the like. But in all cases, the mind performs the operation by an apprehension of some such relations; by singling out the one true relation; by combining the apprehension of the true relation with the facts; by applying to them the Conception of such a relation.

29 In previous writings, I have not only stated this view generally, but I have followed it into detail, exemplifying it in the greater part of the History of the principal Inductive Sciences in succession. I have pointed out what are the Conceptions which have been introduced in every prominent discovery in those sciences; and have noted to which of the above Ideas, or of the like Ideas, each belongs. The performance of this task is the office of the greater part of my *Philosophy of the Inductive Sciences.* For that work, is in reality, no less historical than the *History* which preceded it. The *History of the Inductive Sciences* is the history of the discoveries, mainly so far as concerns the *Facts* which were brought together to form sciences. The *Philosophy* is, in the first ten Books, the history of the *Ideas* and *Conceptions,* by means of which the facts were connected, so as to give rise to scientific truths. It would be easy for me to give a long list of the Ideas and Conceptions thus brought into view, but I may refer any reader who wishes to see such a list, to the Tables of Contents of the *History,* and of the first ten Books of the *Philosophy.*

30 That these Ideas and Conceptions are really distinct elements of the scientific truths thus obtained, I conceive to be proved beyond doubt, not only by considering that the discoveries never were made, nor could be made, till the right Conception was obtained, and by seeing how difficult it often was to obtain this element; but also, by seeing that the Idea and the Conception itself, as distinct from the Facts, was, in almost every science, the subject of long and obstinate controversies;– controversies which turned upon the possible relations of Ideas, much more than upon the actual relations of Facts. The first ten Books of the Philosophy to which I have referred, contain the history of a great number of these controversies. Those controversies make up a large portion of the history of each science; a portion quite as important as the study of the facts; and a portion, at every stage of the science, quite as essential to the progress of truth. Men, in seeking and obtaining scientific knowledge, have always shown that they found the formation

of right conceptions in their own minds to be an essential part of the process.

31 Moreover, the presence of a Conception of the mind as a special element of the inductive process, and as the tie by which the particular facts are bound together, is further indicated, by there being some special new *term* or *phrase* introduced in every induction; or at least some term or phrase thenceforth steadily applied to the facts, which had not been applied to them before; as when Kepler asserted that Mars moved round the sun in an *elliptical orbit,* or when Newton asserted that the planets *gravitate* towards the sun; these new terms, *elliptical orbit,* and *gravitate,* mark the new conceptions on which the inductions depend. I have in the *Philosophy* (B.I.C. iii.), further illustrated this application of "technical terms," that is, fixed and settled terms, in every inductive discovery; and have spoken of theiruse in enabling men to proceed from each such discovery to other discoveries more general. But I notice these terms here for the purpose of showing the existence of a conception in the discoverer's mind, corresponding to the term thus introduced; which conception, the term is intended to convey to the minds of those to whom the discovery is communicated.

32 But this element of discovery,—right conceptions supplied by the mind in order to bind the facts together,—Mr. Mill denies to be an element at all. He says, of Kepler's discovery of the elliptical orbit, (i. 363) "It super-added nothing to the particular facts which it served to bind together;" yet he adds, "except indeed the knowledge that a resemblance existed between the planetary orbit and other ellipses;" that is, except the knowledge that it *was* an ellipse;—precisely the circumstance in which the discovery consisted. Kepler, he says, "asserted as a fact that the planet moved in an ellipse. But this fact, which Kepler did not add to, but found in the motion of the planet. . . .was the very fact, the separate parts of which had been separately observed; it was the sum of the different observations."

33 That the fact of the elliptical motion was not merely the *sum* of the different observations, is plain from this, that other persons, and Kepler himself before this discovery, did not find it by adding together the observations. The fact of the elliptical orbit was not the sum of the observations *merely;* it was the sum of the observations, *seen under a new point of view,* which point of view Kepler's mind supplied. Kepler found it in the facts, because it was there, no doubt, for one reason; but also for another, because he had, in his mind, those relations of thought which enabled him to find it. We may illustrate this by a familiar analogy. We too find the law in Kepler's book; but

if we did not understand Latin, we should not find it there. We must learn Latin in order to find the law in the book. In like manner, a discoverer must know the language of science, as well as look at the book of nature, in order to find scientific truth. All the discussions and controversies respecting Ideas and Conceptions of which I have spoken, may be looked upon as discussions and controversies re specting the grammar of the language in which nature speaks to the scientific mind. Man is the *Interpreter* of Nature; not the Spectator merely, but the In terpreter. The study of the language, as well as the mere sight of the characters, is requisite in order that we may read the inscriptions which are written on the face of the world. And this study of the language of nature, that is, of the necessary coherencies and derivations of the relations of phenomena, is to be pursued by examin-ing Ideas, as well as mere phenomena;—by tracing the formulation of Conceptions, as well as the accumulation of Facts. And this is what I have tried to do in the books already referred to.

34 Mr. Mill has not noticed, in any considerable degree, what I have said of the formation of the Conceptions which enter into the various sciences; but he has, in general terms, denied that the Conception is anything different from the facts themselves. "If," he says, (i. 301) "the facts are rightly classed under the conceptions, it is because there is in the facts themselves, something of which the conception is a copy." But it is a copy which cannot be made by a person without peculiar endowments; just as a person cannot copy an ill-written inscription, so as to make it convey sense, except he understand the language. "Conceptions," Mr. Mill says (ii. 217) "do not develop themselves from within, but are impressed from without." But what comes from without is not enough: they must have both origins, or they cannot make knowledge. "The conception," he says again, (ii. 221) " is not fur-nished *by* the mind till it has been furnished *to* the mind." But it is furnished to the mind by its own activity, operating according to its own laws. No doubt, the conception may be formed, and in cases of discovery, must be formed, by the suggestion and excitement which the facts themselves produce; and must be so moulded as to agree with the facts. But this does not make it superfluous to examine, out of what *materials* such conceptions are formed, and *how* they are capable of being moulded so as to express laws of nature; especially, when we see how large a share this part of discovery—the examination how our ideas can be modified so as to agree with nature,—holds, in the history of science.

REFORMULATION OF THE CLASSICAL CONCEPTION

RETRODUCTION AND GENIUS

Charles Sanders Peirce (1839-1914) was for many years the
forgotten genius of American philosophy, partly because he
lacked an academic affiliation. He taught only briefly (1879-
1884) at Johns Hopkins, America's first graduate center.
Among his students were John Dewey and Thorstein Veblen.
Peirce's voluminous writings have only recently been made
available to the general reading public.

The selection is taken from an article, "A Neglected Argu-
ment for the Reality of God," that first appeared in the
Hibbert Journal *(1908), Vol, vii, pp. 90-112.*

Every inquiry whatsoever takes its rise in the observation, in one
or another of the three Universes, of some surprising phenomenon,
some experience which either disappoints an expectation, or breaks in
upon some habit of expectation of the *inquisiturus;* and each apparent
exception to this rule only confirms it. There are obvious distinctions
between the objects of surprise in different cases; but throughout this
slight sketch of inquiry such details will be unnoticed, especially since
it is upon such that the logic-books descant. The inquiry begins with
pondering these phenomena in all their aspects, in the search of some
point of view whence the wonder shall be resolved. At length a conjecture arises that furnishes a possible Explanation, by which I mean
a syllogism exhibiting the surprising fact as necessarily consequent upon

the circumstances of its occurrence together with the truth of the credible conjecture, as premises. On account of this Explanation, the inquirer is led to regard his conjecture, or hypothesis, with favor. As I phrase it, he provisionally holds it to be "Plausible"; this acceptance ranges in different cases—and reasonably so—from a mere expression of it in the interrogative mood, as a question meriting attention and reply, up through all appraisals of Plausibility, to uncontrollable inclination to believe. The whole series of phenomenon and the acceptance of the hypothesis, during which the usually docile understanding seems to hold the bit between its teeth and to have us at its mercy, the search for pertinent circumstances and the laying hold of them, sometimes without our cognizance, the scrutiny of them, the dark laboring, the bursting out of the startling conjecture, the remarking of its smooth fitting to the anomaly, as it is turned back and forth like a key in a lock, and the final estimation of its Plausibility, I reckon as composing the First Stage of Inquiry. Its characteristic formula of reasoning I term Retroduction, i.e., reasoning from consequent to antecedent. In one respect the designation seems inappropriate; for in most instances where conjecture mounts the high peaks of Plausibility—and is *really* most worthy of confidence—the inquirer is unable definitely to formulate just what the explained wonder is; or can only do so in the light of the hypothesis. In short, it is a form of Argument rather than of Argumentation.

Retroduction does not afford security. The hypothesis must be tested.

This testing, to be logically valid, must honestly start not as Retroduction starts, with scrutiny of the phenomena, but with examination of the hypothesis, and a muster of all sorts of conditional experimental consequences which would follow from its truth. This constitutes the Second Stage of Inquiry. For its characteristic form of reasoning our language has, for two centuries, been happily provided with the name Deduction.

Deduction has two parts. For its first step must be by logical analysis to Explicate the hypothesis, i.e., to render it as perfectly distinct as possible. This process, like Retroduction, is Argument that is not Argumentation. But unlike Retroduction, it cannot go wrong from lack of experience, but so long as it proceeds rightly must reach a true conclusion. Explication is followed by Demonstration, or Deductive Argumentation. Its procedure is best learned from Book I of Euclid's *Elements,* a masterpiece which in real insight is far superior to Aristotle's *Analytics;* and its numerous fallacies render it all the more instructive to a close student. It invariably requires something of the nature of a diagram; that is, an "Icon," or Sign that represents its Object in resembling it. It usually, too, needs "Indices," or Signs that represent their Objects by being actually connected with them. But it is mainly composed of "Symbols," or Signs that represent their Objects essentially because they will be so interpreted. Demonstration should be *Corollarial* when it can. An accurate definition of Corollarial Demonstration would require a long explanation; but it will suffice to say that it limits itself to considerations already introduced or else involved in the Explication of its conclusion; while *Theorematic* Demonstration resorts to a more complicated process of thought.

The purpose of Deduction, that of collecting consequents of the hypothesis, having been sufficiently carried out, the inquiry enters upon its Third Stage, that of ascertaining how far those consequents accord with Experience, and of judging accordingly whether the hypothesis is sensibly correct, or requires some inessential modification, or must be entirely rejected. Its characteristic way of reasoning is Induction. This stage has three parts. For it must begin with Classification, which is an Inductive Non-argumentational kind of Argument, by which general Ideas are attached to objects of Experience; or rather by which the latter are subordinated to the former. Following this will come the testing-argumentations, the Probations; and the whole inquiry will be wound up with the Sentential part of the Third Stage, which, by Inductive reasonings appraises the different Probations singly, then their combinations, then makes self-appraisal of these very appraisals themselves, and passes final judgment on the whole result.

The Probations, or direct Inductive Argumentations, are of two kinds. The first is that which Bacon ill described as *"inductio illa quae procedit per enumerationem simplicem"* [that induction which proceeds by simple enumeration.] So at least he has been understood. For an enumeration of instances is not essential to the argument that, for example, there are no such beings as fairies, or no such events as miracles. The point is that there is no well-established instance of such a thing. I call this Crude Induction. It is the only Induction which concludes a logically Universal Proposition. It is the weakest of arguments, being liable to be demolished in a moment, as happened toward the end of the eighteenth century to the opinion of the scientific world that no stones fall from the sky. The other kind is Gradual Induction, which makes a new estimate of the proportion of truth in the hypothesis with every new instance; and given any degree of error there will *sometime* be an estimate (or would be, if the probation were persisted in) which will be absolutely the last to be infected with so much falsity. Gradual Induction is either Qualitative or Quantitative and the latter either depends on measurements, or on statistics, or on countings.

Concerning the question of the nature of the logical validity possessed by Deduction, Induction, and Retroduction, which is still an arena of controversy, I shall confine myself to stating the opinions which I am prepared to defend by positive proofs. The validity of Deduction was correctly, if not very clearly, analyzed by Kant. This kind of reasoning deals exclusively with Pure Ideas attaching primarily to Symbols and derivatively to other Signs of our own creation; and the fact that man has a power of Explicating his own meaning renders Deduction valid. Induction is a kind of reasoning that may lead us into error; but that it follows a method which, sufficiently persisted in, will be Inductively Certain (the sort of certainty we have that a perfect coin, pitched up often enough, will *sometime* turn up heads) to diminish the error below any predesignate degree, is assured by man's power of perceiving Inductive Certainty. In all this I am inviting the reader to peep through the big end of the telescope; there is a wealth of pertinent detail that must here be passed over.

Finally comes the bottom question of logical Critic. What sort of validity can be attributed to the First Stage of inquiry? Observe that neither Deduction nor Induction contributes the smallest positive item to the final conclusion of the inquiry. They render the indefinite definite; Deduction explicates; Induction evaluates: that is all. Over the chasm that yawns between the ultimate goal of science and such ideas of Man's environment as, coming over him during his primeval wandering in the forest, while yet his very notion of error was of the vaguest, he managed to communicate to some fellow, we are building a cantilever bridge of induction, held together by scientific struts and ties. Yet every plank of its advance is first laid by Retroduction alone, that is to say, by the spontaneous conjectures of instinctive reason; and neither Deduction nor Induction contributes a single new concept to the structure. Nor is this less true or less important for those inquiries that self-interest prompts.

The first answer we naturally give to this question is that we cannot help accepting the conjecture at such a valuation as that at which we do accept it; whether as a simple interrogation, or as more or less Plausible, or, occasionally as an irresistible belief. But far from constituting, by itself, a logical justification such as it becomes a rational being to put forth, this pleading, that we *cannot help* yielding to the suggestion, amounts to nothing more than a confession of having failed to train ourselves to control our thoughts. It is more to the purpose, however, to urge that the strength of the impulse is a symptom of its being instinctive. Animals of all races rise far above the general level of their intelligence in those performances that are their proper function, such as flying and nest-building for ordinary birds; and what is man's proper function if it be not to embody general ideas in art-creations, in utilities, and above all in theoretical cognition? To give the lie to his own consciousness of divining the reasons of phenomena would be as silly in a man as it would be in a fledgling bird to refuse to trust to its wings and leave the nest, because the poor little thing had read Babinet, and judged aerostation to be impossible on hydrodynamical grounds. Yes; it must be confessed that *if we knew* that the impulse to prefer one hypothesis to another really were analogous to the instincts of birds and wasps, it would be foolish not to give it play, within the bounds of reason; especially since we must entertain some hypothesis, or else forego all further knowledge than that which we have already gained by that very means. But is it a fact that man possesses this magical faculty? Not, I reply, to the extent of guessing right the first time, nor perhaps the second; but that the well-prepared mind has wonderfully soon guessed each secret of nature is historical truth. All the theories of science have been so obtained. But may they not have come fortuitously, or by some such modification of chance as the Darwinian supposes? I answer that three or four independent methods of computation show that it would be ridiculous to suppose our science to have so come to pass. Nevertheless, suppose that it can be so "explained," just as that any purposed act of mine is supposed by materialistic necessitarians to have come about. Still, what of it? Does that materialistic explanation, supposing it granted, show that reason has nothing to do with my actions? Even the parallelists will admit that the one explanation leaves the same need of the other that there was before it was given; and this is certainly sound logic. There is a reason, an interpretation, a logic, in the course of scientific advance, and this indisputably proves to him who has perceptions of rational or significant relations, that man's mind must have been attuned to the truth of things in order to discover what he has discovered. It is the very bedrock of logical truth.

Modern science has been builded after the model of Galileo, who founded it, on *il lume naturale.* That truly inspired prophet had said that, of two hypotheses, the *simpler* is to be preferred;[1] but I was formerly one of those who, in our dull self-conceit fancying ourselves more sly than he, twisted the maxim to mean the *logically* simpler, the one that adds the least to what has been observed, in spite of three obvious objections: first, that so there was no support for any hypothesis; secondly, that by the same token we ought to content ourselves with simply formulating the special observations actually made; and thirdly, that every advance of science that further opens the truth to our view discloses a world of unexpected complications. It was not until long experience forced me to realize that subsequent discoveries were every time showing I had been wrong, while those who understood the maxim as Galileo had done, early unlocked the secret, that the scales fell from my eyes and my mind awoke to the broad and flaming daylight that it is the simpler Hypothesis in the sense of the more facile and natural, the one that instinct suggests, that must be preferred; for the reason that, unless man have a natural bent in accordance with nature's, he

---

[1]See "Dialogues Concerning the Two Great Systems of the World," in Mathematical Collections and Translations of Thomas Salisbury, Vol. 1, p. 301 (London, 1661).

has no chance of understanding nature at all. Many tests of this principal and positive fact, relating as well to my own studies as to the researches of others, have confirmed me in this opinion; and when I shall come to set them forth in a book, their array will convince everybody. Oh, no! I am forgetting that armor, impenetrable by accurate thought, in which the rank and file of minds are clad! They may, for example, get the notion that my proposition involves a denial of the rigidity of the laws of association: it would be quite on a par with much that is current. I do not mean that logical simplicity is a consideration of no value at all, but only that its value is badly secondary to that of simplicity in the other sense.

If, however, the maxim is correct in Galileo's sense, whence it follows that man has, in some degree, a divinatory power, primary or derived, like that of a wasp or a bird, then instances swarm to show that a certain altogether peculiar confidence in a hypothesis, not to be confounded with rash cocksureness, has a very appreciable value as a sign of the truth of the hypothesis. I regret I cannot give an account of certain interesting and almost convincing cases.

THE LOGIC OF DISCOVERY

Norwood Russell Hanson (1924-1967) was, before his untimely death, one of the leaders in the recent revival of interest in the history and philosophy of science. He held positions at Cambridge University, the Institute for Advanced Study at Princeton, Indiana University, and Yale University. His published works include Patterns of Discovery *(1958) and* Concept of the Position *(1962).*

The selection, "The Logic of Discovery," appeared in the Journal of Philosophy.*

INTRODUCTION

F.C.S. SCHILLER distinguished the Logic of Proof from the Logic of Discovery[1]. No one, not even Schiller, has been clear about what was intended here. He probably felt his colleagues were too busy sectioning syllogisms—ignoring inferences which mattered in science. He would have approved of the attention philosophers now lavish on inductive inference, and the so-called "hypothetico-deductive method." (For this abominable appellation I substitute "H-D method.") This H-D kind of inquiry would have met Schiller's demand for a study of the

---

*Volume LV, No. 25 (December 4, 1958). It is reprinted here with the permission of the editors, of Stephen Toulmin, and of Mrs. Hanson.

[1] Cf. Studies in the History and Methods of the Sciences, ed. by Charles Singer.

Logic of Discovery. Nonetheless, I doubt whether this H-D method
has anything to do with real discovery in natural science.

The Logic of Proof (i.e., deductive logic) has claimed philosophers
attention more than the Logic of Discovery. And even the latter, with
its analyses of inductive reasoning, the foundations of probability, and
the principles of theory-construction,—all this reads less like a Logic
of Discovery than like a Logic of the Finished Research Report. Logicians of science have described how one might set out reasons in support of an hypothesis once it is proposed. They have said little about
the conceptual considerations pertinent to the initial proposal of an
hypothesis. There are two exceptions: Aristotle and Peirce. When they
discussed what Peirce called "retroduction," both recognized that the
proposal of an hypothesis is often a reasonable affair. One can have
good reasons, or bad, for suggesting an hypothesis initially. These may
be different from reasons which lead one to accept the hypothesis
once suggested; in some cases the two may be different in type. This is
not to deny that sometimes one's reasons for proposing an hypothesis
are identical with his reasons for accepting it.

Neither Aristotle nor Peirce imagined himself to be setting out a
manual to help scientists make discoveries. There could be no such
manual.[2] Nor were they discussing the psychology of discoverers, or
the sociology of discovery. There are such discussions,[3] but they are
not logical discussions. Aristotle and Peirce were doing logic. They
examined characteristics of the reasoning behind the original suggestion
of certain hypotheses. And this is what I should like to do.

I

A. I begin therefore by distinguishing

(1) reasons for accepting an hypothesis H, from
(2) reasons for suggesting H in the first place.

Some philosophers will deny that there is any *logical* difference

---

[2]"There is no science which will enable a man to bethink himself of that which will suit his
purpose" (J.S. Mill, A System of Logic, Book III, Ch. 1, 2).

[3]E.G., those of Hadamard and Poincaré, Helmholtz and Beveridge.

between these two:—this must be faced. But let the distinction be drawn out boldly first.

What are reasons for accepting H? They are just those one might have for thinking H true. But the reasons for suggesting H originally, or even for formulating H, may not be those one would require before thinking H true. They are, rather, those reasons which make H *a plausible conjecture*. No one denies *some* differences between deciding that H is true, and deciding that H is a plausible conjecture. The question is, are these really logical, or more properly called "psychological" or "sociological"?

Thus H will be accepted as true if repeated observations support H— if consequences of H, used as predictions, confirm H—if new phenomena are revealed through operations on H. Again, if H is compatible with, or derivable from, already established theories, this will incline us to accept H as true.

Clearly, all this need not be considered before formulating H as a plausible conjecture. Sometimes one's reasons for proposing that all a's are β's may *just* be that all the a's ever observed were also β's: this will also be his reason for accepting that all a's are β's. But not all cases are like this. Kepler, e.g., could not have set out all the reasons which ultimately supported his elliptical orbit hypothesis *before* the idea of such an orbit for Mars seized him as an at least plausible possibility.

Considerations relevant to Kepler's hypothesis being a plausible possibility, however, might be these:

(1) Does H look as if it might be that from which known phenomena $p_1, p_2 \ldots$ etc., could be shown to follow?

(2) Does H look as if it might explain $p_1, p_2 \ldots$ etc.? (For some values of H the answer at any time would be "No"—an answer for which good reasons could usually be marshaled.)

Or, to follow through with Kepler's *De Motibus Stellae Martis:*

(1) Does the hypothesis of a non-circular orbit for Mars appear to be that from which it would follow that the planet's apparent velocities at 90° and at 270° of eccentric anomaly would be greater than if the orbit were circular? and

(2) Does this hypothesis look as if it might *explain* these facts?

These queries were certainly relevant to Kepler's first formulations of the elliptical orbit idea.[4] And that these considerations are reasonable is seen, in a negative way, from the fact that other values of H (e.g., that Mars' *color* is responsible for its high velocities—or that the disposition of Jupiter's moons are responsible) these would *not* have looked to Kepler as if they would imply or explain the surprising phenomena in question. He would have thought it unreasonable to attempt to develop them; he could have produced good arguments in favor of abandoning them.[5]

B. Now I shall be challenged. Some philosophers will mark as spurious my distinction between reasons for suggesting H and reasons for accepting H.[6] There may be "psychological" factors, they concede, which make certain hypotheses "look" as if they may explain and imply phenomena. Thus Ptolemy knew just as well as did Aristarchus before him and Copernicus after him, that heliocentrism was theoretically simpler, and technically easier to manage, than the hypothesis of a geocentric, geostatic universe. But, say my challengers, for psychological, sociological, or historical reasons, heliocentrism did not "look" to Ptolemy as if it could imply (much less explain) the absence of stellar parallax. This cannot be a matter of logic because for Copernicus heliocentrism did "look" as if it could explain this phenomenon. Insofar as scientists have *reasons* for formulating and entertaining hypotheses (as opposed to having hunches, shrewd suspicions, and inspired intuitions), these are *just* the reasons which show the hypothesis to be true. Thus, if the absence of stellar parallax is thought to constitute more than a psychological reason for Ptolemy's refusal to entertain heliocentrism, then insofar it is equivalent to his reason for rejecting that hypothesis *as false.* Conversely, his reason for developing the geostatic hypothesis

[4]C.F. De Motibus Stellae Martis (Munich), pp. 250 ff.

[5]Braithwaite's view differs: "But exactly which hypothesis was to be rejected was a matter for the 'hunch' of the physicist" (Scientific Explanation, p. 20).

[6]Reichenbach writes that philosophy "cannot be concerned with the first, but only with the latter" (Experience and Prediction, p. 382).

(namely, this absence of stellar parallax) *was* his reason for accepting that hypothesis as true. Again, Kepler's reasons for rejecting Mars' color or Jupiter's moons as responsible for the former's apparent accelerations—if he had reasons and was not simply guessing—were reasons which inductively supported (and also served as reasons finally for accepting as true) the non-circularity hypothesis.

So the objection to my distinction between reasons for proposing H and reasons for accepting H comes to this: *the only logical reasons for proposing H at all is that certain considerations incline one to think H true. Obviously these are the same considerations which (if substantiated) will ultimately lead one to account H as true. The distinction Hanson advocates is at bottom merely psychological, sociological, or historical in nature; it says nothing of logical import about the differences between suggesting and establishing scientific hypotheses.*[7]

Kepler may again illustrate the objection. No historian of planetary theory would deny that the principle of uniform circular motion profoundly affected astronomical thought before 1600. Even young Kepler in 1591 abandons an hypothesis because it entails other-than-uniform-circular motions in the heavens—inconceivable for him. Psychological pressure against forming alternative hypotheses was therefore great. But *logically* Kepler's reasons for entertaining a Martian motion other than uniformly circular were precisely his reasons for accepting that idea as an astronomical truth. He first encountered this hypothesis on perceiving that no simple adjustments of the orthodox epicycle, deferent, and eccentric could square with Mars' observed distances, velocities, and apsidal positions. These were the first reasons which led him ultimately to assert that the planet's orbit is not the effect of uniform-circular motions. Even after scores of other inductive reasons confirmed the truth of the non-circularity hypothesis, these early reasons *were still* reasons for accepting H as true. So they cannot have been merely reasons for proposing H and nothing more.

This objection is made as strong as possible. If the arguments I now bring forward cannot weaken it essentially, my purpose will not have been achieved.

---

[7]Or, as Braithwaite puts it, "The solution of these historical problems involves the individual psychology of thinking and the sociology of thought. None of these questions are our business here." (Scientific Explanation, pp. 20-21.)

C. It still seems to me that in some cases one's reasons for entertaining an hypothesis and his reasons for accepting it are logically different. When Kepler published *De Motibus Stellae Martis* he had completely established that Mars' orbit was an ellipse, inclined to the ecliptic, the sun being in one of the foci. In the *Harmonices Mundi* (1619) Kepler generalized this for *all* the planets. Let us call this general hypothesis H'.

The reasons which led Kepler to formulate and propose H' were many. But they certainly included this one; that H (the limited hypothesis that *Mars'* orbit is elliptical) is true. Since Eudoxos, Mars had been taken to reveal typical planetary behavior. *(We* can see why this would be so. Mars' retardations and retrogradations, its movement at perihelion and around the empty focus—all these we observe particularly clearly because of the actual spatial relations of Earth and Mars.) In a sense Mars is a typical planet. Its dynamical properties are usually found in the other planets. If *its* orbit is ellipsoidal, then it is reasonable to conjecture that the orbits of Mercury, Venus, Jupiter, Saturn, and even Earth, are also ellipsoidal—i.e., it is reasonable to entertain, develop, and suggest H'.

But these reasons would not *establish* the truth of H'. Because what makes it reasonable to propose H' is *analogical* in character. (Mars does *x;* Mars is a typical planet; so (perhaps) all planets do *x.)* Analogies cannot establish hypotheses, only observations can; in this the H-D account is correct. To establish H' one must observe the positions of the other planets, determining that each could be plotted on a smooth curve whose equations approximate to those of an ellipse. When this is done it may be possible to assert H'. But this could not have been done, nor would it be reasonable to expect it, before H' was even proposed initially. Nor is it correct to characterize this difference between H'-as-established as being one of psychology only (as Reichenbach and Braithwaite, among others, seem prepared to do). *Logically,* Kepler's analogical reasons for proposing H' just after 1609 were good ones. But, logically, they would not have been good reasons for asserting the truth of H'—something which could be done confidently only years later. Remember, if the statement "A is a good reason for H'" is true, it is logically true—even when the reasons are inductive. If I say "Jones *has* good reason for H," that is contingently true, if true at all. Jones could have had other reasons for H. But this statement is logically different from "A *is* a good reason for H." What are and are not good reasons is a logical matter. No further observations are required to settle the matter—any more than we require experiments to decide, on the basis of all of Jones' bank statements, whether he is bankrupt. Similarly, whether or not A is a good reason for H's proposal is a purely logical inquiry.

It seems clear, then, that the difference between reasons which make it plausible to propose H and those which establish H is greater than is conveyed by calling them "psychological." Consider how reasoning proceeds from analogies on the one hand, and from observations on the other.

Kepler reasoned initially by analogy. Other kinds of reasons which might make it plausible to propose an hypothesis could be, e.g., the detection of a single formal structure, or symmetry, in sets of equations or arguments; this marked the work of Clerk Maxwell and Einstein. One could even argue reasonably from authority. Kepler's assistant, Bartsch, had a good reason for proposing H': it was Kepler that also proposed H'. Just because a man proposes an hypothesis in "me too" fashion does not make his proposal unreasonable. It all depends on whom he takes his cue from. Even the purest of mathematicians rarely work out their own logarithmic tables. But these considerations would not establish H'. So reasons for proposing H' and for accepting it are not only different, they can be different in type. Consider this further.

Reasoning from observations of a's are β's to the proposal of "all a's are β's" is different in type from reasoning analogically from the fact that γ's are δ's to the proposal of "all a's are β's." (Here it is the *way* in which γ's are a's which seems analogous to the way in which a's are β's.) Both of these are typically different from reasons consisting in the detection of symmetries in equations which describe a's and those describing β's. Again, all these differ from what can also be good reason for proposing that all a's are β's, namely, that all authorities are convinced that a's are β's. Microbiologists, e.g., accept the atomic hypothesis and with good reason. Yet they may discover further reasons for accepting the hypothesis, e.g., the Brownian movement, and the properties of semi-permeable membranes.

SUMMARY

I have distinguished reasons for proposing hypotheses from reasons for accepting them. In some cases the two are identical; in others they can differ in type. There is a difference in type between proposing H as (1) a result of analogical argument, and (2) as a result of symmetry considerations, and (3) by appealing to authority—and between all of these and (4) the acceptance of H because of inductive arguments from observed particulars.

But here an objection obtrudes: "Analogical, authoritative, and symmetry arguments are used in certain cases *because* of inductively established beliefs in their reliability."

This I accept. However, I am not discussing the genesis of our faith in these types of arguments, but rather the logic of the arguments themselves. *Given* an analogical premise, or one based on authority or on symmetry—or indeed on enumeration of particulars,—one argues from these in logically different ways. This is clear once one considers what further moves would be necessary to convince one who doubted the conclusions of such arguments. A challenge to the conclusion "all a's are β's" when this is based on induction by enumeration, could only be a challenge to justify induction, or to show that the particulars are correctly described. These are inappropriate when the argument rests on analogies or on formal symmetries.

Another potent objection is this: "Analogical reasons, and those based on symmetry considerations and on appeals to authorities—all these are *still* reasons for H even after H is (inductively) established. They are thus reasons both for proposing *and* for accepting H." This is also accepted. Nonetheless, analogical, symmetry, and authoritative arguments could never *by themselves* establish an H. Inductive arguments can, by themselves, do this. So they must be different in type. Though any of these could make it reasonable to propose an H, only the inductive argument can by itself establish hypotheses.

Since H-D philosophers have been most articulate on these matters I must draw out a related issue on which their accounts are unsatisfactory.

II

J.S. Mill was wrong in his account of Kepler's discovery.[8] It is impossible to reconcile the labors of the *Astronomia Nova,* and the delicate adjustment between theory, hypothesis, and observation recorded in *De Motibus Stellae Martis,* with Mill's irresponsible statement that Kepler's First Law is just "a compendious expression for the one set of directly observed facts." Mill cannot have understood Kepler.[9] *A System of Logic* is as misleading about scientific research and discovery as any account which proceeded *via* what Bacon called "Inductio per enumerationem simplicem, ubi non reperitur instantia contradictoria."[10] In another way the accounts of H-D theorists are equally misleading.

An H-D account of Kepler's First Law would treat it as a high-level hypothesis in an H-D system. It would be regarded as a quasi-axiom, from the assumption of which observation-statements can be shown to follow. If these are true—if, e.g., they imply that Uranus' orbit is an ellipse and that its apparent velocity at 90° will be greater than at aphelion, —then insofar is the First Law confirmed.[11]

Perhaps this describes physical theory more adequately than did pre-Baconian accounts in terms of simple enumerations, or even post-Millian accounts in terms of ostensibly not-so-simple enumerations. It tells us something about the logic of laws, and what they do in the finished arguments of physicists. H-D accounts do not, however, tell us how laws are proposed in the first place—nor were they intended to.

---

[8]A System of Logic, Bk. III, Ch. 2-3.

[9]As Peirce notes Collected Papers, I, p. 31. It is equally questionable whether Reichenbach understood Kepler: "Kepler's laws of the elliptic motion of celestial bodies were inductive generalizations of observed facts. . .[He] observed a series of. . . positions of the planet Mars and found that they may be connected by a mathematical relation. . ." (Experience and Prediction, p. 371).

[10]Reichenbach observes:"It is the great merit of John Stuart Mill to have pointed out that all empirical inferences are reducible to the inductio per enumerationem simplicem. . ." (op. cit., p. 389)

[11]Thus Braithwaite writes: "A scientific system consists of a set of hypotheses which form a deductive system. . . arranged in such a way that from some of the hypotheses as premises all the other hypotheses logically follow. . . .The establishment of a system as a set of true propositions depends upon the establishment of its lowest-level hypotheses. . ." (Scientific Exploration pp. 12-13).

(Nonetheless those who deny real differences between reasons for suggesting H and reasons for accepting it are also inclined sometimes to suppose that scientific discovery *actually proceeds via* the industrious employment of the H-D method.)

Though the H-D account of scientific theories, laws, and hypotheses does not tell us in what kinds of rational contexts laws and hypotheses are suggested, the induction-by-enumeration story did attempt this. It sought to describe good reasons for initially proposing H. The H-D account ought to be silent on this point. The two accounts are not strict alternatives.[12] The induction-by-enumeration account and the H-D account are compatible. Acceptance of the second is no good reason for rejecting the first. A law *might* have been arrived at, or inferred from, little more than an enumeration of particulars (e.g., Boyle's Law in the 17th century, Bode's Law in the 18th, the Laws of Ampére and Faraday in the 19th, and much of meson theory in the 20th). It could then be built into an H-D system as a higher-order proposition—as indeed has happened with all my examples save the last. So, if there is anything wrong with the older view, H-D accounts do not reveal what this is.

There is something wrong with the older accounts. They are false. Scientists do not always find laws by enumerating and summarizing observables.[13] But this does not strengthen the H-D account of the matter as against the inductive view. There is no H-D account of how "sophisticated generalizations" are *derived*.

If the H-D account were construed as a description of scientific practice it would be misleading.[14] Natural scientists do not "start from" hypotheses. They start from data. And even then not from ordinary commonplace data—but from surprising anomalies. Thus Aristotle remarks[15] that knowledge begins in astonishment. Peirce makes perplexity the trigger of scientific inquiry.[16] And James and Dewey treat intelligence as the result of mastering problem situations.[17]

[12]As Braithwaite suggests they are when he remarks of a certain "higher level" hypothesis that it "will not have been established by induction by simple enumeration; it will have been obtained by the hypothetico-deductive method. . ." (op. cit., p. 303).

[13]Thus Braithwaite says: "sophisticated generalizations (such as that about the proton-electron constitution of the hydrogen atom). . .[were] certainly not derived by simple enumeration of instances. . ." (op. cit., p. 11).

[14]Braithwaite's use of "derived" is thus misleading. So is his announcement (p. 11) that he is going to explain "how we come to make use of sophisticated generalizations."

[15]Metaphysica 982 b 11 ff.

[16]Collected Papers, II, Book III, Ch. 1, Part III.

[17]Dewey, How We Think, pp. 12 ff.

By the time a law gets fixed into an H-D system, the *original* scientific thinking is over. The more pedestrian process of deducting observation-statments begins only after the physicist is convinced that the proposed hypothesis will at least explain the data initially requiring explanation. Thus Kepler's assistant could easily work out the consequences of H′, and check its validity by seeing whether Mercury, Venus, Earth, Jupiter, and Saturn behaved as H′ predicts. This was possible because of Kepler's reasonable conviction that what H had done for Mars, H′ would do for the other planets. The H-D account is helpful here; it analyzes *the argument of a completed research report,* such as Bartsch's report that the consequences of H′ square with the observed positions of the planets. It helps us also to see how the experimentalist elaborates a theoretician's hypotheses. And yet another aspect of science the H-D account illuminates, but its proponents oddly have not stressed it; scientists often dismiss explanations alternative to the one which has won their provisional assent in a way that is almost a model of the H-D method in action. Examples of this are in Ptolemy's *Almagest,* when he rules out a moving earth; in Copernicus' *De Revolutionibus. . . ,* when he demolishes Ptolemy's lunar theory; in Kepler's *De Motibus Stellae Martis,* when he denies that the planes of the planetary orbits intersect in the center of the ecliptic instead of (as he proposed) the center of the sun; and in Newton's *Principia,* when he rejects the idea that the gravitational force law might be of an inverse cube nature. These mirror parts of Mill's *System of Logic,* or Braithwaite's *Scientific Explanation.*

Notwithstanding these merits, however, the H-D analysis leaves undiscussed reasoning which often conditions the discovery of laws.

The induction-by-enumeration story views the important inference as being from observations to the law, from particulars to the general. There is something true about this which the H-D account must ignore. Thus Newton wrote: "the main business of natural philosophy is to argue from phenomena. . .[18]

This inductive view ignores what Newton never ignored; the inference is also from *explicanda* to an *explicans.* Why a beveled mirror shows a spectrum in the sunlight is not explained by saying that all beveled mirrors display spectra in sunlight. Why Mars moves more rapidly at 270° and 90° than could be expected of circular-uniform

---

[18]*Principia,* Preface.

motions is not explained by saying that Mars always moves in this manner—or even that all the planets always move in this manner. On the induction-by-enumeration view, these latter might count as laws. But clearly, only when it is explained why beveled mirrors show spectra in the sunlight, and why planets apparently accelerate at 90°—only then will we have laws of the type suggested; Newton's Laws of Refraction and Kepler's First Law.

So the inductive view rightly suggests that laws are got by inference from data. It wrongly suggests that the law is but a summary of these data, instead of being (what it at least sometimes must be) an explanation of the data.

H-D accounts all agree that physical laws explain data.[19] However, they obscure the initital connection between data and laws. Indeed, they often suggest, that the fundamental inference in science is from higher-order hypotheses to observation-statements. This may be a way of setting out reasons for making a prediction after H is formulated and provisionally established. It need not be a way of setting out reasons in favor of proposing H originally. Bartsch could have justified a prediction that Saturn will appear to move faster at 270° and 90° than the hypothesis of its uniform circular motion indicates. Referring to H' and its success with the other planets, he would show how this conclusion about Saturn is entailed by H'. But he would not have set out thus his reasons for entertaining H' initially— if he had any reasons other than that Kepler was convinced that H' was true. Certainly Kepler himself would not have set out thus his reasons for proposing H originally.

Yet the original suggestion of an hypothesis is often a reasonable affair. It is not as dependent on intuition, hunches, and other imponderables as historians and philosophers suppose when they make it the province of genius but not of logic. If the establishment of H through its predictions has a logic, so has the argument which leads to H's proposal initially. To form the first idea of an elliptical planetary

[19]Thus Braithwaite says: "A hypothesis to be regarded as a natural law must be a general proposition which can be thought to explain its instances; if the reason for believing the general proposition is solely direct knowledge of the truth of its instances, it will be felt to be a poor sort of explanation of these instances. . ." (op. cit., p. 302).

orbit, or of constant acceleration, or of universal gravitational attraction does indeed require genius; nothing less than a Kepler, a Galileo, or a Newton, But this need not entail that reflections leading to these ideas are unreasonable, or a-reasonable. Perhaps *only* Kepler, Galileo, and Newton had intellects mighty enough to fashion these notions initially. To concede this is not to concede that their reasons for first entertaining such concepts surpass rational inquiry.

H-D accounts begin with the hypothesis as given, as cooking recipes begin with the trout as given. In an occasional ripple of culinary humor, however, recipes sometimes begin with "First catch your trout." The H-D account describes a recipe physicists often use after catching hypotheses. However, the ingenuity and conceptual boldness which mark the whole history of physics show more clearly in the ways in which scientists *caught* their hypotheses, than in the ways in which they elaborated these once caught.

To study only the verification of hypotheses is to leave a vital part of the story untold—namely, what were the reasons Kepler, Galileo, and Newton had for suggesting their hypotheses initially. In a letter to Fabricius, Kepler underlines this distinction.

Prague, July 4, 1603

Dear Fabricius,
    . . .You believe that I start with imagining some pleasant hypothesis and please myself in embellishing it, examing it only later by observations. In this you are very much mistaken. The truth is that after having built up an hypothesis on the ground of observations and given it proper foundations, I feel a peculiar desire to investigate whether I might discover some natural, satisfying combination between the two. . . .

If any H-D theorist ever sought to give an account of the way in which hypotheses in science are actually discovered, these words are for him.

THE ROLE OF MODELS IN PHYSICS

James Clerk Maxwell (1831-1879) was one of the greatest of English physicists. Basing his own work on the previous endeavors of Lord Kelvin and Michael Faraday, Maxwell sought to develop the analogies between heat and hydrodynamics. He also developed the revolutionary electromagnetic theory of light, which he described in On a Dynamical Theory of the Electro-magnetic Field *(1864).*

The selection is from On Faraday's Lines of Force *(1856), which is part of* The Scientific Papers *of James Clerk Maxwell (1890).*

I. The present state of electrical science seems peculiarly unfavourable to speculation. The laws of the distribution of electricity on the surface of conductors have been analytically deduced from experiment; some parts of the mathematical theory of magnetism are established, while in other parts the experimental data are wanting; the theory of the conduction of galvanism and that of the mutual attraction of conductors have been reduced to mathematical formulæ, but have not fallen into relation with the other parts of the science. No electrical theory can now be put forth, unless it shows the connexion not only between electricity at rest and current electricity, but between the attractions and inductive effects of electricity in both states. Such a theory must, accurately satisfy those laws, the mathematical form of which is known, and must afford the means of calculating the effects in the limiting cases where the known formulæ are inapplicable. In order therefore to appreciate the requirements of the science, the student must make himself familiar with a considerable body of most intricate mathematics, the mere retention of which in the memory materially interferes with further progress. The first process therefore in the effectual study of the science, must be one of simplification and reduction of the results of previous investigation to a form in which the mind can grasp them. The results of this simplification may take the form of a purely mathematical formula or of a physical hypothesis. In the first case we entirely lose sight of the phenomena to be explained; and though we may trace out the consequences of given laws, we can never obtain more extended views of the connexions of the subject. If, on the other hand, we adopt a physical hypothesis, we see the phenomena only through a medium, and are liable to that blindness to facts and rashness in assumption which a partial explanation encourages. We must therefore discover some method of investigation which allows the mind at every step to lay hold of a clear physical conception, without being committed to any theory founded on the physical science from which that conception is borrowed, so that it is neither drawn aside from the subject in pursuit of analytical subtleties, nor carried beyond the truth by a favourite hypothesis.

In order to obtain physical ideas without adopting a physical theory we must make ourselves familiar with the existence of physical analogies. By a physical analogy I mean that partial similarity between the laws of one science and those of another which makes each of them illustrate the other. Thus all the mathematical sciences are founded on relations between physical laws and laws of numbers, so that the aim of exact science is to reduce the problems of nature to the determination of quantities by operations with numbers. Passing from the most universal of all analogies to a very partial one, we find the same resemblance in mathematical form between two different phenomena giving rise to a physical theory of light.

The changes of direction which light undergoes in passing from one medium to another, are identical with the deviations of the path of a particle in moving through a narrow space in which intense forces act. This analogy, which extends only to the direction, and not to the velocity of motion, was long believed to be the true explanation of the refraction of light; and we still find it useful in the solution of certain problems, in which we employ it without danger, as an artificial method. The other analogy, between light and the vibrations of an elastic medium, extends much farther, but, though its importance and fruitfulness cannot be over-estimated, we must recollect that it is founded only on a resemblance *in form* between the laws of light and those of vibrations. By stripping it of its physical dress and reducing it to a theory of "transverse alternations," we might obtain a system of truth strictly founded on observation, but probably deficient both in the vividness of its conceptions and the fertility of its method. I have said thus much on the disputed questions of Optics, as a preparation for the discussion of the almost universally admitted theory of attraction at a distance.

We have all acquired the mathematical conception of these attractions. We can reason about them and determine their appropriate forms or formulæ. These formulæ have a distinct mathematical significance, and their results are found to be in accordance with natural phenomena. There is no formula in applied mathematics more consistent with nature than the formula of attractions, and no theory better established in the minds of men than that of the action of bodies on one another at a distance. The laws of the conduction of heat in uniform media appear at first sight among the most different in their physical relations from those relating to attractions. The quantities which enter into them are *temperature, flow of heat, conductivity.* The word *force* is foreign to the subject. Yet we find that the mathematical laws of the uniform motion of heat in homogeneous media are identical in form with those of attractions varying inversely as the square of the distance. We have only to substitute *source of heat* for *centre of attraction, flow of heat* for *accelerating effect of attraction* at any point, and *temperature* for *potential,* and the solution of a problem in attractions is transformed into that of a problem in heat.

This analogy between the formulæ of heat and attraction was, I believe, first pointed out by Professor William Thomson in the *Camb. Math. Journal,* Vol. III.

Now the conduction of heat is supposed to proceed by an action between contiguous parts of a medium, while the force of attraction is a relation between distant bodies, and yet, if we knew nothing more than is expressed in the mathematical formulæ, there would be nothing to distinguish between the one set of phenomena and the other.

It is true, that if we introduce other considerations and observe additional facts, the two subjects will assume very different aspects, but the mathematical resemblance of some of their laws will remain, and may still be made useful in exciting appropriate mathematical ideas.

It is by the use of analogies of this kind that I have attempted to bring before the mind, in a convenient and manageable form, those mathematical ideas which are necessary to the study of the phenomena of electricity. The methods are generally those suggested by the processes of reasoning which are found in the researches of Faraday*, and which, though they have been interpreted mathematically by Prof. Thomson and others, are very generally supposed to be of an indefinite and unmathematical character, when compared with those employed by the professed mathematicians. By the method which I adopt, I hope to render it evident that I am not attempting to establish any physical theory of a science in which I have hardly made a single experiment, and that the limit of my design is to show how, by a strict application of the ideas and methods of Faraday, the connexion of the very different orders of phenomena which he has discovered may be clearly placed before the mathematical mind. I shall therefore avoid as much as I can the introduction of anything which does not serve as a direct illustration of Faraday's methods, or of the mathematical deductions which may be made from them. In treating the simpler parts of the subject I shall use Faraday's mathematical methods as well as his ideas. When the complexity of the subject requires it, I shall use analytical notation, still confining myself to the development of ideas originated by the same philosopher.

I have in the first place to explain and illustrate the idea of "lines of force."

---

*See especially Series XXXVIII. of the Experimental Researches, and Phil. Mag. 1852.

When a body is electrified in any manner, a small body charged with positive electricity, and placed in any given position, will experience a force urging it in a certain direction. If the small body be now negatively electrified, it will be urged by an equal force in a direction exactly opposite.

The same relations hold between a magnetic body and the north or south poles of a small magnet. If the north pole is urged in one direction, the south pole is urged in the opposite direction.

In this way we might find a line passing through any point of space, such that it represents the direction of the force acting on a positively electrified particle, or on an elementary north pole, and the reverse direction of the force on a negatively electrified particle or an elementary south pole. Since at every point of space such a direction may be found, if we commence at any point and draw a line so that, as we go along it, its direction at any point shall always coincide with that of the resultant force at that point, this curve will indicate the direction of that force for every point through which it passes, and might be called on that account *a line of force*. We might in the same way draw other lines of force, till we had filled all space with curves indicating by their direction that of the force at any assigned point.

We should thus obtain a geometrical model of the physical phenomena, which would tell us the *direction* of the force, but we should still require some method of indicating the *intensity* of the force at any point. If we consider these curves not as mere lines, but as fine tubes of variable section carrying an incompressible fluid, then, since the velocity of the fluid is inversely as the section of the tube, we may make the velocity vary according to any given law, by regulating the section of the tube, and in this way we might represent the intensity of the force as well as its direction by the motion of the fluid in these tubes. This method of representing the intensity of a force by the velocity of an imaginary fluid in a tube is applicable to any conceivable system of forces, but it is capable of great simplification in the case in which the forces are such as can be explained by the hypothesis of attractions varying inversely as the square of the distance, such as those observed in electrical and magnetic phenomena.

In the case of a perfectly arbitrary system of forces, there will generally be interstices between the tubes; but in the case of electric and magnetic forces it is possible to arrange the tubes so as to leave no interstices. The tubes will then be mere surfaces, directing the motion of a fluid filling tup the whole space. It has been usual to commence the investigation of the laws of these forces by at once assuming that the phenomena are due to attractive or repulsive forces acting between certain points. We may however obtain a different view of the subject, and one more suited to our more difficult inquiries, by adopting for the definition of the forces of which we treat, that they may be represented in magnitude and direction by the uniform motion of an incompressible fluid.

I propose then, first to describe a method by which the motion of such a fluid can be clearly conceived; secondly to trace the consequences of assuming certain conditions of motion, and to point out the application of the method to some of the less complicated phenomena of electricity, magnetism, and galvanism; and lastly to show how by an extension of these methods, and the introduction of another idea due to Faraday, the laws of the attractions and inductive actions of magnets and currents may be clearly conceived, without making any assumptions as to the physical nature of electricity, or adding anything to that which has been already proved by experiment.

By referring everything to the purely geometrical idea of the motion of an imaginary fluid, I hope to attain generality and precision, and to avoid the dangers arising from a premature theory professing to explain the cause of the phenomena. If the results of mere speculation which I have collected are found to be of any use to experimental philosophers, in arranging and interpreting their results, they will have served their purpose, and a mature theory, in which physical facts will be physically explained, will be formed by those who by interrogating Nature herself can obtain the only true solution of the questions which the mathematical theory suggests.

PART II.

On Faraday's "Electro-tonic State."

When a conductor moves in the neighbourhood of a current of electricity, or of a magnet, or when a current or magnet near the conductor is moved, or altered in intensity, then a force acts on the conductor and produces electric tension, or a continuous current, according as the circuit is open or closed. This current is produced only by *changes* of the electric or magnetic phenomena surrounding the conductor, and as long as these are constant there is no observed effect on the conductor. Still the conductor is in different states when near a current or magnet, and when away from its influence, since the removal or destruction of the current or magnet occasions a current, which would not have existed if the magnet or current had not been previously in action.

Considerations of this kind led Professor Faraday to connect with his discovery of the induction of electric currents the conception of a state into which all bodies are thrown by the presence of magnets and currents. This state does not manifest itself by any known phenomena as long as it is undisturbed, but any change in this state is indicated by a current or tendency towards a current. To this state he gave the name of the "Electro-tonic State," and although he afterwards succeeded in explaining the phenomena which suggested it by means of less hypothetical conceptions, he has on several occasions hinted at the probability that some phenomena might be discovered which would render the electro-tonic state an object of legitimate induction. These speculations, into which Faraday had been led by the study of laws which he has well established, and which he abandoned only for want of experimental data for the direct proof of the unknown state, have not, I think, been made the subject of mathematical investigation. Perhaps it may be thought that the quantitative determinations of the various phenomena are not sufficiently rigorous to be made the basis of a mathematical theory; Faraday, however, has not contented himself with simply stating the numerical results of his experiemnts and leaving the law to be discovered by calculation. Where he has perceived a law he has at once stated it, in terms as unambiguous as those of pure mathematics; and if the mathematician, receiving this as a physical truth, deduces from it other laws capable of being tested by experiment, he has merely assisted the physicist in arranging his own ideas, which is confessedly a necessary step in scientific induction.

In the following investigation, therefore, the laws established by Faraday will be assumed as true, and it will be shewn that by following out his speculations other and more general laws can be deduced from them. If it should then appear that these laws, originally devised to include one set of phenomena, may be generalized so as to extend to phenomena of a different class, these mathematical connexions may suggest to physicists the means of establishing physical connexions; and thus mere speculation may be turned to account in experimental science.

EXPERIMENT IN PHYSICS

The second selection from the works of Pierre Duhem is taken from The Aim and Structure of Physical Theory.*

EXPERIMENT IN PHYSICS[1]

1. *An Experiment in Physics Is Not Simply the Observation of a Phenomenon; It Is, Besides, the Theoretical Interpretation of This Phenomenon*

---

*Pages 144-145, 185, 188-190, 211-212; translated by Philip P. Wiener (Princeton: Princeton University Press, 1954). Used by permission of Princeton University Press.

[1]This chapter and the two following it are devoted to the analysis of the experimental method used by the physicist in particular. In this regard, we ask the reader's permission to take note of a few dates. We think we were the first to formulate this analysis in an article entitled "Quelques reflexions au sujet de la Physique experimentale," Revue des Questions scientifiques, 2nd Series, Vol. III (1894). G. Milhaud took as the subject of his course in 1895-96 an exposition of a part of these ideas; he published a summary of his lectures (in which, besides, he quoted us) under the title: "La Science rationelle," Revue de Metaphysica et de Morale, 4th year (1896), p. 290; also in book form in Le Rationnel (Paris, 1898). The same analysis of the experimental method was adopted by Edouard Le Roy in the second part of his article "Science et Philosophie," Revue de Metaphysique et de Morale, 7th year (1899), p. 503, and in another essay entitled "La Science positive et les philosophies de la liberte," Congres international de Philosophie (held in Paris in 1900), Sec. I: "Philosophie generale et Metaphysique," p. 313. E. Wilbois also admits an analogous doctrine in his article "La Methode des Sciences physiques," Revue de Metaphysique et de Morale, 7th year (1899), p. 579. The several authors we have just cited often draw from this analysis of the experimental method used in physics conclusions which go beyond the boundaries of physics; we shall not follow them that far, but shall stay always within the limits of physical science.

The aim of all physical theory is the representation of experimental laws. The words "truth" and "certainty" have only one signification with respect to such a theory; they express concordance between the conclusions of the theory and the rules established by the observers. We could not, therefore, push our critical examination of physical theory further if we did not analyze the exact nature of the laws stated by experimenters, and if we did not note precisely what sort of certainty they can yield. Moreover, a law of physics is but the summary of an infinity of experiments that have been made or will be performable. Hence we are naturally led to raise the question: What exactly is an experiment in physics?

This question will undoubtedly astonish more than one reader. Is there any need to raise it, and is not the answer self-evident? What more does "doing an experiment in physics" mean to anybody than producing a physical phenomenon under conditions such that it may be observed exactly and minutely by means of appropriate instruments?

Go into this laboratory; draw near this table crowded with so much apparatus: an electric battery, copper wire wrapped in silk, vessels filled with mercury, coils, a small iron bar carrying a mirror. An observer plunges the metallic stem of a rod, mounted with rubber, into small holes; the iron oscillates and, by means of the mirror tied to it, sends a beam of light over to a celluloid ruler and the observer follows the movement of the light beam on it. There, no doubt, you have an experiment; by means of the vibration of this spot of light, this physicist minutely observes the oscillations of the piece of iron. Ask him now what he is doing. Is he going to answer; "I am studying the oscillations of the piece of iron carrying this mirror?" No, he will tell you that he is measuring the electrical resistance of a coil. If you are astonished and ask him what meaning these words have, and what relation they have to the phenomena he has perceived and which you have at the same time perceived, he will reply that your question would require some very long explanations, and he will recommend that you take a course in electricity.

It is indeed the case that the experiment you have seen done, like any experiment in physics, involves two parts. In the first place, it consists in the observation of certain facts; in order to make this observation

it suffices for you to be attentive and alert enough with your senses.
It is not necessary to know physics; the director of the laboratory may
be less skillful in this matter of observation than the assistant. In the
second place, it consists in the interpretation of the observed facts;
in order to make this interpretation it does not suffice to have an
alert attention and practiced eye; it is necessary to know the accepted
theories and to know how to apply them, in short, to be a physicist.
Any man can, if he sees straight, follow the motions of a spot of light
on a transparent ruler, and see if it goes to the right or to the left or
stops at such and such a point; for that he does not have to be a great
cleric. But if he does not know electrodynamics, he will not be able
to finish the experiment, he will not be able to measure the resistance
of the coil. . . .

Indeed, the demonstrative value of experimental method is far
from being so rigorous or absolute; the conditions under which it functions are much more complicated than is supposed in what we have
just said; the evaluation of results is much more delicate and subject to
caution.

A physicist decides to demonstrate the inaccuracy of a proposition;
in order to deduce from this proposition the prediction of a phenomenon
and institute the experiment which is to show whether this phenomenon
is or is not produced, in order to interpret the results of this experiment
and establish that the predicted phenomenon is not produced, he does
not confine himself to making use of the proposition in question; he
makes use also of a whole group of theories accepted by him as beyond
dispute. The prediction of the phenomenon, whose nonproduction is
to cut off debate, does not derive from the proposition challenged if
taken by itself, but from the proposition at issue joined to that whole
group of theories; if the predicted phenomena is not produced, not only
is the proposition questioned at fault, but so is the whole theoretical
scaffolding used by the physicist. The only thing the experiment teaches
us is that among the propositions used to predict the phenomenon and
to establish whether it would be produced, there is at least one error;
but where this error lies is just what it does not tell us. The physicist
may declare that this error is contained in exactly the proposition he
wishes to refute, but is he sure it is not in another proposition? If he is,
he accepts implicitly the accuracy of all the other propositions he has
used, and the validity of his conclusion is as great as the validity of his
confidence. . . .

3. A *"Crucial Experiment"* Is Impossible in Physics

Let us press this point further, for we are touching on one of the essential features of experimental method, as it is employed in physics.

Reduction to absurdity seems to be merely a means of refutation, but it may become a method of demonstration: in order to demonstrate the truth of a proposition it suffices to corner anyone who would admit the contradictory of the given proposition into admitting an absurd consequence. We know to what extent the Greek geometers drew heavily on this mode of demonstration.

Those who assimilate experimental contradiction to reduction to absurdity imagine that in physics we may use a line of argument similar to the one Euclid employed so frequently in geometry. Do you wish to obtain from a group of phenomena a theoretically certain and indisputable explanation? Enumerate all the hypotheses that can be made to account for this group of phenomena; then, by experimental contradiction eliminate all except one; the latter will no longer be a hypothesis, but will become a certainty.

Suppose, for instance, we are confronted with only two hypotheses. Seek experimental conditions such that one of the hypotheses forecasts the production of one phenomenon and the other the production of quite a different effect; bring these conditions into existence and observe what happens; depending on whether you observe the first or the second of the predicted phenomena, you will condemn the second or the first hypothesis, the hypothesis not condemned will be henceforth indisputable; debate will be cut off, and a new truth will be acquired by science. Such is the experimental test that the author of the *Novum Organum* called the *"fact of the cross,* borrowing this expression from the crosses which at an intersection indicate the various roads."

We are confronted with two hypotheses concerning the nature of light; for Newton, Laplace, or Biot light consisted of projectiles hurled with extreme speed, but for Huygens, Young, or Fresnel light consisted of vibrations whose waves are propagated within an ether. These are the only two possible hypotheses as far as one can see: either the motion is carried away by the body it excites and remains attached to it, or else it passes from one body to another. Let us pursue the first hypothesis;

it declares that light travels more quickly in water than in air; but if we follow the second, it declares that light travels more quickly in air than in water. Let us set up Foucault's apparatus; we set into motion the turning mirror; we see two luminous spots formed before us, one colorless, the other greenish. If the greenish band is to the left of the colorless one, it means that light travels faster in water than in air, and that the hypothesis of vibrating waves is false. If, on the contrary, the greenish band is to the right of the colorless one, that means that light travels faster in air than in water, and that the hypothesis of emissions is condemned. We look though the magnifying glass used to examine the two luminous spots, and we notice that the greenish spot is to the right of the colorless one; the debate is over; light is not a body, but a vibratory wave motion propagated by the ether; the emission hypothesis has had its day; the wave hypothesis has been put beyond doubt, and the crucial experiment has made it a new article of the scientific credo.

What we have said in the foregoing paragraph shows how mistaken we should be to attribute to Foucault's experiment so simple a meaning and so decisive an importance; for it is not between two hypotheses, the emission and wave hypotheses, that Foucault's experiment judges trenchantly; it decides rather between two sets of theories each of which has to be taken as a whole, i.e., between two entire systems, Newton's optics and Huygens' optics.

But let us admit for a moment that in each of these systems everything is compelled to be necessary by strict logic, except a single hypothesis; consequently, let us admit that the facts, in condemning one of the two systems, condemn once and for all the single doubtful assumption it contains. Does it follow that we can find in the "crucial experiment" an irrefutable procedure for transforming one of the two hypotheses before us into a demonstrated truth? Between two contradictory theorems of geometry there is no room for a third judgment; if one is false, the other is necessarily true. Do two hypotheses in physics ever constitute such a strict dilemma? Shall we ever dare to assert that no other hypothesis is imaginable? Light may be a swarm of projectiles, or it may be a vibratory motion whose waves are propagated in a medium; is it forbidden to be anything else at all? Arago undoubtedly thought so when he formulated this incisive alternative: Does light move more quickly in water than in air? "Light is a body. If the contrary is the case, then light is a wave." But it would be difficult for us to take such a decisive stand; Maxwell, in fact, showed that we might just as well attribute light to a periodical electrical disturbance that is propagated within a dielectric medium.

Unlike the reduction to absurdity employed by geometers, experimental contradiction does not have the power to transform a physical hypothesis into an indisputable truth; in order to confer this power on it, it would be necessary to enumerate completely the various hypotheses which may cover a determinate group of phenomena; but the physicist is never sure he has exhausted all the imaginable assumptions. The truth of a physical theory is not decided by heads or tails.

4. Criticism of the Newtonian Method, First Example: Celestial Mechanics

It is illusory to seek to construct by means of experimental contradiction a line of argument in imitation of the reduction to absurdity; but the geometer is acquainted with other methods for attaining certainty than the method of reducing to an absurdity; the direct demonstration in which the truth of a proposition is established by itself and not by the refutation of the contradictory proposition seems to him the most perfect of arguments. Perhaps physical theory would be more fortunate in its attempts if it sought to imitate direct demonstration. The hypotheses from which it starts and develops its conclusions would then be tested one by one; none would have to be accepted until it presented all the certainty that experimental method can confer on an abstract and general proposition; that is to say, each would necessarily be either a law drawn from observation by the sole use of those two intellectual operations called induction and generalization, or else a corollary mathematically deduced from such laws. A theory based on such hypotheses would then not present anything arbitrary or doubtful; it would deserve all the confidence merited by the faculties which serve us in formulating natural laws.

It was this sort of physical theory that Newton had in mind . . .
We have here nothing more than a particular application of the

principle set down in Section 2 of this chapter. A disagreement between the concrete facts constituting an experiment and the symbolic
representation which theory substitutes for this experiment proves that
some part of this symbol is to be rejected. But which part? This the experiment does not tell us; it leaves to our sagacity the burden of guessing. Now among the theoretical elements entering into the composition
of this symbol there is always a certain number which the physicists of
a certain epoch agree in accepting without test and which they regard
as beyond dispute. Hence, the physicist who wishes to modify this
symbol will surely bring his modification to bear on elements other
than those just mentioned.

But what impels the physicist to act thus is *not* logical vecosity.
It would be awkward and ill inspired for him to do otherwise, but it
would not be doing something logically absurd; he would not for all
that be walking in the footsteps of the mathematician mad enough
to contradict his own definitions. More than this, perhaps some day
by acting differently, by refusing to invoke causes of error and take
recourse to corrections in order to reestablish agreement between the
theoretical scheme and the fact, and by resolutely carrying out a reform
among the propositions declared untouchable by common consent, he
will accomplish the work of a genius who opens a new career for a
theory.

Indeed, we must really guard ourselves against believing forever
warranted those hypotheses which have become universally adopted
conventions, and whose certainty seems to break through experimental
contradiction by throwing the latter back on more doubtful assumptions. The history of physics shows us that very often the human mind
has been led to overthrow such principles completely, though they
have been regarded by common consent for centuries as inviolable
axioms, and to rebuild its physical theories on new hypotheses. . . .

POPPER

CONJECTURES AND REFUTATIONS

Karl R. Popper (1902) is Professor of Logic and Scientific Method at the University of London. Among his latest publications is Conjectures and Refutations, *from which the selection is taken.* *

I have discussed the problem of demarcation in some detail because I believe that its solution is the key to most of the fundamental problems of the philosophy of science. I am going to give you later a list of some of these other problems, but only one of them—*the problem of induction*—can be discussed here at any length.

I had become interested in the problem of induction in 1923. Although this problem is very closely connected with the problem of demarcation, I did not fully appreciate the connection for about five years.

I approached the problem of induction through Hume. Hume, I felt, was perfectly right in pointing out that induction cannot be logically justified. He held that there can be no valid logical[1] arguments allowing us to establish *'that those instances, of which we have had no experience, resemble those, of which we have had experience'.* Consequently *'even after the observation of the frequent or constant conjunction of objects, we have no reason to draw any inference concerning any object beyond those of which we have had experience'.* For 'shou'd it be said that we

*Pages 42-59, (London: Routledge & Kegan Paul Ltd., copyright 1963 by Karl R. Popper). Used by permission.

[1]Hume does not say 'logical' but 'demonstrative', a terminology which, I think, is a little misleading. The following two quotations are from the <u>Treatise of Human Nature</u>, Book I, Part III, sections vi and xii. (The italics are all Hume's.)

have experience'[2] —experience teaching us that objects constantly conjoined with certain other objects continue to be so conjoined—then,
Hume says, 'I wou'd renew my question, *why from this experience we
form any conclusion beyond those past instances, of which we have had
experience'.* In other words, an attempt to justify the practice of induction by an appeal to experience must lead to an *infinite regress.* As a
result we can say that theories can never be inferred from observation
statements, or rationally justified by them.

I found Hume's refutation of inductive inference clear and conclusive. But I felt completely dissatisfied with his psychological explanation of induction in terms of custom or habit.

It has often been noticed that this explanation of Hume's is philos-
ophically not very satisfactory. It is, however, without doubt intended
as a *psychological* rather than a philosophical theory; for it tries to give
us a causal explanation of a psychological fact— *the fact that we believe
in laws,* in statements asserting regularities or constantly conjoined kinds
of events—by asserting that this fact is due to (i.e. constantly conjoined
with) custom or habit. But even this reformulation of Hume's theory is
still unsatisfactory; for what I have just called a 'psychological fact' may
itself be described as a custom or habit—the custom or habit of believing
in laws or regularities; and it is neither very surprising nor very enlight-
ening to hear that such a custom or habit must be explained as due to,
or conjoined with, a custom or habit (even though a different one).
Only when we remember that the words 'custom' and 'habit' are used
by Hume, as they are in ordinary language, not merely to *describe* regular behaviour, but rather to *theorize about its origin* (ascribed to frequent
repetition), can we reformulate his psychological theory in a more
satisfactory way. We can then say that, like other habits, *our habit of
believing in laws is the product of frequent repetition*—of the repeated
observation that things of a certain kind are constantly conjoined with
things of another kind.

This genetico-psychological theory is, as indicated, incorporated
in ordinary language, and it is therefore hardly as revolutionary as Hume
thought. It is no doubt an extremely popular psychological theory—part
of 'common sense', one might say. But in spite of my love of both common sense and Hume, I felt convinced that this psychological theory

---

[2]This and the next quotation are from loc. cit., section vi. See also Hume's Enquiry <u>Concerning
Human Understanding,</u> section iv, Part II, and his Abstract, edited 1938 by J. M. Keynes and
P. Sraffa, p. 15, and quoted in L.Sc.D. [<u>Logic of Scientific Discovery</u>] , new appendix *vii, text
to note 6.

was mistaken; and that it was in fact refutable on purely logical grounds.

Hume's psychology, which is the popular psychology, was mistaken, I felt, about at least three different things: *(a)* the typical result of repetition; *(b)* the genesis of habits; and especially *(c)* the character of those experiences or modes of behaviour which may be described as 'believing in a law' or 'expecting a law-like succession of events'.

(a) The typical result of repetition—say, of repeating a difficult passage on the piano—is that movements which at first needed attention are in the end executed without attention. We might say that the process becomes radically abbreviated, and ceases to be conscious: it becomes 'physiological'. Such a process, far from creating a conscious expectation of law-like succession, or a belief in a law, may on the contrary begin with a conscious belief and destroy it by making it superfluous. In learning to ride a bicycle we may start with the belief that we can avoid falling if we steer in the direction in which we threaten to fall, and this belief may be useful for guiding our movements. After sufficient practice we may forget the rule; in any case, we do not need it any longer. On the other hand, even if it is true that repetition may create unconscious expectations, these become conscious only if something goes wrong (we may not have heard the clock tick, but we may hear that it has stopped).

(b) Habits or customs do not, as a rule, *originate* in repetition. Even the habit of walking, or of speaking, or of feeding at certain hours, *begins* before repetition can play any part whatever. We may say, if we like, that they deserve to be called 'habits' or 'customs' only after repetition has played its typical part; but we must not say that the practices in question originated as the result of many repetitions.

(c) Belief in a law is not quite the same thing as behaviour which betrays an expectation of a law-like succession of events; but these two are sufficiently closely connected to be treated together. They may, perhaps, in exceptional cases, result from a mere repetition of sense impressions (as in the case of the stopping clock). I was prepared to concede this, but I contended that normally, and in most cases of any interest, they cannot be so explained. As Hume admits, even a single striking observation may be sufficient to create a belief or an expectation—a fact which he tries to explain as due to an inductive habit, formed as the result of a vast number of long repetitive sequences which

had been experienced at an earlier period of life.[3] But this, I contended, was merely his attempt to explain away unfavourable facts which threatened his theory; an unsuccessful attempt, since these unfavourable facts could be observed in very young animals and babies—as early, indeed, as we like. 'A lighted cigarette was held near the noses of the young puppies', reports F. Bäge. 'They sniffed at it once, turned tail, and nothing would induce them to come back to the source of the smell and to sniff again. A few days later, they reacted to the mere sight of a cigarette or even of a rolled piece of white paper, by bounding away, and sneezing.'[4] If we try to explain cases like this by postulating a vast number of long repetitive sequences at a still earlier age we are not only romancing, but forgetting that in the clever puppies' short lives there must be room not only for repetition but also for a great deal of novelty, and consequently of non-repetition.

But it is not only that certain empirical facts do not support Hume; there are decisive arguments of a *purely logical* nature against his psychological theory.

The central idea of Hume's theory is that of *repetition, based upon similarity* (or 'resemblance'). This idea is used in a very uncritical way. We are led to think of the water-drop that hollows the stone: of sequences of unquestionably like events slowly forcing themselves upon us, as does the tick of the clock. But we ought to realize that in a psychological theory such as Hume's, only repetition-for-us, based upon similarity-for-us, can be allowed to have any effect upon us. We must respond to situations as if they were equivalent; *take* them as similar; *interpret* them as repetitions. The clever puppies, we may assume, showed by their response, their way of acting or of reacting, that they recognized or interpreted the second situation as a repetition of the first: that they expected its main element, the objectionable smell, to be present. The situation was a repetition-for-them because they responded to it by *anticipating* its similarity to the previous one.

This apparently psychological criticism has a purely logical basis which may be summed up in the following simple argument. (It happens to be the one from which I originally started my criticism.) The kind of repetition envisaged by Hume can never be perfect; the cases he has in mind cannot be cases of perfect sameness; they can only be cases of

---

[3] Treatise, section xiii; section xv, rule 4.

[4] F. Bage, 'Zur Entwicklung, etc.', Zeitschrift f. Hundeforschung, 1933; cp. D. Katz, Animals and Men, ch. vi, footnote.

similarity. Thus *they are repetitions only from a certain point of view.*
(What has the effect upon me of a repetition may not have this effect
upon a spider.) But this means that, for logical reasons, there must
always be a point of view—such as a system of expectations, anticipations, assumptions, or interests—*before* there can be any repetition;
which point of view, consequently, cannot be merely the result of
repetition. (See now also appendix *x, (1), to my *L.Sc.D.*)

We must thus replace, for the purposes of a psychological theory
of the origin of our beliefs, the naive idea of events which *are* similar.
But if this is so (and I can see no escape from it) then Hume's psychological theory of induction leads to an infinite regress, precisely analogous to that other infinite regress which was discovered by Hume himself, and used by him to explode the logical theory of induction. For
what do we wish to explain? In the example of the puppies we wish to
explain behaviour which may be described as *recognizing or interpreting*
a situation as a repetition of another. Clearly, we cannot hope to explain this by an appeal to earlier repetitions, once we realize that the
earlier repetitions must also have been repetitions-for-them, so that
precisely the same problem arises again: that of *recognizing or interpreting* a situation as a repetition of another.

To put it more concisely, similarity-for-us in the product of a respons
involving interpretations (which may be inadequate) and anticipations or
expectations (which may never be fulfilled). It is therefore impossible to
explain anticipations, or expectations, as resulting from many repetitions,
as suggested by Hume. For even the first repetition-for-us must be based
upon similarity-for-us, and therefore upon expectations—precisely the
kind of thing we wished to explain.

This shows that there is an infinite regress involved in Hume's
psychological theory.

Hume, I felt, had never accepted the full force of his own logical
analysis. Having refuted the logical idea of induction he was faced with
the following problem: how do we actually obtain our knowledge, as a
matter of psychological fact, if induction is a procedure which is logically
invalid and rationally unjustifiable? There are two possible ansers: (1)
We obtain our knowledge by a non-inductive procedure. This answer
would have allowed Hume to retain a form of rationalism. (2) We obtain our knowledge by repetition and induction, and therefore by a
logically invalid and rationally unjustifiable procedure, so that all ap-

parent knowledge is merely a kind of belief—belief based on habit. This answer would imply that even scientific knowledge is irrational, so that rationalism is absurd, and must be given up. (I shall not discuss here the age-old attempts, now again fashionable, to get out of the difficulty by asserting that though induction is of course logically invalid if we mean by 'logic' the same as 'deductive logic', it is not irrational by its own standards, as may be seen from the fact that every reasonable man applies it *as a matter of fact:* it was Hume's great achievement to break this uncritical identification of the question of fact—*quid facti*—and the question of justification or validity—*quid juris*. (See below, point (13) of the appendix to the present chapter.)

It seems that Hume never seriously considered the first alternative. Having cast out the logical theory of induction by repetition he struck a bargain with common sense, meekly allowing the re-entry of induction by repetition, in the guise of a psychological theory. I proposed to turn the tables upon this theory of Hume's. Instead of explaining our propensity to expect regularities as the result of repetition, I proposed to explain repetition-for-us as the result of our propensity to expect regularities and to search for them.

Thus I was led by purely logical considerations to replace the psychological theory of induction by the following view. Without waiting, passively, for repetitions to impress or impose regularities upon us, we actively try to impose regularities upon the world. We try to discover similarities in it, and to interpret it in terms of laws invented by us. Without waiting for premises we jump to conclusions. These may have to be discarded later, should observation show that they are wrong.

This was a theory of trial and error—of *conjectures and refutations*. It made it possible to understand why our attempts to force interpretations upon the world were logically prior to the observation of similarities. Since there were logical reasons behind this procedure, I thought that it would apply in the field of science also; that scientific theories were not the digest of observations, but that they were inventions—conjectures boldly put forward for trial, to be eliminated if they clashed with observations; with observations which were rarely accidental but as a rule undertaken with the definite intention of testing a theory by obtaining, if possible, a decisive refutation.

The belief that science proceeds from observation to theory is still so widely and so firmly held that my denial of it is often met with incredulity. I have even been suspected of being insincere—of denying what nobody in his senses can doubt.

But in fact the belief that we can start with pure observations alone, without anything in the nature of a theory, is absurd; as may be illustrated by the story of the man who dedicated his life to natural science, wrote down everything he could observe, and bequeathed his priceless collection of observations to the Royal Society to be used as inductive evidence. This story should show us that though beetles may profitably be collected, observations may not.

Twenty-five years ago I tried to bring home the same point to a group of physics students in Vienna by beginning a lecture with the following instructions: 'Take pencil and paper; carefully observe, and write down what you have observed!' They asked of course, *what* I wanted them to observe. Clearly the instruction, 'Observe!' is absurd.[5] (It is not even idiomatic, unless the object of the transitive verb can be taken as understood.) Observation is always selective. It needs a chosen object, a definite task, an interest, a point of view, a problem. And its description presupposes a descriptive language, with property words; it presupposes similarity and classification, which in its turn presupposes interests, points of view, and problems. 'A hungry animal', writes Katz,[6] 'divides the environment into edible and inedible things. An animal in flight sees roads to escape and hiding places. . . .Generally speaking, objects change. . .according to the needs of the animal.' We may add that objects can be classified, and can become similar or dissimiliar, *only* in this way—by being related to needs and interests. This rule applies not only to animals but also to scientists. For the animal a point of view is provided by its needs, the task of the moment, and its expectations; for the scientist by his theoretical interests, the special problem under investigation, his conjectures and anticipations, and the theories which he accepts as a kind of background: his frame of reference his 'horizon of expectations'.

The problem 'Which comes first, the hypothesis *(H)* or the observation *(O)*,'is soluble; as is the problem, 'Which comes first, the hen *(H)* or the egg *(O)*'. The reply to the latter is, 'An earlier kind of egg'; to the former, 'An earlier kind of hypothesis'. It is quite true that any

---

[5]See section 30 of L.Sc.D.

[6]Katz, loc. cit.

particular hypothesis we choose will have been preceded by observations—
the observations, for example, which it is designed to explain. But these
observations, in their turn, presupposed the adoption of a frame of
reference: a frame of expectations: a frame of theories. If they were
significant, if they created a need for explanation and thus gave rise to
the invention of a hypothesis, it was because they could not be explained
within the old theoretical framework, the old horizon of expectations.
There is no danger here of an infinite regress. Going back to more and
more primitive theories and myths we shall in the end find unconscious,
inborn expectations.

The theory of inborn *ideas* is absurd, I think; but every organism
has inborn *reactions* or *responses;* and among them, responses adapted
to impending events. These responses we may describe as 'expectations'
without implying that these 'expectations' are conscious. The new-born
baby 'expects', in this sense, to be fed (and, one could even argue, to
be protected and loved). In view of the close relation between expectation and knowledge we may even speak in quite a reasonable sense of
'inborn knowledge'. This 'knowledge' is not, however, *valid a priori;* an
inborn expectation, no matter how strong and specific, may be mistaken.
(The newborn child may be abandoned, and starve.)

Thus we are born with expectations; with 'knowledge' which,
although not *valid a priori,* is *psychologically or genetically a priori,*
i.e. prior to all observational experience. One of the most important of
these expectations is the expectation of finding a regularity. It is connected with an inborn propensity to look out for regularities, or with
a *need* to *find* regularities, as we may see from the pleasure of the child
who satisfies this need.

This 'instinctive' expectation of finding regularities, which is
psychologically *a priori,* corresponds very closely to the 'law of causality'
which Kant believed to be part of our mental outfit and to be *a priori*
valid. One might thus be inclined to say that Kant failed to distinguish
between psychologically *a priori* ways of thinking or responding and
a priori valid beliefs. But I do not think that his mistake was quite as
crude as that. For the expectation of finding regularities is not only
psychologically *a priori,* but also logically *a priori:* It is logically prior
to all observational experience, for it is prior to any recognition of
similarities, as we have seen; and all observation involves the recognition
of similarities (or dissimilarities). But in spite of being logically *a priori*
in this sense the expectation is not valid *a priori.* For it may fail; we

can easily construct an environment (it would be a lethal one) which, compared with our ordinary environment, is so chaotic that we completely fail to find regularities. (All natural laws could remain valid: environments of this kind have been used in the animal experiments mentioned in the next section.)

Thus Kant's reply to Hume came near to being right; for the distinction between an *a priori* valid expectation and one which is both genetically *and* logically prior to observation, but not *a priori* valid, is really somewhat subtle. But Kant proved too much. In trying to show how knowledge is possible, he proposed a theory which had the unavoidable consequence that our quest for knowledge must necessarily succeed, which is clearly mistaken. When Kant said, 'Our intellect does not draw its laws from nature but imposes its laws upon nature', he was right. But in thinking that these laws are necessarily true, or that we necessarily succeed in imposing them upon nature, he was wrong.[7] Nature very often resists quite successfully, forcing us to discard our laws as refuted; but if we live we may try again.

To sum up this logical criticism of Hume's psychology of induction we may consider the idea of building an induction machine. Placed in a simplified 'world' (for example, one of sequences of coloured counters) such a machine may through repetition 'learn', or even 'formulate', laws of succession which hold in its 'world'. If such a machine can be constru (and I have no doubt that it can) then, it might be argued, my theory must be wrong; for if a machine is capable of performing inductions on the basis of repetition, there can be no logical reasons preventing us from doing the same.

The argument sounds convincing, but it is mistaken. In constructin an induction machine we, the architects of the machine, must decide *a priori* what constitutes its 'world'; what things are to be taken as similar or equal; and what *kind* of 'laws' we wish the machine to be able to 'discover' in its 'world'. In other words we must build into the machine a framework determining what is relevant or interesting in its world: the

---

[7]Kant believed that Newton's dynamics was a priori valid. (See his Metaphysical Foundations of Natural Science, published between the first and the second editions of the Critique of Pure Reason.) But if, as he thought, we can explain the validity of Newton's theory by the fact that our intellect imposes its laws upon nature, it follows, I think, that our intellect must succeed in this; which makes it hard to understand why a priori knowledge such as Newton's should be so hard to come by. A somewhat fuller statement of this criticism can be found in ch. 2, especially section ix, and chs. 7 and 8 of the present volume.

machine will have its 'inborn' selection principles. The problems of
similarity will have been solved for it by its makers who thus have interpreted the 'world' for the machine.

Our propensity to look out for regularities, and to impose laws
upon nature, leads to the psychological phenomenon of *dogmatic
thinking* or, more generally, dogmatic behaviour: we expect regularities
everywhere and attempt to find them even where there are none; events
which do not yield to these attempts we are inclined to treat as a kind
of 'background noise'; and we stick to our expectations even when
they are inadequate and we ought to accept defeat. This dogmatism is
to some extent necessary. It is demanded by a situation which can only
be dealt with by forcing our conjectures upon the world. Moreover, this
dogmatism allows us to approach a good theory in stages, by way of
approximations: if we accept defeat too easily, we may prevent ourselves
from finding that we were very nearly right.

It is clear that this *dogmatic attitude,* which makes us stick to our
first impressions, is indicative of a strong belief; while a *critical attitude,*
which is ready to modify its tenets, which admits doubt and demands
tests, is indicative of a weaker belief. Now according to Hume's theory,
and to the popular theory, the strength of a belief should be a product
of repetition; thus it should always grow with experience, and always
be greater in less primitive persons. But dogmatic thinking, an uncon-
trolled wish to impose regularities, a manifest pleasure in rites and in
repetition as such, are characteristic of primitives and children; and
increasing experience and maturity sometimes create an attitude of
caution and criticism rather than of dogmatism.

I may perhaps mention here a point of agreement with psycho-
analysis. Psycho-analysts assert that neurotics and others interpret the
world in accordance with a personal set pattern which is not easily
given up, and which can often be traced back to early childhood. A
pattern or scheme which was adopted very early in life is maintained
throughout, and every new experience is interpreted in terms of it;
verifying it, as it were, and contributing to its rigidity. This is a description of what I have called the dogmatic attitude, as distinct from the
critical attitude, which shares with the dogmatic attitude the quick
adoption of a schema of expectations—a myth, perhaps, or a conjecture
or hypothesis—but which is ready to modify it, to correct it, and even
to give it up. I am inclined to suggest that most neuroses may be due

to a partially arrested development of the critical attitude; to an arrested rather than a natural dogmatism; to resistance to demands for the modification and adjustment of certain schematic interpretations and responses. This resistance in its turn may perhaps be explained, in some cases, as due to an injury or shock, resulting in fear and in an increased need for assurance or certainty, analogous to the way in which an injury to a limb makes us afraid to move it, so that it becomes stiff. (It might even be argued that the case of the limb is not merely analogous to the dogmatic response, but an instance of it.) The explanation of any concrete case will have to take into account the weight of the difficulties involved in making the necessary adjustments—difficulties which may be considerable, especially in a complex and changing world: we know from experiments on animals that varying degrees of neurotic behaviour may be produced at will by correspondingly varying difficulties.

I found many other links between the psychology of knowledge and psychological fields which are often considered remote from it— for example the psychology of art and music; in fact, my ideas about induction originated in a conjecture about the evolution of Western polyphony. But you will be spared this story.

My logical criticism of Hume's psychological theory, and the considerations connected with it (most of which I elaborated in 1926-7, in a thesis entitled 'On Habit and Belief in Laws'[8]) may seem a little removed from the field of the philosophy of science. But the distinction between dogmatic and critical thinking, or the dogmatic and the critical attitude, brings us right back to our central problem. For the dogmatic attitude is clearly related to the tendency to *verify* our laws and schema by seeking to apply them and to confirm them, even to the point of neglecting refutations, whereas the critical attitude is one of readiness to change them—to test them; to refute them; to *falsify* them, if possible. This suggests that we may identify the critical attitude with the scienti attitude, and the dogmatic attitude with the one which we have describe as pseudo-scientific.

It further suggests that genetically speaking the pseudo-scientific attitude is more primitive than, and prior to, the scientific attitude: that it is a pre-scientific attitude. And this primitivity or priority also

---

[8]A thesis submitted under the title 'Gewohnheit und Gesetzerlebnis' to the Institute of Educat of the City of Vienna in 1927. (Unpublished.)

has its logical aspect. For the critical attitude is not so much opposed to the dogmatic attitude as super-imposed upon it: criticism must be directed against existing and influential beliefs in need of critical revision—in other words, dogmatic beliefs. A critical attitude needs for its raw material, as it were, theories or beliefs which are held more or less dogmatically.

Thus science must begin with myths, and with the criticism of myths; neither with the collection of observations, nor with the invention of experiments, but with the critical discussion of myths, and of magical techniques and practices. The scientific tradition is distinguished from the pre-scientific tradition in having two layers. Like the latter, it passes on its theories; but it also passes on a critical attitude towards them. The theories are passed on, not as dogmas, but rather with the challenge to discuss them and improve upon them. This tradition is Hellenic: it may be traced back to Thales, founder of the first *school* (I do not mean 'of the first *philosophical* school', but simply 'of the first school') which was not mainly concerned with the preservation of a dogma.[9]

The critical attitude, the tradition of free discussion of theories with the aim of discovering their weak spots so that they may be improved upon, is the attitude of reasonableness, of rationality. It makes far-reaching use of both verbal argument and observation—of observation in the interest of argument, however. The Greeks' discovery of the critical method gave rise at first to the mistaken hope that it would lead to the solution of all the great old problems; that it would establish certainty; that it would help to *prove* our theories, to *justify* them. But this hope was a residue of the dogmatic way of thinking; in fact nothing can be justified or proved (outside of mathematics and logic). The demand for rational proofs in science indicates a failure to keep distinct the broad realm of rationality and the narrow realm of rational certainty: it is an untenable, an unreasonable demand.

Nevertheless, the role of logical argument, of deductive logical reasoning, remains all-important for the critical approach; not because it allows us to prove our theories, or to infer them from observation statements, but because only by purely deductive reasoning is it possible for us to discover what our theories imply, and thus to criticize them effectively. Criticism, I said, is an attempt to find the weak spots in a theory, and these, as a rule, can be found only in the more remote

[9]Further comments on these developments may be found in chs. 4 and 5 below.

logical consequences which can be derived from it. It is here that
purely logical reasoning plays an important part in science.

Hume was right in stressing that our theories cannot be validly
inferred from what we can know to be true—neither from observations
nor from anything else. He concluded from this that our belief in them
was irrational. If 'belief' means here our inability to doubt our natural
laws, and the constancy of natural regularities, then Hume is again right;
this kind of dogmatic belief has, one might say, a physiological rather
than a rational basis. If, however, the term 'belief' is taken to cover our
critical acceptance of scientific theories—a *tentative* acceptance combined with an eagerness to revise the theory if we succeed in designing
a test which it cannot pass—then Hume was wrong. In such an acceptance
of theories there is nothing irrational. There is not even anything irrational
in relying for practical purposes upon well-tested theories, for no more
rational course of action is open to us.

Assume that we have deliberately made it our task to live in this
unknown world of ours; to adjust ourselves to it as well as we can; to
take advantage of the opportunities we can find in it; and to explain it,
if possible (we need not assume that it is), and as far as possible, with
the help of laws and explanatory theories. *If we have made this our
task, then there is no more rational procedure than the method of
trial and error—of conjecture and refutation:* of boldly proposing
theories; of trying our best to show that these are erroneous; and of
accepting them tentatively if our critical efforts are unsuccessful.

From the point of view here developed all laws, all theories, remain
essentially tentative, or conjectural, or hypothetical, even when we feel
unable to doubt them any longer. Before a theory has been refuted we
can never know in what way it may have to be modified. That the sun
will always rise and set within twenty-four hours is still proverbial as a
law 'established by induction beyond reasonable doubt'. It is odd that
this example is still in use, though it may have served well enough in
the days of Aristotle and Pytheas of Massalia—the great traveller who
for centuries was called a liar because of his tales of Thule, the land of
the frozen sea and the *midnight sun.*

The method of trial and error is not, of course, simply identical
with the scientific or critical approach—with the method of conjecture
and refutation. The method of trial and error is applied not only by
Einstein but, in a more dogmatic fashion, by the amoeba also. The differen

lies not so much in the trials as in a critical and constructive attitude towards errors; errors which the scientist consciously and cautiously tries to uncover in order to refute his theories with searching arguments, including appeals to the most severe experimental tests which his theories and his ingenuity permit him to design.

The critical attitude may be described as the conscious attempt to make our theories, our conjectures, suffer in our stead in the struggle for the survival of the fittest. It gives us a chance to survive the elimination of an inadequate hypothesis—when a more dogmatic attitude would eliminate it by eliminating us. (There is a touching story of an Indian community which disappeared because of its belief in the holiness of life, including that of tigers.) We thus obtain the fittest theory within our reach by the elimination of those which are less fit. (By 'fitness' I do not mean merely 'usefulness' but truth; see chapters 3 and 10, below.) I do not think that this procedure is irrational or in need of any further rational justification.

Let us now turn from our logical criticism of the *psychology of experience* to our real problem—the problem of *the logic of science*. Although some of the things I have said may help us here, in so far as they may have eliminated certain psychological prejudices in favour of induction, my treatment of the *logical problem of induction* is completely independent of this criticism, and of all psychological considerations. Provided you do not dogmatically believe in the alleged psychological fact that we make inductions, you may now forget my whole story with the exception of two logical points: my logical remarks on testability or falsifiability as the criterion of demarcation; and Hume's logical criticism of induction.

From what I have said it is obvious that there was a close link between the two problems which interested me at that time: demarcation, and induction or scientific method. It was easy to see that the method of science is criticism, i.e. attempted falsifications. Yet it took me a few years to notice that the two problems—of demarcation and of induction —were in a sense one.

Why, I asked, do so many scientists believe in induction? I found they did so because they believed natural science to be characterized by the inductive method—by a method starting from, and relying upon, long sequences of observations and experiments. They believed that the difference between genuine science and metaphysical or pseudo-scientific speculation depended solely upon whether or not the inductive method was employed. They believed (to put it in my own terminology) that only the inductive method could provide a satisfactory *criterion of demarcation.*

I recently came across an interesting formulation of this belief in a remarkable philosophical book by a great physicist—Max Born's *Natural Philosophy of Cause and Chance.*[10] He writes: 'Induction allows us to generalize a number of observations into a general rule: that night follows day and day follows night. . .But while everyday life has no definite criterion for the validity of an induction,. . .science has worked out a code, or rule of craft, for its application.' Born nowhere reveals the contents of this inductive code (which, as his wordings shows, contains a 'definite criterion for the validity of an induction'); but he stresses that 'there is no logical argument' for its acceptance: 'it is a question of faith'; and he is therefore 'willing to call induction a metaphysical principle'. But why does he believe that such a code of valid inductive rules must exist? This becomes clear when he speaks of the 'vast communities of people ignorant of, or rejecting, the rule of science, among them the members of anti-vaccination societies and believers in astrology. It is useless to argue with them; I cannot compel them to accept the same criteria of valid induction in which I believe: the code of scientific rules.' This makes it quite clear that *'valid induction' was here meant to serve as a criterion of demarcation between science and pseudo-science.*

But it is obvious that this rule or craft of 'valid induction' is not even metaphysical: it simply does not exist. No rule can ever guarantee that a generalization inferred from true observations, however often repeated, is true. (Born himself does not believe in the truth of Newtonian physics, in spite of its success, although he believes that it is based on induction.) And the success of science is not based upon rules of induction, but depends upon luck, ingenuity, and the purely deductive rules of critical argument.

I may summarize some of my conclusions as follows:

(1) Induction, i.e. inference based on many observations, is a myth. It is neither a psychological fact, nor a fact of ordinary life, nor one of scientific procedure.

---

[10]Max Born, <u>Natural Philosophy of Cause and Chance,</u> Oxford 1949, p. 7.

(2) The actual procedure of science is to operate with conjectures: to jump to conclusions—often after one single observation (as noticed for example by Hume and Born).

(3) Repeated observations and experiments function in science as *tests* of our conjectures or hypotheses, i.e. as attempted refutations.

(4) The mistaken belief in induction is fortified by the need for a criterion of demarcation which, it is traditionally but wrongly believed, only the inductive method can provide.

(5) The conception of such an inductive method, like the criterion of verifiability, implies a faulty demarcation.

(6) None of this is altered in the least if we say that induction makes theories only probable rather than certain. (See especially chapter 10, below.)

If, as I have suggested, the problem of induction is only an instance or facet of the problem of demarcation, then the solution to the problem of demarcation must provide us with a solution to the problem of induction. This is indeed the case, I believe, although it is perhaps not immediately obvious.

For a brief formulation of the problem of induction we can turn again to Born, who writes: '. . . no observation or experiment, however extended, can give more than a finite number of repetitions'; therefore, 'the statement of a law—B depends on A—always transcends experience. Yet this kind of statement is made everywhere and all the time, and sometimes from scanty material.'[11]

In other words, the logical problem of induction arises from (a) Hume's discovery (so well expressed by Born) that it is impossible to justify a law by observation or experiment, since it 'transcends experience'; (b) the fact that science proposes and uses laws 'everywhere and all the time'. (Like Hume, Born is struck by the 'scanty material', i.e. the few observed instances upon which the law may be based.) To this we have to add (c) *the principle of empiricism* which asserts that in science, only observation and experiment may decide upon the *acceptance or rejection* of scientific statements, including laws and theories.

These three principles, (a), (b), and (c), appear at first sight to clash; and this apparent clash constitutes the *logical problem of induction.*

---

[11] Natural Philosophy of Cause and Chance, pl 6.

Faced with this clash, Born gives up (c), the principle of empiricism (as Kant and many others, including Bertrand Russell, have done before him), in favour of what he calls a 'metaphysical principle'; a metaphysical principle which he does not even attempt to formulate; which he vaguely describes as a 'code or rule of craft'; and of which I have never seen any formulation which even looked promising and was not clearly untenable

But in fact the principles (a) to (c) do not clash. We can see this the moment we realize that the acceptance by science of a law or of a theory is *tentative only;* which is to say that all laws and theories are conjectures, or tentative *hypotheses* (a position which I have sometimes called 'hypotheticism'); and that we may reject a law or theory on the basis of new evidence, without necessarily discarding the old evidence which originally led us to accept it.[12]

The principle of empiricism (c) can be fully preserved, since the fate of a theory, its acceptance or rejection, is decided by observation and experiment—by the result of tests. So long as a theory stands up to the severest tests we can design, it is accepted; if it does not, it is rejected. But it is never inferred, in any sense, from the empirical evidence. There is neither a psychological nor a logical induction. *Only the falsity of the theory can be inferred from empirical evidence, and this inference is a purely deductive one.*

Hume showed that it is not possible to infer a theory from observation statements; but this does not affect the possibility of refuting a theory by observation statements. The full appreciation of this possibility makes the relation between theories and observations perfectly clear.

This solves the problem of the alleged clash between the principles (a), (b), and (c), and with it Hume's problem of induction.

Thus the problem of induction is solved. But nothing seems less wanted than a simple solution to an age-old philosophical problem. Wittgenstein and his school hold that genuine philosophical problems do not exist,[13] from which it clearly follows that they cannot be solved. Others among my contemporaries do believe that there are philosophical problems,

---

[12]I do not doubt that Born and many others would agree that theories are accepted only tentatively. But the widespread belief in induction shows that the far-reaching implications of this view are rarely seen.

[13]Wittgenstein still held this belief in 1946; see note 8 to ch. 1, below.

and respect them; but they seem to respect them too much; they seem to believe that they are insoluble, if not taboo; and they are shocked and horrified by the claim that there is a simple, neat, and lucid, solution to any of them. If there is a solution it must be deep, they feel, or at least complicated.

However this may be, I am still waiting for a simple, neat and lucid criticism of the solution which I published first in 1933 in my letter to the Editor of *Erkenntnis,*[14] and later in *The Logic of Scientific Discovery.*

Of course, one can invent new problems of induction, different from the one I have formulated and solved. (Its formulation was half its solution.) But I have yet to see any reformulation of the problem whose solution cannot be easily obtained from my old solution. I am now going to discuss some of these re-formulations.

One question which may be asked is this: how do we really jump from an observation statement to a theory?

Although this question appears to be psychological rather than philosophical, one can say something positive about it without invoking psychology. One can say first that the jump is not from an observation statement, but from a problem-situation, and that the theory must allow us *to explain* the observations which created the problem (that is, *to deduce* them from the theory strengthened by other accepted theories and by other observation statements, the so-called initial conditions). This leaves, of course, an immense number of possible theories, good and bad; and it thus appears that our question has not been answered.

---

[14]My Logic of Scientific Discovery (1959, 1960, 1961), here usually referred to as L.Sc.D., is the translation of Logik der Forschung (1934), with a number of additional notes and appendices, including (on pp. 312-14) the letter to the Editor of Erkenntnis mentioned here in the text; it was first published in Erkenntnis, 3, 1933, pp. 426f.

Concerning my never published book mentioned here in the text, see R. Carnap's paper 'Ueber Protokollstäze' (On Protocol-Sentences), Erkenntnis, 3, 1932, pp. 215-28 where he gives an outline of my theory on pp. 223-8, and accepts it. He calls my theory 'procedure B', and says (p. 224, top): 'Starting from a point of view different from Neurath's' (who developed what Carnap calls on p. 223 'procedure A'), 'Popper developed procedure B as part of his system.' And after describing in detail my theory of tests, Carnap sums up his views as follows (p. 228): 'After weighing the various arguments here discussed, it appears to me that the second language form with procedure B—that is in the form here described—is the most adequate among the forms of scientific language at present advocated. . .in the theory of knowledge.' This paper of Canap's contained the first published report of my theory of critical testing. (See also my critical remarks in L.Sc.D., note 1 to section 29, p. 104, where the date '1933' should read '1932'; and ch. 11, below, text to note 39.)

But this makes it fairly clear that when we asked our question we had more in mind than, 'How do we jump from an observation statement to a theory?' The question we had in mind was, it now appears, 'How do we jump from an observation statement to a *good* theory?' But to this the answer is: by jumping first to *any* theory and then testing it, to find whether it is good or not; i.e. by repeatedly applying the critical method, eliminating many bad theories, and inventing many new ones. Not everybody is able to do this; but there is no other way.

Other questions have sometimes been asked. The original problem of induction, it was said, is the problem of *justifying* induction, i.e. of justifying inductive inference. If you answer this problem by saying that what is called an 'inductive inference' is always invalid and therefore clearly not justifiable, the following new problem must arise: how do you justify your method of trial and error? Reply: the method of trial and error is a *method of eliminating false theories* by observation statements; and the justification for this is the purely logical relationship of deducibility which allows us to assert the falsity of universal statements if we accept the truth of singular ones.

Another question sometimes asked is this: why is it reasonable to prefer non-falsified statements to falsified ones? To this question some involved answers have been produced, for example pragmatic answers. But from a pragmatic point of view the question does not arise, since false theories often serve well enough: most formulae used in engineering or navigation are known to be false, although they may be excellent approximations and easy to handle; and they are used with confidence by people who know them to be false.

The only correct answer is the straightforward one: because we search for truth (even though we can never be sure we have found it), and because the falsified theories are known or believed to be false, while the non-falsified theories may still be true. Besides, we do not prefer *every* non-falsified theory—only one which, in the light of criticism, appears to be better than its competitors: which solves our problems, which is well tested, and of which we think, or rather conjecture or hope (considering other provisionally accepted theories), that it will stand up to further tests.

It has also been said that the problem of induction is, 'Why is it *reasonable* to believe that the future will be like the past?'', and that a satisfactory answer to this question should make it plain that such a belief is, in fact, reasonable. My reply is that it is reasonable to believe that the future will be very different from the past in many vitally important respects. Admittedly it is perfectly reasonable to *act* on the assumption that it will, in many respects, be like the past, and that well-tested laws will continue to hold (since we can have no better assumption to act upon); but it is also reasonable to believe that such a course of action will lead us at times into severe trouble, since some of the laws upon which we now heavily rely may easily prove unreliable. (Remember the midnight sun!) One might even say that to judge from past experience, and from our general scientific knowledge, the future will *not* be like the past, in perhaps most of the ways which those have in mind who say that it will. Water will sometimes not quench thirst, and air will choke those who breathe it. An apparent way out is to say that the future will be like the past *in the sense that the laws of nature will not change,* but this is begging the question. We speak of a 'law of nature' only if we think that we have before us a regularity which does not change; and if we find that it changes then we shall not continue to call it a 'law of nature'. Of course our search for natural laws indicates that we hope to find them, and that we believe that there are natural laws; but our belief in any particular natural law cannot have a safer basis than our unsuccessful critical attempts to refute it.

I think that those who put the problem of induction in terms of the *reasonableness* of our beliefs are perfectly right if they are dissatisfied with a Humean, or post-Humean, sceptical despair of reason. We must indeed reject the view that a belief in science is as irrational as a belief in primitive magical practices—that both are a matter of accepting a 'total ideology', a convention or a tradition based on faith. But we must be cautious if we formulate our problem, with Hume, as one of the reasonableness of our *beliefs.* We should split this problem into three—our old problem of demarcation, or of how to *distinguish* between science and primitive magic; the problem of the rationality of the scientific or critical *procedure,* and of the role of observation within it; and lastly the problem of the rationality of our *acceptance* of theories for scientific and for practical purposes. To all these three problems solutions have been offered here.

One should also be careful not to confuse the problem of the reasonableness of the scientific procedure and the (tentative) acceptance of the results of this procedure —i.e. the scientific theories—with the problem of the rationality or otherwise *of the belief that this procedure will succeed.* In practice, in practical scientific research, this belief is no doubt unavoidable and reasonable, there being no better alternative. But the belief is certainly unjustifiable in a theoretical sense, as I have argued (in section v). Moreover, if we could show, on general logical grounds, that the scientific quest is likely to succeed, one could not understand why anything like success has been so rare in the long history of human endeavours to know more about our world.

Yet another way of putting the problem of induction is in terms of probability. Let *t* be the theory and *e* the evidence: we can ask for *P(t,e)*, that is to say, the probability of *t*, given *e*. The problem of induction, it is often believed, can then be put thus: construct a *calculus of probability* which allows us to work out for any theory *t* what its probability is, relative to any given empirical evidence *e;* and show that *P(t,e)* increases with the accumulation of supporting evidence, and reaches high values—at any rate values greater than ½.

In *The Logic of Scientific Discovery* I explained why I think that this appraoch to the problem is fundamentally mistaken.[15] To make this clear, I introduced there the distinction between *probability* and *degree of corroboration or confirmation.* (The term 'confirmation' has lately been so much used and misused that I have decided to surrender it to the verificationists and to use for my own purposes 'corroboration' only. The term 'probability' is best used in some of the many senses which satisfy the well-known calculus of probability, axiomatized, for example, by Keynes, Jeffreys, and myself; but nothing of course depends on the choice of words, as long as we do not *assume,* uncritically, that degree of corroboration must also be a probability—that is to say, that it must satisfy the calculus of probability.)

I explained in my book why we are interested in theories with a *high degree of corroboration.* And I explained why it is a mistake to conclude from this that we are interested in *highly probable* theories. I pointed out that the probability of a statement (or set of statements) is always the greater the less the statement says: it is inverse to the content of the deductive power of the statement, and thus to its explanatory power. Accordingly every interesting and powerful statement

---

[15] L.Sc.D. (see note 14 above), ch. x, especially sections 80 to 83, also section 34 ff. See also my note 'A Set of Independent Axioms for Probability', Mind, N.S. 47, 1938, p. 275. (This note has since been reprinted, with corrections, in the new appendix *ii of L.Sc.D.

must have a low probability; and *vice versa:* a statement with a high probability will be scientifically uninteresting, because it says little and has no explanatory power. Although we seek theories with a high degree of corroboration, *as scientists we do not seek highly probable theories but explanation; that is to say, powerful and improbable theories.* [16] The opposite view—that science aims at high probability—is a characteristic development of verificationism: if you find that you cannot verify a theory, or make it certain by induction, you may turn to probability as a kind of *'Ersatz'* for certainty, in the hope that induction may yield at least that much.

I have discussed the two problems of demarcation and induction at some length. Yet since I set out to give you in this lecture a kind of report on the work I have done in this field I shall have to add, in the form of an Appendix, a few words about some other problems on which I have been working, between 1934 and 1953. I was led to most of these problems by trying to think out the consequences of the solutions to the two problems of demarcation and induction. But time does not allow me to continue my narrative, and to tell you how my new problems arose out of my old ones. Since I cannot even start a discussion of these further problems now, I shall have to confine myself to giving you a bare list of them, with a few explanatory words here and there. But even a bare list may be useful, I think. It may serve to give an idea of the fertility of the approach. It may help to illustrate what our prob-

---

[16] A definition, in terms of probabilities of $C(t,e)$, i.e. of the degree of corroboration (of a theory t relative to the evidence e) satisfying the demands indicated in my L.Sc.D., sections 82 to 83, is the following:

$$C(t,e) = E(t,e) \, (1 + P(t)P(t,e)),$$

where $E(t,e) = (P(e,t) - P(e))/P(e,t) + P(e))$ is a (non-additive) measure of the explanatory power of t with respect to e. Note that $C(t,e)$ is not a probability: it may have values between -1 (refuation of t by e) and $C(t,t) \leqslant + 1$. Statements t which are lawlike and thus non-verifiable cannot even reach $C(t,e) = C(t,t)$ upon empirical evidence e. $C (t,t)$ is the *degree of corroborability* of t and is equal to the degree of testability of t, or to the content of t. Because of the demands implied in point (6) at the end of section I above, I do not think, however, that it is possible to give a complete formalization of the idea of corroboration (or, as I previously used to say, of confirmation).

(Added 1955 to the first proofs of this paper:)

See also my note 'Degree of Confirmation', British Journal for the Philosophy of Science, 5, 1954, pp. 143 ff. (See also 5, pp. 334). I have since simplified this definition as follows (B.J.P.S., 1955, 5, p. 359):

$$C(t,e) = (P(e,t) - P(e))/(P(e,t) - P(et) + P(e))$$

For a further improvement, see B.J.P.S. 6, 1955, p. 56.

lems look like; and it may show how many there are, and to convince you that there is no need whatever to worry over the question whether philosophical problems exist, or what philosophy is really about. So this list contains, by implication, an apology for my unwillingness to break with the old tradition of trying to solve problems with the help of rational argument, and thus for my unwillingness to participate wholeheartedly in the developments, trends, and drifts, of contemporary philosophy.

PART III

SCIENCE AND MATHEMATICS

INTRODUCTION

SECTION 1.

One of the most pervasive features of modern science is its extensive use of mathematics. This feature has become so prevalent that many people judge the degree of development and success of a given science by the extent and sophistication of its use of mathematics. Thus, many psychologists have claimed that their discipline has not made enough progress, and the proof and explanation of this is that it has not found enough ways to study its subject matter mathematically.

This feature of science naturally gives rise to many philosophical puzzles: (1) Why does the scientist use mathematics as extensively as he does? (2) How does the scientist use mathematics? (3) Are there any limitations on the use of mathematics?

Nor are these the only problems raised by the use of mathematics in the sciences. After all, the scientist who uses mathematical tools is clearly committed to the view that the mathematical propositions, whose truth is presupposed in the use of these tools, are in fact true. This commitment naturally raises many additional philosophical puzzles, the most prominent of which are:(4) What do these mathematical propositions mean? (5) How does the scientist know that they are true? In particular, is the method the scientist uses to ascertain the truth of mathematical propositions the same as, or different from, the method he uses to ascertain the truth of ordinary scientific hypotheses?

In this section we are concerned with various answers that have been given to these five questions. Although each selection is not explicitly concerned with all five of the issues, the views taken by an author on some of them often have implications for other issues as well.

Before turning to a more detailed consideration of these issues, it is necessary *not* to assume that all of the mathematical tools used by the scientist are alike; it is quite possible that the answers to our questions may depend on the particular part of mathematics we have in mind. Indeed, some of the authors we will be reading have answered these questions differently for different parts of mathematics. For example, Professor Carl Hempel's answers to questions 4 and 5 in the case of the geometrical truths presupposed in the scientist's use of geometry is quite different from the answer that he gives to these questions in the case of the truths of arithmetic, algebra, and analysis presupposed in the scientist's use of these areas of mathematics. Nor is Professor Hempel alone in drawing this distinction between geometry and these other areas of mathematics. This distinction has been made by many scientists and philosophers. Therefore, in the readings devoted to these issues (Mill through Reichenbach), geometry and these other areas are considered separately. But this is not the only relevant distinction that can be drawn. You should be alert to the possibility that what is said in the selections about one area of mathematics is not relevant to some other area of mathematics.

SECTION 2.

It will help the discussion of these problems considerably if we begin by considering a concrete example of the actual use by the scientist of mathematical tools. The example we will use has to do with the scientific study of relations between the pressure, volume, and temperature of a gas, the relations summarized in the gas laws.

Long before scientists had systematically studied this area, people had noted that there are important relations between these properties of a gas. If, for example, you apply heat to a container full of some gas, the gas exerts more pressure on the walls of the container than it did before. The same thing happens if you decrease the volume of the container (think what happens when you press one side of a closed balloon full of gas). But merely saying this does not even express the amount of knowledge that we can gain about these matters by presystematic observation. The volume of the container, when it changes, does not merely change; it changes more in some cases than in others, and often we can observe this. When we study this matter scientifically, we want to be able to say something more precise than has been said so far. What we need is some method of measuring the extent of the change and of expressing the results of our measurements. This is the first motive for introducing mathematics into the sciences: mathematical concepts are used to express more precisely the degree to which a change has occurred, or simply the degree or extent to which the object has the property in question (for if we can express the extent to which the object had the property before the change and the extent to which it had it after the change, we can express the extent of the change).

In this process, two distinct aspects must be noted. To begin with, we must adopt a set of numbers that can be assigned to objects so as to represent the degree to which they have a property. We might call this aspect the adoption of a scale. Second, we must adopt a process whereby we can pick out the appropriate number in that set to be assigned to a given object at a given time. We can call this process the measurement process. As Professor S.S. Stevens puts it: "measurement, in the broadest sense, is defined as the assignment of numerals to objects or events according to rules."

There are many questions that can be raised about each aspect of this process. We will begin by considering questions about scales. We have to distinguish various types of scales, for all scales are not the same. In order to understand why there are various possible types of scales, we should recall the original purpose for assigning numbers to objects—to express the degree to which an object has changed or simply the degree to which it has a certain property. But this has to be amplified. Sometimes, numbers are only used to indicate whether or not one object has the property in question to a greater degree than another object; that is, numbers are not used to indicate *how much more* one object has the property than another. An example of such a scale is Moh's hardness scale, by which numbers are assigned to objects in such a way that the order of the assigned numbers corresponds to the order of hardness of the objects; but we cannot infer that an object with the assigned number 2 is twice as hard as an object with the assigned number 4. We cannot even infer that the difference between the hardness of an object that has 6 assigned to it and the hardness of an object that has 4 assigned to it is the same as the difference between the hardness

of an object that has 4 assigned to it and the hardness of an object
that has 2 assigned to it. Sometimes, however, the assignment of numbers tells us more than merely which object has the property to a greater
degree than the other. In the centrigrade scale an object (a_1) that has
a temperature of 60°C is certainly warmer than an object (a_2) that has
a temperature of 40°C, and that object is certainly warmer than an object (a_3) that has a temperature of 20°C. But this assignment of numbers
tells us more than that. We know that the difference in temperature betwee
a_1 and a_2 is the same as the difference in temperature between a_2 and
a_3. So the centrigrade scale is certainly more informative than Moh's
scale. It is not, however, the most informative type of scale, since we
cannot infer that a_2 is two thirds as warm as a_1. If, however, we use
the Kelvin scale, then we know that an object whose temperature is
40°K is two thirds as warm as an object whose temperature is 60°K.
The Kelvin scale is therefore even more informative than the centrigrade
scale. Professor Stevens' article contains a detailed discussion of the
differences among these three scales (he also includes a fourth scale),
and points out why certain statistical techniques can be used if we have
one type of scale but cannot be used if we have a less informative type
of scale.

You might wonder why these less informative scales are used at
all if more informative ones are available. Sometimes they are used
simply because we are not concerned with the additional information.
But they may also be used because we are unable to devise a method
of assigning the numbers in the more informative scales to objects with
respect to a given property; that is, there may be conditions for the use
of the more informative scales that we cannot fulfill. Stevens suggests,
for example, that we need an absolute zero point to use the most informative type of scale. In going through the Stevens article, therefore,
you should try to figure out what conditions are presupposed in the
use of each of these types of scales and to see whether or not these
presuppositions explain why we sometimes use one type of scale and
sometimes another.

Even when we have only one type of scale, there often seem to be
several different scales possible. Consider, for example, the Fahrenheit
and centrigrade scales. Careful reflection shows that these two scales
are not different. After all, a scale is nothing more than a set of number
and the set of numbers in the Fahrenheit scale is the same as the set of

numbers in the centigrade scale. The difference is really about which number is to be assigned to a given temperature; that is, it is a difference in the rules governing the measurement process. Having now seen what the real difference is, we can meaningfully ask whether there are any reasons for preferring one to the other. It has often been said that this is simply a matter of convenience and simplicity. What this means and whether it is true is something that you should consider carefully.

Turning to the process of measurement, we must consider several questions. The first was raised by Pierre Duhem. In order to understand it, we must draw the distinction between quantities (such as length and volume) and qualities (such as heat and hardness). In the case of a quantity like length, there is a process by which we can take an object a_1 that has assigned to it by our measurement procedure the length l_1 and an object a_2 that has assigned to it by our measurement procedure the length l_2 and join them so as to form an object that will have assigned to it by our measurement procedures the length $l_1 + l_2$. This process is simply putting a_1 end to end with a_2. We will call such a process an additive process. But there is no such process in the case of a quality like heat. If you take an object whose temperature is 60°C and an object whose temperature is 40°C, you have no way of joining them to form an object whose temperature is 100°C. To generalize, a quantity is a property with an additive process, whereas a quality is a property that has no additive process.

Duhem points out that the founders of modern science, men like Galileo and Descartes, thought that science should be based on a study of quantities, and not qualities, and that the study of the former would lead to an understanding of the latter. Scientists abandoned this program a long time ago, and Duhem thinks that this was justified. A more reasonable program would consist in trying to understand all phenomena in terms of properties that can be treated mathematically, that is, properties for which we have scales and measurement procedures. But not all of these properties are quantities.

Is there any significance to the distinction between quantities and qualities, or is Duhem right is dismissing this distinction as insignificant? S.S. Stevens, near the end of his article, briefly considers the view that this distinction is significant because it explains the distinction between fundamental and derivative measurement. When we measure the heat of a gas by use of a mercury thermometer, the assignment of a temperature to the gas depends on the previous assignment of a length to the column of mercury. Strictly speaking, we first measure the length of the column and then use the result to determine the temperature of the gas. We forget about this procedure only because the thermometer manufacturers have put the temperature numbers corresponding to the various lengths of the mercury column on the glass tube.

Since the measurement of temperature depends on the measurement of length, we say that temperature measurement is derivative. On the other hand, we do not need to measure anything else in order to measure the length of an object, so we say that the measurement of length is fundamental. The suggestion that Stevens rejects is that some properties can be measured fundamentally because they are quantities; a quality can only be measured derivatively. You should note carefully Stevens' reason for rejecting this view. If we agree with him, we are left with two extremely interesting questions: (1) Is there any significance to the distinction between quantities and qualities? (2) Is there any explanation for the fact that some properties can only be measured derivatively while others can be measured fundamentally?

In this section, we have briefly considered some of the questions that arise out of the scientist's use of mathematics to represent what he has observed. We shall consider other aspects of the scientist's use of mathematics in the next section. First, however, we should note that we have only explicitly considered the use of arithmetic to represent the data. But the scientist who says that the angle of reflection of a certain light ray was 40° is using geometrical concepts for this same purpose. You must decide for yourself whether these cases are analogous, or whether there are special problems that arise when geometrical concepts are used to represent the data.

SECTION 3.

Let us return to our example in order to find additional uses of mathematics by the scientist. Having assigned numerical values to the pressure, volume, and temperature of several gases, the scientist may note certain definite relations among these values. As long as the temperature is kept constant, for example, the pressure and volume are inversely proportional; that is the pressure multiplied by the volume equals a constant. The scientist may come to adopt this as a general principle and then use it to make such predictions as "if the volume is changed from v_α to v_β, then the pressure will change from p_α to p_β."

What has happened throughout this whole process? The scientist notes in several cases that the pressure multiplied by the volume has (as long as the temperature is kept constant) a constant value. But he certainly cannot observe this. All that he can observe, given the appropriate instruments for measuring pressure and volume, is the pressure and volume in each case. He can observe p_1 and v_1, p_2 and v_2, p_3 and v_3, and so on. That $p_1 \times v_1 = p_2 \times v_2 = p_3 \times v_3$ and so on is a truth of mathematics, not something he observes by use of his instruments. In other words, in order for the scientist to justify his claim that in the cases he has observed so far, the pressure multiplied by the volume equals a constant, he must presuppose that certain mathematical statements are true.

This assumption is not the only part of the process just described in which the scientist must presuppose the truth of certain mathematical statements. He must also do this when he makes the predictions. After all, his argument for the prediction is that the pressure must change from p_α to p_β (and not to some other p_ϵ) because only p_β is such that it multiplied by v_β equals p_α multiplied by v_α. This, however, is certainly a mathematical statement whose truth the scientist is presupposing.

We see in this example a phenomenon that is common to a great many cases. Having used mathematical concepts to represent the data, the scientist presupposes the truth of certain mathematical statements in order to use the data to justify a certain hypothesis and then presupposes the truth of additional mathematical statements in order to derive predictions from the hypothesis. In our case, the mathematical statements are elementary truths of arithmetic; in other cases, they may be geometrical truths, truths of analysis, and so on. Indeed, the scientist may often have to interrupt his research to prove mathematical theorems (or even to begin new areas of mathematical research) so that he can continue this process.

What do these statements mean and how does the scientist know that they are true? These two questions are fundamental to the philosophy of science and mathematics, and the remainder of our introduction (together with the selections from Mill through Reichenbach) are devoted to them. In this section (along with the selections by Mill,

Poincaré, and Hempel) we will consider the non-geometrical statements. In the next section (along with the selection by Kant, Poincaré. and Reichenbach) we will consider the geometrical statements.

To meaningfully follow the discussion of these issues, we must draw two elementary distinctions (they are discussed at some length in the first part of the selection from Kant). One is the distinction between *a priori* and *a posteriori* statements. An *a priori* statement is one whose truth or falsity is ascertainable independently of any appeal to our experiences (e.g., the truth of "All red objects are colored" and the falsity of "This book is red all over and blue all over at the same time" is ascertainable without any appeal to experience). An *a posteriori* statement is one whose truth or falsity is ascertainable only by an appeal to our experience (e.g., the truth of "Some toys are red" is ascertainable only by an appeal to our experiences.) As we saw in an earlier part of this book, practically all (if not all) of the ordinary scientific hypotheses are *a posteriori* statements.

The other distinction is between *analytic* and *synthetic* statements. An analytic statement is one whose truth or falsity is due solely to the meaning of the statement (e.g., the truth of "All bachelors are males" and the falsity of "Some women are husbands" are due solely to the meaning of these statements). A synthetic statement is one whose truth or falsity is not due solely to the meaning of the statement; that is, given the meaning of a synthetic statement, it might still be either true or false (e.g., the truth of "This book is about scientific methodology" and the falsity of "All books are about scientific methodology" are not due solely to the meaning of these statements). It is fairly obvious that practically all (if not all) of the ordinary scientific hypotheses are synthetic statements.

Although these distinctions have recently been challenged by various philosophers, it will be useful for us to employ them in the discussion here. We shall put our problems as follows: What do arithmatical statements mean, and are they, like ordinary scientific hypotheses, synthetic *a posteriori* statements?

There is obviously a very close relation between these two questions, for the way that you can know whether a statement is true or false clearly depends (among other things) on the meaning of the statement. This close connection can be seen very clearly in the views on the nature of arithmetical knowledge advocated by John Stuart Mill. Mill believed that all mathematical truths are synthetic *a posteriori* truths. One of his basic underlying arguments for this view in the case of arithmetic is the following: an arithmetical statement like "half of ten is five" seems to be about an abstract object, the number ten. But there are no such objects; a statement about the number ten must, therefore, be a shorthand version of a general statement about groups having ten numbers. "Half of ten is five" really means "If you take a group of ten objects and divide in into two equal parts, each group will have five objects in it." Such a statement is, according to Mill, a clear example of a synthetic *a posteriori* truth (known by induction from those cases in which we have seen this happen); therefore, Mill concludes, the truths of arithmetic are synthetic *a posteriori* truths.

This argument clearly rests on Mill's view that statements about numbers are really statements about groups of objects having that number of members. It is just this view (at least in the form adopted by Mill) that has been denied by most philosophers, and it is not difficult to see why. Let us imagine that there are microbes that can only exist in pairs and that we have a group of ten of them. If we divide this group into two equal groups, there will be only four in each group. This is however, no objection to the claim that half of ten is five, although it seems that it would be if Mill's view were right. Consequently, we must reject Mill's view and grant that "half of ten is five" is about the number ten, and not about groups of ten objects.

Before you agree with this criticism of Mill's argument (a criticism based upon Carl Hempel's remarks at the end of Section 3 of his article), remember that this alternative position has its own difficulties: (a) It seems to follow from this alternative conception of mathematics that the truths of mathematics presuppose the existence of numbers as abstract objects. But do these objects really exist? (b) If mathematical statements are about numbers, how can we use them in empirical investigations in the way sketched at the beginning of this section? Hempel attempts to deal with this difficulty at the end of his paper; you should see if his reply is satisfactory before you agree that Mill was mistaken on this point.

There are two general objections to Mill's view, objections that were raised in his time and to which he replied. The first is that his view cannot explain the presence of deductive proofs and the absence of experimentation in mathematics. If the truths of mathematics are synthetic *a posteriori* truths, why does not the mathematician establish their truth by inductive arguments based on experimental findings, rather than by deductive proofs? Mill's reply to this criticism is that it is based on a failure to distinguish between the axioms of mathematics and its theorems. All that a mathematician proves deductively is that the theorems follow from the axioms; that is that the theorems must be true if the axioms are true. But the truth of the axioms, and therefore of the theorems, is only known inductively. To be sure, it is not an induction from experimental findings, but this is only because we can infer the axioms' truth inductively from ordinary observations and therefore do not need to carry out any experiments.

The second objection is a much more serious one. It begins by pointing out that the laws of science, even if true, are not necessarily true. They could have been false. In general, synthetic *a posteriori* statements are not necessarily true. But the truths of mathematics are necessary truths. Therefore, they cannot be synthetic *a posteriori* truths. Mill did not actually reply to this argument in the case of arithmetic, but he did reply to it in the case of geometry (this reply is included at the end of the Mill selection). His reply is that the necessity of the truths of mathematics consists solely in the fact that we cannot imagine their turning out to be false. This type of necessity can, however, characterize synthetic *a posteriori* statements. Consequently, said Mill, the necessity of mathematical truths is compatible with their being synthetic *a posteriori* truths.

Mill's reply clearly depends on his view of the nature of the necessity of mathematical truths and on his view that synthetic *a posteriori* truths can have this type of necessity. Whether he was right or wrong is something you will have to decide for yourself. Many philosophers have rejected this reply and have therefore concluded that Mill's theory of mathematics is mistaken. We can now consider the alternative view they have proposed.

Whereas Mill maintained that the truths of mathematics are synthe *a posteriori* truths, Gottfried Wilhelm von Leibniz (the seventeenth-century physicist, mathematician, and philosopher) believed that they were analytic *a priori* truths. In particular, he believed that they were true solely by virtue of the definitions of the numbers.* In order to see what

---

*Leibniz's position was actually somewhat more sophisticated than this. But it is this more simplified theory that has usually been attributed to him, so we are therefore leaving out some of the finer points of his position.

Leibniz had in mind, we must begin by listing his definitions of the various numbers (when "1" is treated as basic and undefined).

"2" means "1 + 1"
"3" means "2 + 1"
"4" means "3 + 1"
"5" means "4 + 1"

Leibniz claimed that all of the truths of mathematics follow directly from these definitions. As an example of what he had in mind, consider the following proof of "3 + 2 = 5":

(1) 5 = 4 + 1 (by the definition of "5")
(2) 5 = 3 + 1 + 1 (by the definition of "4")
(3) 5 = 3 + 2 (by the definition of "2")

It is not clear how Leibniz hoped to generalize this pattern of proof so as to prove all of the truths of mathematics. But we need not consider that question in order to see that his position is in error. Even the proof just given is invalid: "3 + 2 = 5" does not follow deductively from the definitions given. In particular, step 3 does not follow from step 2 by the definition of "2". Step 2 really should be written "5 = (3 + 1) + 1", and in that formula there is no occurrence of the expression "1 + 1" for which we can substitute "2" by the definition of "2". A valid proof along the lines suggested by Leibniz would be:

(1') 5 = 4 + 1 (by the definition of "5")
(2') 5 = (3 + 1) + 1 (by the definition of "4")
(3') 5 = 3 + (1 + 1) (by the principle of the associativity
                              of addition)
(4') 5 = 3 + 2 (by the definition of "2")

In other words, in order to prove that 5 = 3 + 2, we need something more than Leibniz's definitions. We could do it if we had the assumption that addition is associative; that is, that (a + b) + c = a + (b + c), but this does not follow from Leibniz's definitions of the numbers given earlier.

This criticism of Leibniz only shows that even the truths of arithmetic (and certainly the truths of all mathematics) do not follow directly from the definitions of the numbers. It does not show that they do not follow from these definitions together with some additional definitions. These additional definitions might entail the truth of the general statements about addition and multiplication needed for proofs of the type given by Leibniz (e.g., the associativity of addition), or they might make it possible to carry through these proofs without the use of these general truths. In either case, since the truths of mathematics would still be consequences of a set of definitions, they would still be analytic.

Henri Poincaré tried to show that adding these definitions would not do the job. In particular, he was concerned with the attempt to drive all arithmetical truths from definitions by use of the definitions of the numbers together with the following equations, which define addition and multiplication:

$$(D_1) \quad x + a = [x + (a - 1)] + 1$$

$$(D_2) \quad x \circ 1 = x$$

$$(D_3) \quad x \circ y = [x \circ (y - 1)] + y$$

Given these definitions, we can offer the following proof of $5 = 3 + 2$:

(1*) $5 = 4 + 1$ (by definition of "5")
(2*) $5 = (3 + 1) + 1$ (by definition of "4")
(3*) $5 = 3 + 2$ (by D_1 and the fact that $2 - 1 = 1$)

This proof follows directly from the definitions and does not require the principle of the associativity of addition. It would look therefore as though "$5 = 3 + 2$" is an analytic statement.

Poincaré agreed that these mathematical truths about particular numbers are analytic. His point was, however, that these are not the only mathematical truths. There are, in addition, important general truths about numbers, truths like the associativity of addition. He claimed that these do not follow from any of the definitions, so they must be synthetic *a priori* truths.

How, according to Poincaré, do we know that they are true? We prove their truth by recurrence (mathematical induction). In doing this, we first prove that they hold of 1, then prove that if they of n, they must hold of $n + 1$, and finally conclude that they hold of all numbers. We are clearly assuming in this proof that any theorem that holds of 1 and holds of $n + 1$ if it holds of n must hold of all numbers. This assumption (to be called the principle of mathematical induction) is, according to Poincaré, synthetic *a priori,* and is known only on the basis of a rational intuition. Therefore, all the general truths known on the basis of this assumption are also synthetic *a priori* truths.

Poincaré's position has been rejected by many philosophers who

claim that our intuitions cannot serve as a basis for any knowledge.
Hempel puts their point of view as follows.

> . . .*It would be pertinent to remark that judgments as to what
> may be considered as self-evident, are subjective; they may
> vary from person to person and certainly cannot constitute
> an adequate basis for decisions as to the objective validity
> of mathematical propositions.*

How then do these philosophers explain our knowledge of general
mathematical statements? Unless they return to Mill's empiricist point
of view, they seem forced to claim that the principle of mathematical
induction is analytic. Yet it does not follow from the definitions we
have already discussed, so they must introduce additional definitions.

The principle of mathematical induction (at least in the form used
by Hempel, where we begin with 0 rather than with 1) involves three
previously undefined terms, "0", "successor", and "number". In his
article Hempel shows that we can replace the definitions we have been
using so far with definitions that involve only these three terms. It
would seem, therefore, that these terms are somehow basic to mathematics and that we should try to derive the principle of mathematical induction from the definition of these three terms. Hempel briefly explains in his article how Frege and Russell tried to do this.

Was this attempt successful? Without going into some of the finer
points (ones not mentioned by Hempel), it is difficult for us to discuss
this question. But there is one objection that we should consider. Hempel
is obviously supposing that his definitions are not merely arbitrary ones
invented to prove the principle of mathematical induction (and four
other postulates that are also assumed by the mathematician), but ones
that correctly define these basic mathematical terms. This supposition
raises fundamental issues that you must certainly consider: What is
the criterion by which we judge such a definition, and are Hempel's
definitions correct according to this criterion? Until these questions
are answered, we cannot decide whether or not the attempt described
by Hempel was successful.

We seem to have returned to a point that was raised at the beginning of this section: questions about the nature of mathematical knowledge cannot be decided independently of questions about the meaning
of mathematical propositions. We will see the same thing in the next section concerning the nature of our knowledge of geometrical propositions.

SECTION 4.

We can now discuss the truths of geometry that are often assumed by the scientist in his work—in particular, various accounts of what they mean and how we can know that they are true. Most of the discussion of these issues has as its point of departure the views of Immanuel Kant. Kant claimed that the truths of geometry are synthetic *a priori* truths. He argued that they are *a priori* because they are necessarily true and only *a priori* truths are necessarily true. (We have discussed the validity of this type of argument in the preceding section.) He also argued for the view that they are synthetic. This argument is contained in section 5 of the Introduction to his *Critique of Pure Reason,* and you should note it carefully; something more will be said about it later in our discussion.

How, according to Kant, can we know the truth of these synthetic *a priori* propositions? Kant's answer is that we can intuit their truth. But Kant was not satisfied with saying just this, for he found it very perplexing that we could intuit the truth of synthetic propositions about the world. In order to do away with this perplexity, Kant introduced his famous theory of space: Space is a form that we impose upon the world as we can know it.

This theory has often puzzled people, for they do not see why a theory of space is relevant to our knowledge of geometrical truths. To understand its relevance, we must remember that Kant thought that the laws of geometry are the laws of space. "A straight line is the shortest distance between two points" should be analyzed, according to Kant, as "the smallest distance between any two points in space is the spatial configuration we call a straight line." Kant then argued: "If space were an objective aspect of reality, then there could be no way of knowing by intuition the laws governing it (the laws of geometry); but if space is a form we impose on objects, then we can intuit the laws governing this form and we do not need any experience to teach us about them."

There certainly are many obscure points in Kant's position. What does he mean by his claim that space is a form that we impose upon the world? Why does he think that we can have knowledge by intuition of this form but not of objective reality? Enough has been said, however, about his views to enable us to go on and discuss the reasons why various philosophers have rejected them, reasons that are based on the fact that there seem to be many alternatives to our standard Euclidean geometry.

In the first half of the nineteenth centrury, several mathematicians constructed non-Euclidean geometries. To understand why they did this, and why what they did is so significant in a consideration of our problem, we must keep in mind certain facts about the history of geometry. Unlike arithmetic, which was not axiomatized until the latter part of the nineteenth century, geometry was axiomatized by Euclid at the end of the fourth century B.C. To be sure, Euclid's axiomatization was not complete, and many nineteenth-century mathematicians were able to offer improved axiomatizations. Nevertheless, we did have, after Euclid's time, a rough idea of at least some of the axioms required in Euclidean geometry. One of the axioms, Euclid's famous fifth postulate, troubled mathematicians for a long time because it did not have the intuitive certainty that the others had. Many mathematicians tried to show that it could be derived from the other axioms, but none of these attempts were successful. Finally, mathematicians began to consider the possibility of constructing alternative geometries in which this postulate did not hold.

The version of Euclid's fifth postulate that they considered states that there is one and only one straight line through a given point parallel to a given line. The Russian geometrician Lobachewsky constructed a geometrical system that contains an axiom that states that there are two straight lines through a given point parallel to a given line. His system contains many theorems that seem to contradict the standard Euclidean theorems. In his system, for example, the sum of the angles of a triangle is always less than two right angles (and not equal to two right angles, as it is in Euclidean geometry), and this sum is proportional to the area of the triangle. Another system, constructed by the German mathematician Georg F.B. Riemann, contains an axiom that states that there are no straight lines through a given point parallel to a given line. This system also contains many theorems that seem to contradict the standard Euclidean theorems. In Riemannian geometry, for example, the sum of the angles of a triangle is always greater than two right angles, and this sum is proportional to the area of the triangle.

When these geometries were first developed, many thought that they would turn out to be inconsistent. In 1869, however, Eugenio

Beltrami proved that if Euclidean geometry is consistent, then so is
Lobachewskian geometry. The selection from Henri Poincaré contains
a brief sketch of Beltrami's proof. Other mathematicians proved that
the same thing holds for Riemannian geometry.

Given the existence of these seemingly alternative geometries,
many philosophers have concluded that Kant's position must be mistaken. There is, they claim, no way of knowing *a priori* which of these
geometries is ture. One of the earliest proponents of this view, Hermann
von Helmholtz, put his objection to Kant's position as follows.

But if we can imagine such spaces of other sorts, it cannot
be maintained that the axioms of geometry are necessary
consequences of an a priori *transcendental form of intuition,*
as Kant thought.

How then do we know the truth of geometrical statements? The
answer that was adopted by many mathematicians and philosophers
was that geometrical statements are synthetic *a posteriori* statements
known to be true or false, like ordinary scientific hypotheses, on the
basis of experimental evidence.

What type of experimental evidence could enable us to determine
which is the correct geometry? Let us consider the following experiment
first suggested by the German mathematician Christian Gauss: we
measure the angles of a very large triangle (one sufficiently large so that
the difference between the results seemingly implied by the various
geometrical systems would be noticeable) and ascertain the sum of
these angles. As a matter of fact, it might be impossible to carry out
such an experiment at present; we might not, for example, be able to
measure the angles of a large enough triangle. But in principle, and
perhaps someday in practice, such an experiment could be carried
through. Would it not enable us to decide which geometry was the
correct one?

Although it might seem so, further consideration suggests otherwi∫
When we measure the angles between objects at a great distance, we
use an instrument like a sextant, and we suppose that the light rays
traveling from the object to the sight device in the sextant travel along
straight lines and can therefore be used to define the sides of the
triangle. But this supposition could be challenged: Perhaps light rays
do not travel along straight lines. Given this possibility, the experiment

can never be conclusive. We can continue to maintain that a given geometry is the correct one, even if the experiment seems to show otherwise, providing that we are prepared to deny that the light rays are, as a matter of fact, travelling along straight lines.

The following objection might be raised: Could we not test to see if the path of the light ray is a straight line? After all, a straight line, in all of the geometries, is the shortest distance between two points. All we have to do, then, is use measuring rods (or other measuring instruments) to determine whether or not the path of the light ray is the shortest distance between two points. This might, again, be difficult in practice, but it could be done in principle, and perhaps someday in practice. If this were done, and if we determined that the path of the light ray is a straight line, then we could use the original experiment as a method for determining which geometry is the correct one.

This suggestion, although promising, faces serious difficulties. In order to measure the distance covered by the light ray to see if it is the shortest distance between the two points, we have to transport some measuring rod (or other measuring instrument) along the path of the light ray and along other possible paths. This measurement will be conclusive only if we assume that the lengths of the measuring rods are not changed throughout the whole process; that is, we must assume the rigidity of these measuring rods throughout the whole process. This assumption can, however, be challenged, and the experiment will therefore continue to be inconclusive.

We seem to face the difficulty that in order to carry through Gauss's experiment, we need additional principles. They may be viewed as physical hypotheses or, following Reichenbach,* as definitions. In any case, they are needed. Since this is true, it would seem to follow that we cannot use this experiment (nor perhaps any other experiment) to determine which is the correct geometry, since no matter what results are obtained, we can still maintain, by giving up some of these additional principles, the truth of any of the geometries in question.

The need for these additional principles was noted by Poincaré. In the second part of the selection from his writings on geometry he used this need for additional principles as one of the bases for his

---

*We should note Reichenbach's reasons for treating these principles as definitions rather than as physical hypotheses. Something more will be said about this issue later.

claim that the adoption of a particular geometry is solely a matter of
convention. After all, he argued, we always have a choice open to us.
We can give up a geometry and keep the additional principles, or we
can keep the geometry and drop the principles. Which option we choose
is solely a matter of convention (*conventionalism*). Poincaré added to
this assertion the claim that we would always keep Euclidean geometry.
In reading his discussion you should carefully note the reasons he gave
for this additional assertion, and should consider the question whether
this claim is compatible with the conventionalist position.

One of the main objectives of Hans Reichenbach's article is to
refute Poincaré's conventionalism. Reichenbach begins by agreeing
with Poincaré that it is solely a matter of convention whether we say
that (1) Euclidean geometry is correct, but the path of a light ray is
not a straight line and the measuring rods are not rigid; or that (2) non-
Euclidean geometry is correct, and the path of a light ray is a straight
line and the measuring rods are rigid.

Reichenbach claims, however, that it is a matter of convention
which of these we say only because these are just two ways of saying
the same thing. There is, he claims, no difference in meaning between
these two assertions because they describe the same state of affairs. If,
however, we were considering two claims that did not mean the same
thing, two claims that did not describe the same state of affairs, then
it would be an empirical issue whether one or the other is correct;
adopting one or the other would not then be merely a matter of
adopting a convention.

Why did Reichenbach claim that there is no difference in meaning
between (1) and (2)? His line of reasoning seems to have been the following: the meaning of a geometrical statement like (1) or (2) is simply
its empirically observable consequences.* But (1) and (2) have the same
empirically observable consequences. That is why they are both compatible with the same experimental results. Therefore, (1) and (2) mean
the same thing.

Reichenbach's criticism of Poincaré seems to have, as its underlying
basis, a theory of the meaning of geometrical statements, and this cer-

---

*Reichenbach noted that simple geometrical statements do not have, independently of the
additional principles, any empirically observable consequences, and therefore any meaning.
Only these additional principles give the geometrical statements meaning. For this reason, he
suggested that we view these principles as a special way of defining the basic geometrical notio

tainly strengthens his argument.* Once we realize this, however, we
can see that the validity of Reichenbach's argument depends on the
correctness of his claims about the meaning of geometrical statements.
This is a very important point, for Poincaré would, as we shall see, definitely deny Reichenbach's theory of the meaning of geometrical statements.
If he is right in this denial, then Reichenbach's whole account of our
knowledge of geometrical statements is mistaken.

In order to understand Poincaré's theory of the meaning of geometrical
statements, we must turn to a consideration of his views on the nature
of the axioms of geometry. Poincaré claimed that the axioms of a geometrical system define the basic notions of that system. For this reason,
Poincaré calls the axioms of geometry "definitions in disguise." The
theorems are simply statements of the consequence of these definitions.
Now if Euclidean geometry has one axiom about straight lines and
Lobachewskian geometry has another, then "straight line" in Euclidean
geometry does not mean the same thing as "straight line" in Lobachewskian
geometry, and the two systems do not really conflict. Moreover, if the
axioms are merely stipulative definitions of the basic geometrical notions,
then they are neither true nor false. Consequently, all of Reichenbach's
talk about conflicting geometries and the acceptance of one as true
together with the rejection of the others as false is clearly mistaken.
The adoption of one geometrical system rather than any of the others
is simply the adoption of one set of definitional conventions rather
than the other.

What would happen, according to Poincaré, when the adoption of
a geometrical system and certain additional principles led us to a certain
expectation about the results of an experiment, like Gauss's experiment—
but the experiment turned out otherwise? We could drop some of the
additional principles, and this would be a case of the rejection of an
empirical hypothesis. We could also keep the principles**and change
our geometry; but this, according to Poincaré, would simply be a change
of definition, not the rejection of an empirical hypothesis.

---

*This can be seen by comparing it with Kant's argument for the syntheticity of geometrical
statements, an argument that is weak precisely because it cannot draw support from a detailed
theory of the meaning of these statements since Kant has no such theory.

**Poincaré, as we noted in the foregoing, felt that we would, as a matter of fact, never do this.
But this does not, of course, prevent us from asking what would be involved in doing this.

We can now see what is really at issue in the dispute between Poincaré and Reichenbach. Reichenbach viewed the additional principles as definitions of the basic geometrical notions like "straight line" and the geometrical statements as empirical hypotheses. Poincaré, however, viewed the geometrical statements as definitions of the basic geometrical notions and the additional principles as empirical hypotheses. Neither, however, denied the possibility of giving up either on the basis of experimental evidence.

We seem to come, therefore, to the conclusion that the dispute about our knowledge of geometrical statements really revolves around a more fundamental dispute about the meaning of these statements. In this respect, if in no other, geometrical statements are like nongeometrical mathematical statements.

MEASUREMENT

ON THE THEORY OF SCALES OF MEASUREMENT

*S.S. Stevens (1906-　　) is one of the leading workers in,
and theoreticians of, mathematical psychology and psycho-
physics; he is director of the Psycho-Acoustic Laboratory at
Harvard University and has edited the extremely important
reference book,* Handbook of Experimental Psychology. *The
present selection first appeared in* Science, *Vol. 103 (1946);
it is reprinted here by permission of the editor.*

For seven years a committee of the British Association for the
Advancement of Science debated the problem of measurement. Ap-
pointed in 1932 to represent Section A (Mathematical and Physical
Sciences) and Section J (Psychology), the committee was instructed
to consider and report upon the possibility of "quantitative estimates
of sensory events"—meaning simply: Is it possible to measure human
sensation? Deliberation led only to disagreement, mainly about what
is meant by the term measurement. An interim report in 1938 found
one member complaining that his colleagues "came out by that same
door as they went in," and in order to have another try at agreement,
the committee begged to be continued for another year.

For its final report (1940) the committee chose a common bone
for its contentions, directing its arguments at a concrete example of
a sensory scale. This was the Sone scale of loudness (S.S. Stevens
and H. Davis. *Hearing.* New York: Wiley, 1938), which purports to
measure the subjective magnitude of an auditory sensation against a
scale having the formal properties of other basic scales, such as those

used to measure length and weight. Again the 19 members of the committee came out by the routes they entered, and their views ranged
widely between two extremes. One member submitted "that any law
purporting to express a quantitative relation between sensation intensity and stimulus intensity is not merely false but is in fact meaningless unless and until a meaning can be given to the concept of addition
as applied to sensation" (Final Report, p. 245).

It is plain from this and from other statements by the committee
that the real issue is the meaning of measurement. This, to be sure, is
a semantic issue, but one susceptible of orderly discussion. Perhaps
agreement can better be achieved if we recognize that measurement
exists in a variety of forms and that scales of measurement fall into
certain definite classes. These classes are determined both by the
empirical operations invoked in the process of "measuring" and by the
formal (mathematical) properties of the scales. Furthermore—and this
is of great concern to several of the sciences—the statistical manipula-
tions that can legitimately be applied to empirical data depend upon
the type of scale against which the data are ordered.

A CLASSIFICATION OF SCALES OF MEASUREMENT

Paraphrasing N.R. Campbell (Final Report, p. 340), we may say
that measurement, in the broadest sense, is defined as the assignment
of numerals to objects or events according to rules. The fact that
numerals can be assigned under different rules leads to different kinds
of scales and different kinds of measurement. The problem then becomes that of making explicit (a) the various rules for the assignment
of numerals, (b) the mathematical properties (or group structure) of
the resulting scales, and (c) the statistical operations applicable to
measurements made with each type of scale.

Scales are possible in the first place only because there is a certain
isomorphism between what we can do with the aspects of objects and
the properties of the numeral series. In dealing with the aspects of
objects we invoke empirical operations for determing equality (classifying), for rank-ordering, and for determining when differences and
when ratios between the aspects of objects are equal. The conventional
series of numerals yields to analogous operations: We can identify the
members of a numeral series and classify them. We know their order

as given by convention. We can determine equal differences, as $8-6 = 4-2$, and equal ratios, as $8/4 = 6/3$. The isomorphism between these properties of the numeral series and certain empirical operations which we perform with objects permits the use of the series as a *model* to represent aspects of the empirical world.

The type of scale achieved depends upon the character of the basic empirical operations performed. These operations are limited ordinarily by the nature of the thing being scaled and by our choice of procedures, but, once selected, the operations determine that there will eventuate one or another of the scales listed in Table 1.

TABLE 1[1]

Scale	Basic Empirical Operations	Mathematical Group Structure	Permissible Statistics (invariantive)
NOMINAL	Determination of equality	*Permutation group* $x' = f(x)$ $f(x)$ means any one-to-one substitution	Number of cases Mode Contingency correlation
ORDINAL	Determination of greater or less	*Isotonic group* $x' = f(x)$ $f(x)$ means any monotonic increasing function	Median Percentiles
INTERVAL	Determination of equality of intervals or differences	*General linear group* $x' = ax + b$	Mean Standard deviation Rank-order correlation Product-moment correlation
RATIO	Determination of equality of ratios	*Similarity group* $x' = ax$	Coefficient of variation

[1] A classification essentially equivalent to that contained in this table was presented before the International Congress for the Unity of Science, September 1941. The writer is indebted to the late Prof. G.D. Birkhoff for a stimulating discussion which led to the completion of the table in essentially its present form.

The decision to discard the scale names commonly encountered in writings on measurement is based on the ambiguity of such terms as "intensive" and "extensive." Both ordinal and interval scales have at times been called intensive, and both interval and ratio scales have sometimes been labeled extensive.

It will be noted that the column listing the basic operations needed to create each type of scale is cumulative: to an operation listed opposite a particular scale must be added all those operations preceding it. Thus, an interval scale can be erected only provided we have an operation for determining equality of intervals, for determining greater or less, and for determining equality (not greater and not less). To these operations must be added a method for ascertaining equality of ratios if a ratio scale is to be achieved.

In the column which records the group structure of each scale are listed the mathematical transformations which leave the scale-form invariant. Thus, any numeral, x, on a scale can be replaced by another numeral, x', where x' is the function of x listed in this column. Each mathematical group in the column is contained in the group immediately above it.

The last column presents examples of the type of statistical operations appropriate to each scale. This column is cumulative in that *all* statistics listed are admissible for data scaled against a ratio scale. The criterion for the appropriateness of a statistic is *invariance* under the transformations in Column 3. Thus, the case that stands at the median (mid-point) of a distribution maintains its position under all transformations which preserve order (isotonic group), but an item located at the mean remains at the mean only under transformations as restricted as those of the linear group. The ratio expressed by the coefficient of variation remains invariant only under the similarity transformation (multiplication by a constant). (The rank-order correlation coefficient is usually deemed appropriate to an ordinal scale, but actually this statistic assumes equal intervals between successive ranks and therefore calls for an interval scale.)

Let us now consider each scale in turn.

NOMINAL SCALE

The *nominal scale* represents the most unrestricted assignments of numerals. The numerals are used only as labels or type numbers, and words or letters would serve as well. Two types of nominal assignments are sometimes distinguished, as illustrated (a) by the 'numbering' of football players for the identification of the individuals, and (b) by the 'numbering' of types or classes, where each member of a class is assigned the same numeral. Actually, the first is a special case of the second, for when we label our football players we are dealing with unit classes of one member each. Since the purpose is just as well served when any two designating numerals are interchanged, this scale form remains invariant under the general substitution or permutation group (sometimes called the symmetric group of transformations). The only statistic relevant to nominal scales of Type A is the number of cases, e.g. the number of players assigned numerals. But once classes containing several individuals have been formed (Type B), we can determine the most numerous class (the mode), and under certain conditions we can test, by the contingency methods, hypotheses regarding the distribution of cases among the classes.

The nominal scale is a primitive form, and quite naturally there are many who will urge that it is absurd to attribute to this process of assigning numerals the dignity implied by the term measurement. Certainly there can be no quarrel with this objection, for the naming of things is an arbitrary business. However we christen it, the use of numerals as names for classes is an example of the "assignment of numerals according to rule." The rule is: Do not assign the same numeral to different classes or different numerals to the same class. Beyond that, anything goes with the nominal scale.

ORDINAL SCALE

The *ordinal scale* arises from the operation of rank-ordering. Since any 'order-preserving' transformation will leave the scale form invariant, this scale has the structure of what may be called the isotonic or order-preserving group. A classic example of an ordinal scale is the scale of hardness of minerals. Other instances are found among scales of intelligence, personality traits, grade or quality of leather, etc.

As a matter of fact, most of the scales used widely and effectively by psychologists are ordinal scales. In the strictest propriety the ordinary statistics involving means and standard deviations ought not to be used with these scales, for these statistics imply a knowledge of something more than the relative rank-order of data. On the other hand, for this 'illegal' statisticizing there can be invoked a kind of pragmatic sanction: In numerous instances it leads to fruitful results. While the outlawing of this procedure would probably serve no good purpose, it is proper to point out that means and standard deviations computed on an ordinal scale are in error to the extent that the successive intervals on the scale are unequal in size. When only the rank-order of data is known, we should proceed cautiously with our statistics, and especially with the conclusions we draw from them.

Even in applying those statistics that are normally appropriate for ordinal scales, we sometimes find rigor compromised. Thus, although it is indicated in Table 1 that percentile measures may be applied to rank-ordered data, it should be pointed out that the customary procedure of assigning a value to a percentile by interpolating linearly within a class interval is, in all strictness, wholly out of bounds. Likewise, it is not strictly proper to determine the mid-point of a class interval by linear interpolation, because the linearity of an ordinal scale is precisely the property which is open to question.

INTERVAL SCALE

With the *interval scale* we come to a form that is "quantitative" in the ordinary sense of the word. Almost all the usual statistical measures are applicable here, unless they are the kinds that imply a knowledge of a 'true' zero point. The zero point on an interval scale is a matter of convention or convenience, as is shown by the fact that the scale form remains invariant when a constant is added.

This point is illustrated by our two scales of temperature, Centigrade and Fahrenheit. Equal intervals of temperature are scaled off by noting equal volumes of expansion; an arbitrary zero is agreed upon for each scale; and a numerical value on one of the scales is transformed into a value on the other by means of an equation of the form $x' = ax + b$. Our scales of time offer a similar example. Dates on one calendar are transformed to those on another by way of this same equation. On these scales, of course, it is meaningless to say that one value is twice or some other proportion greater than another.

Periods of time, however, can be measured on ratio scales and one period may be correctly defined as double another. The same is probably true of temperature measured on the so-called Absolute Scale.

Most psychological measurement aspires to create interval scales, and it sometimes succeeds. The problem usually is to devise operations for equalizing the units of the scales—a problem not always easy of solution but one for which there are several possible modes of attack. Only occasionally is there concern for the location of a 'true' zero point, because the human attributes measured by psychologists usually exist in a positive degree that is large compared with the range of its variation. In this respect these attributes are analogous to temperature as it is encountered in everyday life. Intelligence, for example, is usefully assessed on ordinal scales which try to approximate interval scales, and it is not necessary to define what zero intelligence would mean.

RATIO SCALE

Ratio scales are those most commonly encountered in physics and are possible only when there exist operations for determining all four relations: equality, rank-order, equality of intervals, and equality of ratios. Once such a scale is erected, its numerical values can be transformed (as from inches to feet) only by multiplying each value by a constant. An absolute zero is always implied, even though the zero value on some scales (e.g. Absolute Temperature) may never be produced. All types of statistical measures are applicable to ratio scales, and only with these scales may we properly indulge in logarithmic transformations such as are involved in the use of decibels.

Foremost among the ratio scales is the scale of number itself— cardinal number—the scale we use when we count such things as eggs, pennies, and apples. This scale of the numerosity of aggregates is so basic and so common that it is ordinarily not even mentioned in discussions of measurement.

It is conventional in physics to distinguish between two types of ratio scales: *fundamental* and *derived.* Fundamental scales are represented by length, weight, and electrical resistance, whereas derived scales are represented by density, force, and elasticity.

These latter are *derived* magnitudes in the sense that they are mathematical functions of certain fundamental magnitudes. They are actually more numerous in physics than are the fundamental magnitudes, which are commonly held to be basic because they satisfy the criterion of *additivity*. Weights, lengths, and resistances can be added in the physical sense, but this important empirical fact is generally accorded more prominence in the theory of measurement than it deserves. The so-called fundamental scales are important instances of ratio scales, but they are only instances. As a matter of fact, it can be demonstrated that the fundamental scales could be set up even if the physical operation of addition were ruled out as impossible of performance. Given three balances, for example, each having the proper construction, a set of standard weights could be manufactured without it ever being necessary to place two weights in the same scale pan at the same time. The procedure is too long to describe in these pages, but its feasibility is mentioned here simply to suggest that physical addition, even though it is sometimes possible, is not necessarily the basis of all measurement. Too much measuring goes on where resort can never be had to the process of laying things end-to-end or of piling them up in a heap.

Ratio scales of psychological magnitudes are rare but not entirely unknown. The Sone scale discussed by the British committee is an example founded on a deliberate attempt to have human observers judge the loudness ratios of pairs of tones. The judgment of equal intervals had long been established as a legitimate method, and with the work on sensory ratios, started independently in several laboratories, the final step was taken to assign numerals to sensations of loudness in such a way that relations among the sensations are reflected by the ordinary arithmetical relations in the numeral series. As in all measurement, there are limits imposed by error and variability, but within these limits the Sone scale ought properly to be classed as a ratio scale.

To the British committee, then, we may venture to suggest by way of conclusion that the most liberal and useful definition of measurement is, as one of its members advised, "the assignment of numerals to things so as to represent facts and conventions about them." The problem as to what is and is not measurement then reduces to the simple question: What are the rules, if any, under which numerals are assigned? If we can point to a consistent set of rules, we are obviously concerned with measurement of some sort, and we can then proceed to the more interesting question as to the kind of measurement it is. In most cases a formulation of the rules of assignment discloses directly the kind of measurement and hence the kind of scale involved. If there remains any ambiguity, we may seek the final and definitive answer in the mathematical group-structure of the scale form: In what ways can we transform its values and still have it serve all the functions previously fulfilled? We know that the values of all scales can be multiplied by a constant, which changes the size of the unit. If, in addition, a constant can be added (or a new zero point chosen), it is proof positive that we are not concerned with a ratio scale. Then, if the purpose of the scale is still served when its values are squared or cubed, it is not even an interval scale. And finally, if any two values may be interchanged at will, the ordinal scale is ruled out and the nominal scale is the sole remaining possibility.

This proposed solution to the semantic problem is not meant to imply that all scales belonging to the same mathematical group are equally precise or accurate or useful or "fundamental." Measurement is never better than the empirical operations by which it is carried out, and operations range from bad to good. Any particular scale, sensory or physical, may be objected to on the grounds of bias, low precision, restricted generality, and other factors, but the objector should remember that these are relative and practical matters and that no scale used by mortals is perfectly free of their taint.

DUHEM

QUANTITY AND QUALITY

This third selection from Pierre Duhem's work is taken from Part II, Chapter I, of his book, The Aim and Structure of Physical Theory.*

1. Theoretical Physics Is Mathematical Physics

The discussions developed in the first part of this book have informed us exactly about the aim the physicist should have when he constructs a theory.

A physical theory will then be a system of logically linked propositions and not an incoherent series of mechanical or algebraic models. This system will have for its object not the furnishing of an explanation but the representation and natural classification of experimental laws, taken in a group.

To require that a great number of propositions be linked in a perfect logical order is not a slight or easy condition to satisfy. The experience of centuries testifies how easily a fallacy slips into what appears to be the most irreproachable series of syllogisms.

There is, however, one science in which logic attains a degree of perfection which makes it easy to avoid error and easy to recognize it when it has been committed, namely, the science of numbers, arithmetic, with its extension in algebra. It owes this perfection to an extremely abbreviated symbolic language in which each idea is represented by an unambiguously defined sign, and in which each sentence of the deductive reasoning is replaced by an operation combining the signs in accord with strictly fixed rules and by a calculation whose accuracy

*Translated by Philip Wiener; reprinted here by permission of the Princeton University Press.

is always easy to test. This rapid and precise symbolism of algebra guarantees progress which disregards almost entirely the opposing doctrines of competing schools.

One of the claims to fame of the geniuses who made the sixteenth and seventeenth centuries distinguished was the recognition of the truth that physics would not become a clear and precise science, exempt from the perpetual, sterile disputes characterizing its history till then, and would not be capable of demanding universal assent for its doctrines so long as it would not speak the language of geometers. They created a true theoretical physics by their understanding that it had to be mathematical physics.

Created in the sixteenth century, mathematical physics proved it was the sound method of physics by the wonderful, steady progress it made in the study of nature. Today it would be impossible, without shocking the plainest good sense, to deny that physical theories should be expressed in mathematical language.

In order for a physical theory to be able to present itself in the form of a chain of algebraic calculations, all the ideas employed in the theory must be capable of being represented by numbers. This leads us to ask ourselves the following question: Under what conditions may a physical attribute be signified by a numerical symbol?

2. Quantity and Measurement

The first answer to this question appears at once to the mind to be as follows: In order that an attribute found in a body may be expressed by a numerical symbol, it is necessary and sufficient that this attribute belong, in Aristotle's language, to the category of quantity and not to the category of quality. In the more readily accepted language of modern geometry, it is necessary and sufficient that this attribute be a magnitude.

What are the essential characteristics of a magnitude? By what mark do we recognize that the length of a line, for example, is a magnitude?

By comparing different lengths with one another we come across the notions of equal and unequal lengths which present the following characteristics:

Two lengths equal to the same length are equal to each other.

If the first length is greater than the second and the second greater than a third, the first is greater than the third.

These two characteristics already permit us to express the fact that two lengths are equal to each other by making use of the arithmetical symbol =, and by writing $A = B$. They permit us to express the fact that A is greater than B in length by writing $A > B$ or $B < A$. In fact, the only properties of the signs of equality or inequality invoked in arithmetic or in algebra are the following:

1. The two equalities $A = B$ and $B = C$ imply the equality $A = C$.

2. The two inequalities $A > B$ and $B > C$ imply the inequality $A > C$.

These properties still belong to the signs of equality and inequality when we make use of them in the study of lengths.

Let us place several lengths end to end; we obtain a new length S which is greater than each of the component lengths A, B, and C. S does not change if we change the order in which we put the components end to end; neither does it change if we replace some of the component lengths (e.g., B and C) by the length obtained by putting them end to end.

These several characteristics authorize us to employ the arithmetical sign of addition to represent the operation which consists in putting several lengths end to end, and to write $S = A + B + C + \ldots$.

In fact, from what we have just said, we can write

$$A + B > A, \ A + B > B$$
$$A + B = B + A$$
$$A + (B + C) = (A + B) + C$$

Now these equalities and inequalities represent the only fundamental postulates of arithmetic. All the rules of calculation conceived in arithmetic to combine numbers are going to be extended to lengths.

The most immediate of these extensions is that of multiplication; the length obtained by placing end to end n lengths, equal to one another and to A, may be represented by the symbol $n \times A$. This extension is the starting point for the measurement of lengths and will permit us to represent each length by a number accompanied by the name of a certain standard or unit of length chosen once for all lengths.

Let us choose such a standard of length, for example, the meter, which is the length given to us under very specific conditions by a certain metal bar deposited in the International Bureau of Weights and Measures.

Certain lengths may be reproduced by placing n lengths equal to a meter end to end; the number n followed by the name meter will adequately represent such a length; we say that it is a length of n meters.

Other lengths cannot be represented in that way, but they can be reproduced by placing end to end p equal segments when q of these same segments subsequently placed one after the other would reproduce the length of a meter. Such a length will be entirely known when we state the fraction p/q followed by the name meter; it will be a length of p/q meters.

An incommensurable number, still followed by the name of the standard, will permit us to represent as well any length not belonging to either of the two categories we have just defined. In short, any length whatsoever will be perfectly known when we say it is a length of x meters, whether x is an integer, fraction, or incommensurable number.

Then the symbolic addition of $A + B + C + \ldots$, by which we represent the operation of bringing several lengths end to end, will be replaceable by a true arithmetic sum. It will suffice to measure each of the lengths A, B, C, $\ldots$ with the same unit, the meter, for example; we thus obtain numbers of meters $a, b, c, \ldots$. The length S which is formed by placing A, B, C, $\ldots$ end to end, measured also in meters, will be represented by a number s equal to the arithmetic sum of the numbers a, b, c, $\ldots$, which measure the lengths A, B, C, $\ldots$. For the symbolic equality

$$A + B + C + \ldots = S$$

between the component lengths and the resultant length, we substitute

$$a + b + c + \ldots = s$$

the arithmetic equality of the numbers of meters representing these lengths.

Thus, through the choice of a standard length and through measurement, we give to the signs of arithmetic and algebra, set up to represent operations done with numbers, the power to represent operations performed with lengths.

What we have just said about lengths could be repeated concerning surfaces, volumes, angles, and times; all the physical attributes which are magnitudes would show analogous characteristics. In every case we should see the different states of a magnitude show relations of equality or inequality susceptible of representation by the signs $=$, $>$, and $<$; we should always be able to submit this magnitude to an

operation having the double property of being commutative and associative, and consequently, capable of being represented by the arithmetic symbol of addition, the sign +. Through this operation, measurement would be introduced into the study of this magnitude, and would
enable one to define it fully by means of the union of an integer, fraction, or surd, and a unit of measurement; such a union is known by
the name of a concrete number.

3. Quantity and Quality

The essential character of any attribute belonging to the category
of quantity is therefore the following: Each state of a quantity's magnitude may always be formed through addition by means of other
smaller states of the same quantity; each quantity is the union through
a commutative and associative operation of quantities smaller than the
first but of the same kind as it is, and they are parts of it.

The Aristotelian philosophy expressed this in a formula, too concise to give in full all the details of the thought, by saying: Quantity
is that which has parts external to one another.

Every attribute that is not *quantity* is *quality*.

"Quality," said Aristotle, "is one of those words which are taken
in many senses." The shape of a geometrical figure which makes a
circle or a triangle of it is a quality; the observable properties of bodies,
such as being warm or cold, light or dark, red or blue, are qualities; to
be in good health is a quality; to be virtuous is a quality; to be a gram-
marian, mathematician, or musician—all are qualities.

"There are qualities," added the Stagirite, "which are not susceptible of more or less: a circle is not more or less circular; a triangle
is not more or less triangular. But most qualities are susceptible of
more or less; they are capable of intensity; a white thing can become
whiter."

At first blush, we are tempted to establish a correlation between
the various intensities of the same quality and the various states of
the same quantity's magnitude, that is, to compare the heightening
of intensity (*intensio*) or the lowering of intensity (*remissio*) to the
increase or diminution of length, surface or volume.

$A,B,C,\ldots$ are different mathematicians. A may be as good a
mathematician as B, or a better, or not so good a mathematician.

If A is as good a mathematician as B, and B is as good as C, then A is as good as C. If A is a better mathematician than B and B is better than C, than A is a better mathematician than C.

$A, B, C, \ldots$ are red materials whose shades we are comparing. Material A may be as brilliant a red as B, or less, or more brilliant than the material B. If the shade of A is as brilliant as the shade of B and that of B as brilliant as the shade of C, then the shade of A is as brilliant as the shade of C. If the material A is a deeper red than the material B, and the latter is a deeper hue of red than the material C, then the material A is a deeper red than the material C.

Thus, in order to express the fact that two qualities of the same kind do or do not have the same intensity, we can employ the signs $=, >$, and $<$, which will preserve the same properties they have in arithmetic.

The analogy between quantities and qualities stops there.

A large quantity, we have seen, may always be formed by the addition of a certain number of small quantities of the same kind. The large number of grains inside a sack of wheat may always be obtained by the summation of piles of wheat each containing a smaller number of grains. A century is a succession of years; a year is a succession of days, hours, and minutes. A road several miles long is traveled by putting end to end the short segments which the hiker crosses with each step. A field which has a large surface may be broken up into pieces of smaller surface.

Nothing like this applies to the category of quality. Bring together in a vast meeting as many mediocre mathematicians as you can find, and you will not have the equal of an Archimedes or of a Lagrange. Sew together the cloth remnants of a dark red hue, and the piece obtained will not be a brilliant red.

No quality of a certain kind and intensity results in any manner from several qualities of the same kind but of lesser intensity. Each intensity of quality has its own individual characteristics which make it absolutely unlike lesser and greater intensities. A quality of a certain intensity does not include as an integral part of itself the same quality made more intense. Boiling water is hotter than boiling alcohol and the latter hotter than boiling ether, but neither the boiling point of alcohol nor that of ether is part of the boiling point of water. Whoever would say that the heat of boiling water is the sum of the heat of boiling alcohol and the heat of boiling ether would be talking nonsense.[1] Diderot used to ask jokingly how many snowballs would be required to heat an oven; the question is embarrassing only for one who confuses quantity with quality.

Thus, in the category of quality we find nothing which resembles the formation of a large quantity by means of the small quantities which are its parts. We find no operation both commutative and associative which merits the name "addition" and may be represented by the + sign. Measurement stemming from the idea of addition cannot capture quality.

4. Purely Quantitative Physics

Every time an attribute is capable of being measured, or is a quantity, algebraic language becomes apt for expressing different states of this attribute. Is this aptitude for algebraic expression peculiar to quantities, and are qualities entirely deprived of it? The philosophers who in the seventeenth century created mathematical physics certainly thought so. Hence, in order to realize the mathematical physics to which they aspired, they had to require their theories to deal exclusively with quantities and to rigorously banish any qualitative notion.

Moreover, these same philosophers all saw in physical theory not the representation but the explanation of empirical laws. The ideas combined in the propositions of physical theory were not, for them, the signs and symbols of observable properties, but the very expression of the reality hidden under appearances. The physical universe, which our senses present to us as an immense assemblage of qualities, had therefore to be offered to the mind as a system of quantities.

These common aspirations of the great scientific reformers who ushered in the seventeenth century culminated in the creation of the Cartesian philosophy.

To eliminate qualities completely from the study of material things is the aim and virtually the defining character of Cartesian physic

Among the sciences only arithmetic, with its extension to algebra is free from any notion borrowed from the category of quality, and it alone conforms to the ideal which Descartes proposed for the complete science of nature.

[1]It is, of course, understood that we are taking the word "heat" in its everyday meaning, which has nothing in common with what physicists attribute to "quantity of heat."

When it comes to geometry the mind runs into a qualitative element, for this science remains "so confined to the consideration of diagrams that it cannot exercise the understanding without fatiguing the imagination a great deal." "The scruples the ancients had against using arithmetical terms in geometry, which could only come from their not seeing clearly their relationships, caused much obscurity and difficulty in the manner with which they explained themselves." This obscurity and difficulty are to disappear when we get rid of the qualitative notion of geometrical form and shape, and keep only the quantitative notion of distance and the equations which connect the mutual distances of the different points studied. Although their objects are of different natures, the various branches of mathematics do not consider in these objects "anything else than the various relations or proportions found in them," so that it suffices to deal with these proportions in general with the methods of algebra, without being concerned about the objects in which they are encountered or the diagrams in which they are embodied; consequently, "everything which mathematicians have to consider is reduced to problems of one and the same kind, namely, to finding the values of the roots of some equation." All mathematics is reduced to the science of numbers in which only quantities are dealt with; qualities no longer have any place in it.

Qualities having been eliminated from geometry, they must now be banned from physics. In order to succeed in this, it suffices to reduce physics to mathematics, which has become the science of quantity alone. That is the task Descartes set out to accomplish:

"I admit no principles in physics which are not also accepted in mathematics." "For I profess plainly not to recognize any other substance in material things than the matter capable of all sorts of divisions, configurations, and motions which the geometers call quantity and which they take as the object of their demonstrations; and in this matter I consider absolutely nothing but these divisions, configurations, and motions. Concerning them, I admit nothing as true which cannot be deduced from axioms impossible for us to doubt and deduced in so evident a manner that the deduction amounts to a mathematical demonstration. And as all the phenomena of nature may be explained in that way, as we shall see in the sequel, I think we should admit no other principles in physics, nor wish for any other sort."[2]

---

[2]R. Descartes, Principia Philosophiae, Part II, Art. IXIV.

What, then, is matter, first of all? "Its nature does not consist in hardness, nor in weight, heat, or other qualities of this kind," but only in "extension in length, breadth, and depth," in what "the geometers call quantity"[3] or volume. Matter is therefore quantity; the quantity of a certain portion of matter is the volume it occupies. A vessel contains as much matter as its volume, whether it is filled with mercury or filled with air. "Those who claim to distinguish material substance from extension or from quantity either have no idea of what comes under the name substance or else have a confused idea of immaterial substance.[4]

What is motion? Also a quantity. Multiply the quantity of matter that each of the bodies of a system contains by the speed with which it is set in motion, add together all the products, and you will have the quantity of motion of the system. So long as the system will not collide with any external body which may give motion to it or take motion away from it, it will conserve an invariable quantity of motion.

Thus, there is spread throughout the universe a single, homogeneous, incompressible, and inelastic matter about which we know nothing except that it is extended. This matter is divisible into parts of various shapes, and these parts can be moved into different relations with one another. Such are the only genuine properties of what constitutes bodies, and all the apparent qualities affecting our senses reduce to these properties. The object of Cartesian physics is to explain how this reduction is made.

What is gravitation? The effect produced on bodies by vortices of ethereal matter. What is a hot body? A body "composed of small parts which agitate one another with a very sudden and violent motion." What is light? A pressure exerted on the ether by the motion of fiery bodies and transmitted instantaneously through the greatest distances. All the qualities of bodies without a single exception are explained by a theory in which we consider only geometric extension, the different configurations that can be traced in it, and the different motions which these can have. "The universe is a machine in which there is nothing at all to consider except the shapes and motions of its parts." Thus the entire science of material nature is reduced to a sort of universal arithmetic from which the category of quality radically is banned.

---

[3]ibid., Part II, Art. IV.
[4]ibid., Part II, Art. IX.

5. The Various Intensities of the Same Quality Are Expressible in Numbers

Theoretical physics, as we conceive it, does not have the power to grasp the real properties of bodies underneath the observable appearances; it cannot, therefore, without going beyond the legitimate scope of its methods, decide whether these properties are qualitative or quantative. By insisting that it could decide for the quantitative, Cartesianism was making claims which do not appear tenable to us.

Theoretical physics does not grasp the reality of things; it is limited to representing observable appearances by signs and symbols. Now, we wish our theoretical physics to be a mathematical physics starting with symbols that are algebraic symbols or numerical combinations. If, therefore, only magnitudes can be expressed in numbers, we ought not to introduce into our theories any notion which is not a magnitude. Without asserting that everything at the very bottom of material things is merely quantity, we should admit nothing but what is quantitative in the picture we make of the totality of physical laws; quality would have no place in our system.

Now, there is no good ground on which to subscribe to this conclusion; the purely qualitative character of a notion is not opposed to the use of numbers to symbolize its various states. The same quality may appear with an infinity of different intensities. We can affix a label and number, so to speak, to each of these various intensities, registering the same number in two circumstances where the same quality is found with the same intensity, and identifying a second case, where the quality considered is more intense than in the first case, by a second number greater than the first.

Take, for example, the quality of being a mathematician. When a certain number of young mathematicians take a competitive examination, the examiner who is to judge gives a mark to each of them, assigning the same mark to two candidates who seem to him to be equally good mathematicians, and giving a better mark to one or the other if one appears to him to be a better mathematician than the other.

These pieces of material are red in varying degrees of intensity; the merchant who arranges them on his racks assigns numbers to them; to each number a very definite shade of red corresponds, and the higher the number, the more intense the brightness of red.

Here are some heated bodies. This first one is as hot as the second, hotter or colder than it; that body is hotter or colder at this instant than this one. Each part of a body, small as we suppose it to be, seems to us endowed with a certain quality which we call heat, and the intensity of this quality is not the same at a given instant when we compare one part of the body to another; at the same point of the body, it varies from one instant to the next.

We might in our reasoning speak of this quality of heat and of its various intensities, but wishing to employ the language of algebra as much as possible, we proceed to substitute for this quality of heat that of a numerical symbol, the temperature.

Temperature will then be a number assigned to each point of a body at each instant; it will be correlated to the heat prevailing at that point and in that instant. To two equally intense heats will be correlated two numerically equal temperatures. If it is hotter at one point than at another, the temperature at the first point will be a greater number than the temperature at the second point.

If, therefore, M, M', M'' are different points, and if T, T', T'' are the numbers expressing the temperatures at those points, the equality $T = T'$ has the same meaning as the following sentence: It is as warm at point M' as at point M. The inequality $T' > T''$ is equivalent to the sentence: It is warmer at point M' than at point M''.

The use of a number, the temperature, to represent an intensity of heat as a quality rests entirely on the following two propositions:

If body A is as warm as body B and body B is as warm as body C, then body A is as warm as body C.

These two propositions, in fact, suffice to enable the signs $=$, $>$, and $<$ to represent the possible relations of different intensities of heat, as they permit representation of either the mutual relations of numbers or the mutual relations of different states of magnitude of the same quantity.

If I am told that two lengths are respectively measured by the numbers 5 and 10, without any further indication, I am being given certain information about these lengths: I know that the second is longer than the first, and even that it is double the first. This information is, however, very incomplete; it will not permit me to reproduce one of these lengths, or even to know whether it is large or small.

This information will be more complete if, not content with being given the numbers 5 and 10 as measuring two lengths, I am told that these lengths are measured in meters, and if I am shown the standard meter or a copy of it. Then I shall be able to reproduce and bring into existence these two lengths whenever I wish.

Thus, the numbers measuring magnitudes of the same kind inform us fully about these magnitudes only when we join to them concrete knowledge of the standard which represents the unit.

Some mathematicians have been examined in a competition; I am told they have earned the marks 5, 10, and 15, and that furnishes me certain information about them which will allow me, for example, to classify them. But this information is not complete, and does not allow me to form an idea of each one's talent. I do not know the absolute value of the marks which have been given to them; I lack knowledge of the scale to which these marks refer.

Similarly, if I am told simply that the temperatures of different bodies are represented by the numbers 10, 20, and 100, I learn that the first body is not as hot as the second and the second not as hot as the third. But is the first warm or cold? Can it melt ice or not? Would the last one burn me? Would it cook an egg? I do not know these things so long as I am not given the thermometric scale to which these temperatures 10, 20 and 100 refer, that is to say, a procedure allowing me to realize in a concrete manner the intensities of heat indicated by the numbers 10, 20 and 100. If I am given a graduated glass tube containing mercury and if I am taught that the temperature of a mass of water should be taken as equal to 10, 20, and 100 every time I see the mercury rise to these calibrations when the thermometer is plunged into the water, my doubts will be completely dissipated. Every time the numerical value of a temperature is indicated to me, I shall be able, if I wish, to realize in fact that a mass of water will have that temperature, since I possess the thermometer on which it is read.

So, just as a magnitude is not defined simply by an abstract number but by a number joined to concrete knowledge of a standard in the same way the intensity of a quality is not entirely represented by a numerical symbol, but to this symbol must be joined a concrete procedure suitable for obtaining the scale of these intensitites. Only the knowledge of this scale allows one to give a physical meaning to the algebraic propositions which we state concerning the numbers representing the different intensities of the quality studied.

Naturally, the scale which serves to calibrate the different intensities of a quality is always some quantitative effect having this quality as its cause. We choose this effect in such a way that its magnitude increases in time as the quality which causes it becomes more intense. Thus, in a glass vessel surrounded by a warm body, the mercury undergoes an apparent expansion which becomes greater as the body becomes warmer; this is the quantitative phenomenon provided by a thermometer which allows us to construct a scale of temperatures suitable for calibrating numerically different intensities of heat.

In the domain of quality, there is no room for addition; the latter does apply, however, when we study the quantitative phenomenon which provides a suitable scale on which to calibrate the different intensities of a quality. The various intensities of heat are not additive; we can get the sum of several numbers representing the temperatures.

Thus, the choice of a scale allows us to substitute for the study of the various intensities of a quality the consideration of numbers subject to the rules of algebraic calculation. The advantages sought by past physicists when they substituted a hypothetical quantity for the qualitative property revealed to the senses, and measured the magnitude of that quantity, can very often be obtained without employing that hypothetical quantity, simply by the choice of a suitable scale.

The electric charge will furnish us with an example of this.

What experiment shows us at first in very small bodies electrically charged is something qualitative. Soon, this quality of being charged electrically ceases to appear simple; it is capable of two forms which oppose and destroy each other; the resinous (negative) and the vitreous (positive).

Whether it is resinous or vitreous, the charged state of a small body may be more or less powerful; it is capable of different intensities.

Franklin, Oepinus, Coulomb, Laplace, Poisson—all the creators of the science of electricity thought that qualities could not be admitted into the constitution of a physical theory and that only quantities have the right of entry. Hence, underneath this quality of electric charge manifest to their senses, their reason sought a quantity, "the quantity of electricity." In order to arrive at an understanding of this quantity, they imagined that each of the two charges was due to the presence within the charged body of a certain "electrical fluid"; that the charged body showed an intensity of charge that varied with the mass of the

the electrical fluid; and that the magnitude of this mass then yielded the quantity of electricity.

The study of this quantity enjoyed a central role in the theory, a role which proceeded from these two laws:

The algebraic sum of the quantities of electricity spread over a group of bodies (a sum in which the quantities of vitreous electricity are prefixed by the + sign, and the quantities of resinous electricity have the − sign) does not change so long as this group is isolated from other bodies.

At a given distance two small charged bodies repel each other with a force proportional to the product of the quantities of electricity they carry.

Well now, these two propositions can be preserved intact without appealing to hypothetical and very improbable electrical fluids, and without depriving the electrical charge of the qualitative character our immediate observations confer on it. All we have to do is choose a suitable scale to which we refer the intensities of the electrical quality.

Let us take a small body charged vitreously (positively) in a manner that is always the same; at a fixed distance, we cause to act on it each one of the small bodies whose electrical state we wish to study. Each one of them will exert on the first body a force whose magnitude we shall be able to measure and to which we shall attach the + sign when there is a repulsion and a − sign when there is an attraction. Then each small body charged vitreously will exert on the first body a positive force whose magnitude will be greater as its charge is greater in intensity; each small body charged resinously will exert a negative force whose absolute value will increase in proportion as the charge on it is more powerful.

It is this force, a quantitative element which is measurable and additive, which we shall choose an an electrometric scale and which will supply different positive numbers to represent the diverse intensities of vitreous electricity, and different negative numbers to calibrate the diverse degrees of resinous electrical charge. To these numbers or readings, furnished by this electrometric method, we can, if we wish, give the name "quantities of electricity"; and then the two essential propositions that the doctrine of electrical fluids formulated will become meaningful and true again.

No better example seems to us to make evident the following

truth: In order to make a universal arithmetic out of physics, as Descartes desired to do, it is not at all necessary to imitate the great philosopher and to reject all quality, for the language of algebra allows us to reason as well about the various intensities of a quality as about the various magnitudes of a quantity.

ARITHMETIC

ARITHMETIC AS AN EMPIRICAL SCIENCE

This second selection from Mill is taken from Chapters 5 and 6 of Book II of his A System of Logic *(1843).*

CHAPTER VI.

§ I. In the examination which formed the subject of the last chapter into the nature of the evidence of those deductive sciences which are commonly represented to be systems of necessary truth, we have been led to the following conclusions. The results of those sciences are indeed necessary, in the sense of necessarily following from certain first principles, commonly called axioms and definitions; that is, of being certainly true if those axioms and definitions are so; for the word necessity, even in this acceptation of it, means no more than certainty. But their claim to the character of necessity in any sense beyond this, as implying an evidence independent of and superior to observation and experience, must depend on the previous establishment of such a claim in favour of the definitions and axioms themselves. With regard to axioms, we found that, considered as experimental truths, they rest on superabundant and obvious evidence. We inquired whether, since this is the case, it be imperative to suppose any other evidence of those truths than experimental evidence, any other origin for our belief of them than an experimental origin. We decided that the burden of proof lies with those who maintain the affirmative, and we examined, at considerable length, such arguments as they have produced. The examination having led to the rejection of those arguments, we have thought ourselves warranted in concluding that axioms are but a class, the most universal class, of inductions from experience; the simplest and easiest

cases of generalisation from the facts furnished to us by our senses or
by our internal consciousness.

While the axioms of demonstrative sciences thus appeared to be
experimental truths, the definitions, as they are incorrectly called, in
those sciences, were found by us to be generalisations from experience
which are not even, accurately speaking, truths; being propositions in
which, while we assert of some kind of object some property or properties which observation shows to belong to it, we at the same time deny
that it possesses any other properties, though in truth other properties
do in every individual instance accompany, and in almost all instances
modify, the property thus exclusively predicated. The denial, therefore,
is a mere fiction or supposition, made for the purpose of excluding the
consideration of those modifying circumstances, when their influence
is of too trifling amount to be worth considering, or adjourning it, when
important, to a more convenient moment.

From these considerations it would appear that Deductive or
Demonstrative Sciences are all, without exception, Inductive Sciences;
that their evidence is that of experience; but that they are also, in virtue
of the peculiar character of one indispensable portion of the general
formulæ according to which their inductions are made, Hypothetical
Sciences. Their conclusions are only true on certain suppositions, which
are, or ought to be, approximations to the truth, but are seldom, if ever,
exactly true; and to this hypothetical character is to be ascribed the
peculiar certainty which is supposed to be inherent in demonstration.

What we have now asserted, however, cannot be received as universally true of Deductive or Demonstrative Sciences, until verified by
being applied to the most remarkable of all those sciences, that of
Numbers; the theory of the Calculus; Arithmetic and Algebra. It is
harder to believe of the doctrines of this science than of any other,
either that they are not truths *a priori*, but experimental truths, or that
their peculiar certainty is owing to their being not absolute, but only
conditional truths. This, therefore, is a case which merits examination
apart; and the more so, because on this subject we have a double set
of doctrines to contend with; that of the *a priori* philosophers on one
side; and on the other, a theory the most opposite to theirs, which was
at one time very generally received, and is still far from being altogether
exploded among metaphysicians.

§ 2. This theory attempts to solve the difficulty apparently inhere in the case, by representing the propositions of the science of numbers as merely verbal, and its processes as simple transformations of language, substitutions of one expression for another. The proposition, Two and one is equal to three, according to these writers, is not a truth, is not the assertion of a really existing fact, but a definition of the word three; a statement that mankind have agreed to use the name three as a sign exactly equivalent to two and one; to call by the former name whatever is called by the other more clumsy phrase. According to this doctrine the longest process in algebra is but a succession of changes in terminology, by which equivalent expressions are substituted one for another; a series of translations of the same fact, from one into another language; though how, after such a series of translations, the fact itself comes out changed, (as when we demonstrate a new geometrical theorem by algebra,) they have not explained; and it is a difficulty which is fatal to their theory.

It must be acknowledged that there are peculiarities in the processes of arithmetic and algebra which render the theory in question very plausible, and have not unnaturally made those sciences the stronghold of Nominalism. The doctrine that we can discover facts, detect the hidden processes of nature, by an artful manipulation of language, is so contrary to common sense, that a person must have made some advances in philosophy to believe it; men fly to so paradoxical a belief to avoid, as they think, some even greater difficulty, which the vulgar do not see. What has led many to believe that reasoning is a mere verbal process is, that no other theory seemed reconcilable with the nature of the Science of Numbers. For we do not carry any ideas along with us when we use the symbols of arithmetic or of algebra. In a geometrical demonstration we have a mental diagram, if not one on paper; AB, AC, are present to our imagination as lines, intersecting other lines, forming an angle with one another, and the like; but not so a and b. These may represent line or any other magnitudes, but those magnitudes are never thought of; nothing is realised in our imagination but a and b. The ideas which, on the particular occasion, they happen to represent, are banished from the mind during every intermediate part of the process, between the beginning, when the premises are translated from things into signs, and the end, when the conclusion is translated back from signs into things. Nothing, then, being in the reasoner's mind but the symbols, what can seem more inadmissible than to contend that the

reasoning process has to do with anything more? We seem to have come
to one of Bacon's Prerogative Instances; an *experimentum crucis* on the
nature of reasoning itself.

Nevertheless, it will appear on consideration, that this apparently
so decisive instance is no instance at all; that there is in every step of
an arithmetical or algebraical calculation a real induction, a real inference of facts from facts; and that what disguises the induction is simply
its comprehensive nature and the consequent extreme generality of the
language. All numbers must be numbers of something; there are no
such things as numbers in the abstract. *Ten* must mean ten bodies, or
ten sounds, or ten beatings of the pulse. But though numbers must be
numbers of something, they may be numbers of anything. Propositions
therefore, concerning numbers have the remarkable peculiarity that
they are propositions concerning all things whatever; all objects, all
existences of every kind, known to our experience. All things possess
quantity; consist of parts which can be numbered; and in that character
possess all the properties which are called properties of numbers. That
half of four is two, must be true whatever the word four represents,
whether four hours, four miles, or four pounds weight. We need only
conceive a thing divided into four equal parts (and all things may be
conceived as so divided) to be able to predicate of it every property of
the number four, that is, every arithmetical proposition in which the
number four stands on one side of the equation. Algebra extends the
generalisation still farther: every number represents that particular
number of all things without distinction, but every algebraical symbol
does more, it represents all numbers without distinction. As soon as
we conceive a thing divided into equal parts, without knowing into
what number of parts, we may call it a or x, and apply to it, without
danger of error, every algebraical formula in the books. The proposition
$2 (a + b) = 2 a + 2 b$, is a truth co-extensive with all nature. Since then
algebraical truths are true of all things whatever, and not, like those of
geometry, true of lines only or of angles only, it is no wonder that the
symbols should not excite in our minds ideas of any things in particular
When we demonstrate the forty-seventh proposition of Euclid, it is not
necessary that the words should raise in us an image of all right-angled
triangles, but only of some one right-angled triangle, so in algebra we
need not, under the symbol a, picture to ourselves all things whatever,
but only some one thing; why not, then, the letter itself? The mere

written characters, *a, b, x, y, z,* serve as well for representatives of Things in general, as any more complex and apparently more concrete conception. That we are conscious of them, however, in their character of things, and not of mere signs, is evident from the fact that our whole process of reasoning is carried on by predicating of them the properties of things. In resolving an algebraic equation, by what rules do we proceed? By applying at each step to *a, b,* and *x,* the proposition that equals added to equals make equals; that equals taken from equals leave equals; and other propositions founded on these two. These are not properties of language, or of signs as such, but of magnitudes, which is as much as to say, of all things. The inferences, therefore, which are successively drawn, are inferences concerning things, not symbols; though as any Things whatever will serve the turn, there is no necessity for keeping the idea of the Thing at all distinct, and consequently the process of thought may, in this case, be allowed without danger to do what all processes of thought, when they have been performed often, will do if permitted, namely, to become entirely mechanical. Hence the general language of algebra comes to be used familiarly without exciting ideas, as all other general language is prone to do from mere habit, though in no other case than this can it be done with complete safety. But when we look back to see from whence the probative force of the process is derived, we find that at every single step, unless we suppose ourselves to be thinking and talking of the things, and not the mere symbols, the evidence falls.

There is another circumstance, which, still more than that which we have now mentioned, gives plausibility to the notion that the propositions of arithmetic and algebra are merely verbal. That is, that when considered as propositions respecting Things, they all have the appearance of being identical propositions. The assertion, Two and one is equal to three, considered as an assertion respecting objects, as for instance "Two pebbles and one pebble are equal to three pebbles," does not affirm equality between two collections of pebbles, but absolute identity. It affirms that if we put one pebble to two pebbles, those very pebbles are three. The objects, therefore, being the very same, and the mere assertion that "objects are themselves" being insignificant, it seems but natural to consider the proposition Two and one is equal to three, as asserting mere identity of signification between the two names.

This, however, though it looks so plausible, will not bear examination.

The expression "two pebbles and one pebble," and the expression "three pebbles," stand indeed for the same aggregation of objects, but they by no means stand for the same physical fact. They are names of the same objects, but of those objects in two different states: though they *de*note the same things, their *con*notation is different. Three pebbles in two separate parcels, and three pebbles in one parcel, do not make the same impression on our senses; and the assertion that the very same pebbles may by an alteration of place and arrangement be made to produce either the one set of sensations or the other, though a very familiar proposition, is not an identical one. It is a truth known to us by early and constant experience—an inductive truth; and such truths are the foundation of the science of Numbers. The fundamental truths of that science all rest on the evidence of sense; they are proved by showing to our eyes and our fingers that any given number of objects, ten balls, for example, may by separation and rearrangement exhibit to our senses all the different sets of numbers the sum of which is equal to ten. All the improved methods of teaching arithmetic to children proceed on a knowledge of this fact. All who wish to carry the child's *mind* along with them in learning arithmetic; all who wish to teach numbers, and not mere ciphers—now teach it through the evidence of the senses, in the manner we have described.

We may, if we please, call the proposition, "Three is two and one," a definition of the number three, and assert that arithmetic, as it has been asserted that geometry, is a science founded on definitions. But they are definitions in the geometrical sense, not the logical; asserting not the meaning of a term only, but along with it an observed matter of fact. The proposition, "A circle is a figure bounded by a line which has all its points equally distant from a point within it," is called the definition of a circle; but the proposition from which so many consequences follow, and which is really a first principle in geometry, is, that figures answering to this description exist. And thus we may call "Three is two and one" a definition of three, but the calculations which depend on that proposition do not follow from the definition itself, but from an arithmetical theorem presupposed in it, namely, that collections of objects exist, which while they impress the senses thus, ◇◇◇ , may be separated into two parts, thus, ◇◇ ◇. This proposition being granted, we term all such parcels Threes, after which the enunciation of the above mentioned physical fact will serve also for a definition of the word Three.

The Science of Numbers is thus no exception to the conclusion
we previously arrived at, that the processes even of deductive sciences
are altogether inductive, and that their first principles are generalisations
from experience. It remains to be examined whether this science resembles geometry in the further circumstance that some of its inductions are not exactly true; and that the peculiar certainty ascribed to it,
on account of which its propositions are called necessary truths, is fictitious and hypothetical, being true in no other sense than that those
propositions legitimately follow from the hypothesis of the truth of
premises which are avowedly mere approximations to truth.

§ 3. The inductions of arithmetic are of two sorts: first, those
which we have just expounded, such as One and one are two, Two and
one are three, &c., which may be called the definitions of the various
numbers, in the improper or geometrical sense of the word Definition;
and secondly, the two following axioms: The sums of equals are equal,
The differences of equals are equal. These two are sufficient; for the
corresponding propositions respecting unequals may be proved from
these by a *reductio ad absurdum.*

These axioms, and likewise the so-called definitions, are, as has
already been said, results of induction; true of all objects whatever, and
as it may seem, exactly true, without the hypothetical assumption of
unqualified truth where an approximation to it is all that exists. The
conclusions, therefore, it will naturally be inferred, are exactly true,
and the science of numbers is an exception to other demonstrative
sciences in this, that the categorical certainty which is predicable of its
demonstrations is independent of all hypothesis.

On more accurate investigation, however, it will be found that,
even in this case, there is one hypothetical element in the ratiocination.
In all propositions concerning numbers, a condition is implied, without
which none of them would be true; and that condition is an assumption
which may be false. The condition is, that $I = I$; that all the numbers are
numbers of the same or of equal units. Let this be doubtful, and not
one of the propositions of arithmetic will hold true. How can we know
that one pound and one pound make two pounds, if one of the pounds
may be troy, and the other avoirdupois? They may not make two
pounds of either, or of any weight. How can we know that a forty-
horse power is always equal to itself, unless we assume that all horses

are of equal strength? It is certain that I is always equal in *number* to I; and where the mere number of objects, or of the parts of an object, without supposing them to be equivalent in any other respect, is all that is material, the conclusions of arithmetic, so far as they go to that alone, are true without mixture of hypothesis. There are such cases in statistics; as, for instances an inquiry into the amount of the population of any country. It is indifferent to that inquiry whether they are grown people or children, strong or weak, tall or short; the only thing we want to ascertain is their number. But whenever, from equality or inequality of number, equality or inequality in any other respect is to be inferred, arithmetic carried into such inquiries becomes as hypothetical a science as geometry. All units must be assumed to be equal in that other respect; and this is never accurately true, for one actual pound weight is not exactly equal to another, nor one measured mile's length to another; a nicer balance, or more accurate measuring instruments, would always detect some difference.

What is commonly called mathematical certainty, therefore, which comprises the twofold conception of unconditional truth and perfect accuracy, is not an attribute of all mathematical truths, but of those only which relate to pure Number, as distinguished from Quantity in the more enlarged sense; and only so long as we abstain from supposing that the numbers are a precise index to actual quantities. The certainty usually ascribed to the conclusions of geometry, and even to those of mechanics, is nothing whatever but certainty of inference. We can have full assurance of particular results under particular suppositions, but we cannot have the same assurance that these suppositions are accurately true, nor that they include all the data which may exercise an influence over the result in any given instance.

§4. It appears, therefore, that the method of all Deductive Science is hypothetical. They proceed by tracing the consequences of certain assumptions; leaving for separate consideration whether the assumptions are true or not, and if not exactly true, whether they are a sufficiently near approximation of the truth. The reason is obvious. Since it is only in questions of pure number that the assumptions are exactly true, and even there, only so long as no conclusions except purely numerical ones are to be founded on them; it must, in all other cases of deductive investigation, form a part of the inquiry to determine how much the assumptions want of being exactly true in the case in hand. This is generally a matter of observation, to be repeated in every fresh case; or if it has to be settled by argument instead of observation, may require in every different case different evidence and present every degree of difficulty from the lowest to the highest. But the other part of the process—namely to determine what else may be concluded if we find, and in proporition as we find, the assumptions to be true—may be performed once for all, and the results held ready to be employed as the occasions turn up for use. We thus do all beforehand that can be so done, and leave the least possible work to be performed when cases arise and press for a decision. This inquiry into the inferences which can be drawn from assumptions is what properly constitutes Demonstrative Science.

It is of course quite as practicable to arrive at new conclusions from facts assumed, as from facts observed; from fictitious, as from real, inductions. Deduction, as we have seen, consists of a series of inferences in this form—*a* is a mark of *b, b* of *c, c* of *d,* which last may be a truth inaccessible to distinct observation. In like manner it is allowable to say, *suppose* that *a* were a mark of *b, b* of *c,* and *c* of *d, a* would be a mark of *d,* which last conclusion was not thought of by those who laid down the premises. A system of propositions as complicated as geometry might be deduced from assumptions which are false; as was done by Ptolemy, Descartes, and others, in their attempts to explain synthetically the phenomena of the solar system on the supposition that the apparent motions of the heavenly bodies were the real motions or were produced in some way more or less different from the true one. Sometimes the same thing is knowingly done for the purpose of showing the falsity of the assumption; which is called a *reductio ad absurdum.* In such cases the reasoning is as follows: *a* is a mark of *b,* and *b* of *c;* now if *c* were also a mark of *d, a* would be a mark of *d;* but *d* is known to be a mark of the absence of *a;* consequently *a* would be a mark of its own absence, which is a contradiction, therefore *c* is not a mark of *d.*

§ 5. It has even been held by some writers—that all ratiocination rests in the last resort on a *reductio ad absurdum,* since the way to enforce assent to it, in case of obscurity, would be to show that if the conclusion be denied we must deny some one at least of the premises, which, as they are all supposed true, would be a contradiction. And in accordance with this, many have thought that the peculiar nature of the evidence of ratiocination consisted in the impossibility of admitting the premises and rejecting the conclusion without a contradiction in terms. This theory, however, is admissible as an explanation of the grounds on which ratiocination itself rests. If any one denies the conclusion notwithstanding his admission of the premises, he is not involved in any direct and express contradiction until he is compelled to deny some premise; and he can only be forced to do this by a *reductio ad absurdum,* that is, by another ratiocination: now, if he denies the validity of the reasoning process itself, he can no more be forced to assent to the second syllogism that to the first. In truth, therefore, no one is ever forced to a contradiction in terms: he can only be forced to a contradiction (or rather an infringement) of the fundamental maxim of ratiocination, namely that whatever has a mark, has what it is a mark of; or, (in the case of universal propositions,) that whatever is a mark of anything, is a mark of whatever else that thing is a mark of. For in the case of every correct argument, as soon as thrown into the syllogistic form, it is evident without the aid of any other syllogism, that he who, admitting the premises, fails to draw the conclusion, does not conform to the above axiom.

We have now proceeded as far in the theory of Deduction as we can advance in the present stage of our inquiry. Any further insight into the subject requires that the foundation shall have been laid of the philosophic theory of Induction itself; in which theory that of Deduction, as a mode of Induction, which we have now shown it to be, will assume spontaneously the place which belongs to it, and will receive its share of whatever light may be thrown upon the great intellectual operation of which it forms so important a part. . . .

§ 6. The first of the two arguments in support of the theory that axioms are *a priori* truths, having, I think, been sufficiently answered, I proceed to the second, which is usually the most relied on. Axioms (it is asserted) are conceived by us not only as true, but as universally and necessarily true. Now, experience cannot possibly give to any proposition this character. I may have seen snow a hundred times, and may have seen that it was white, but this cannot give me entire assurance even that all snow is white; much less that snow *must* be white.

"However many instances we may have observed of the truth of a proposition, there is nothing to assure us that the next case shall not be an exception to the rule. If it be strictly true that every ruminant animal yet known has cloven hoofs, we still cannot be sure that some creature will not hereafter be discovered which has the first of these attributes, without having the other. . .Experience must always consist of a limited number of observations; and, however numerous these may be, they can show nothing with regard to the infinite number of cases in which the experiment has not been made." Besides, Axioms are not only universal, they are also necessary. Now "experience cannot offer the smallest ground for the necessity of a proposition. She can observe and record what has happened; but she cannot find, in any case, or in a any accumulation of cases, any reason for what *must* happen. She may see objects side by side; but she cannot see a reason why they must ever be side by side. She finds certain events to occur in succession; but the succession supplies, in its occurrence, no reason for its recurrence. She contemplates external objects; but she cannot detect any internal bond, which indissolubly connects the future with the past, the possible with the real. To learn a proposition by experience, and to see it to be necessarily true, are two altogether different processes of thought."* And Dr. Whewell adds, "If any one does not clearly comprehend this distinction of necessary and contingent truths, he will not be able to go along with us in our researches into the foundations of human knowledge; nor, indeed, to pursue with success any speculation on the subject."†

In the following passage we are told what the distinction is, the non-recognition of which incurs this denunciation. "Necessary truths are those in which we not only learn that the proposition *is* true, but see that it *must be* true; in which the negation of the truth is not only false, but impossible; in which we cannot, even by an effort of imagination, or in a supposition, conceive the reverse of that which is asserted. That there are such truths cannot be doubted. We may take, for example, all relations of number. Three and Two added together made Five. We cannot conceive it to be otherwise. We cannot, by any freak of thought, imagine Three and Two to make Seven."‡

---

* History of Scientific Ideas, i. 65-67.
† Ibid, 60.
‡ Ibid. 58, 59.

Although Dr. Whewell has naturally and properly employed a variety of phrases to bring his meaning more forcibly home, he would, I presume allow that they are all equivalent; and that what he means by a necessary truth, would be sufficiently defined, a proposition the negation of which is not only false but inconceivable. I am unable to find in any of his expressions, turn them what way you will, a meaning beyond this, and I do not believe he would contend that they mean anything more.

This, therefore, is the principle asserted: that propositions, the negation of which is inconceivable, or in other words, which we cannot figure to ourselves as being false, must rest on evidence of a higher and more cogent description than any which experience can afford.

Now I cannot but wonder that so much stress should be laid on the circumstance of inconceivableness, when there is such ample experience to show that our capacity or incapacity of conceiving a thing has very little to do with the possibility of the thing in itself, but is in truth very much an affair of accident, and depends on the past history and habits of our own minds. There is no more generally acknowledged fact in human nature than the extreme difficulty at first felt in conceiving anything as possible which is in contradiction to long-established and familiar experience, or even to old familiar habits of thought. And this difficulty is a necessary result of the fundamental laws of the human mind. When we have often seen and thought of two things together, and have never in any one instance either seen or thought of them separately, there is by the primary law of association an increasing difficulty, which may in the end become insuperable, of conceiving the two things apart. This is most of all conspicuous in uneducated persons who are in general utterly unable to separate any two ideas which have once become firmly associated in their minds; and if persons of cultivated intellect have any advantage on the point, it is only because having seen and heard and read more, and being more accustomed to exercise their imagination, they have experienced their sensations and thoughts in more varied combinations, and have been prevente from forming many of these inseparable associations. But this advantage has necessarily its limits. The most practised intellect is not exempt from the universal laws of our conceptive faculty. If daily habit present to any one for a long period two facts in combination, and if he is not led during that period either by accident or by his voluntary mental operations to think of them apart, he will probably in time become incapable of doing so even by the strongest effort; and the supposition that the two facts can be separated in nature will at last present itself to his mind with all the characters of an inconceivable phenomenon. There are remarkable instances of this in the history of science: instances in which the most instructed men rejected as impossible, because inconceivable, things which their posterity, by earlier practice and longer perseverance in the attempt, found it quite easy to conceive, and which everybody now knows to be true. There was a time when men of the most cultivated intellects, and the most emancipated from the dominion of early prejudice, could not credit the existence of antipodes; were unable to conceive, in opposition to old association, the force of gravity acting upwards instead of downwards. The Cartesians long rejected the Newtonian doctrine of the gravitation of all bodies towards one another, on the faith of a general proposition, the reverse of which seemed to them to be inconceivable—the proposition that a body cannot act where it is not. All the cumbrous machinery of imaginary vortices, assumed without the smallest particle of evidence, appeared to these philosophers a more rational mode of explaining the heavenly motions, than one which involved what seemed to them so great an absurdity. And they no doubt found it is impossible to conceive that a body should act upon the earth from the distance of the sun or moon, as we find it to conceive an end to space or time, or two straight lines enclosing a space. Newton himself had not been able to realise the conception, or we should not have had his hypothesis of a subtle ether, the occult cause of gravitation; and his writings prove, that though he deemed the particular nature of the intermediate agency a matter of conjecture, the necessity of *some* such agency appeared to him indubitable.

If, then, it be so natural to the human mind, even in a high state of culture, to be incapable of conceiving, and on that ground to believe impossible, what is afterwards not only found to be conceivable but proved to be true; what wonder if in cases where the association is still older, more confirmed, and more familiar, and in which nothing ever occurs to shake our conviction, or even suggest to us any conception at variance with the association, the acquired incapacity should continue, and be mistaken for a natural incapacity? It is true, our experience of the varieties in nature enables us, within certain limits, to conceive other varieties analogous to them. We can conceive the sun or moon falling; for though we never saw them fall, nor ever perhaps imagined them falling, we have seen so many other things fall, that we have innumerable familiar analogies to assist the conception; which, after all, we should probably have some difficulty in framing, were we not well accustomed to see the sun and moon move, (or appear to move,) so that we are only called upon to conceive a slight change in the direction of motion, a circumstance familiar to our experience. But when experience affords no model on which to shape the new conception, how is it possible for us to form it? How, for example, can we imagine an end to space or time? We never saw any object without something beyond it, nor experienced any feeling without something following it. When, therefore, we attempt to conceive the last point of space, we have the idea irresistibly raised of other points beyond it. When we try to imagine the last instant of time, we cannot help conceiving another instant after it. Nor is there any necessity to assume, as is done by a modern school of metaphysicians, a peculiar fundamental law of the mind to account for the feeling of infinity inherent in our conceptions of space and time; that apparent infinity is sufficiently accounted for by simpler and universally acknowledged laws.

Now, in the case of a geometrical axiom, such, for example, as that two straight lines cannot enclose a space,—a truth which is testified to us by our very earliest impressions of the external world,—how is it possible (whether those external impressions be or be not the ground of our belief) that the reverse of the proposition *could* be otherwise than inconceivable to us? What analogy have we, what similar order of facts in any other branch of our experience, to facilitate to us the conception of two straight lines enclosing a space? Nor is even this all. I have already called attention to the peculiar property of our impressions of form, that the ideas of mental images exactly resemble their prototypes, and adequately represent them for the purposes of scientific observation. From this, and from the intuitive character of the observation, which in this case reduces itself to simple inspection, we cannot so much as call up in our imagination two straight lines, in order to attempt to conceive them enclosing a space, without by that very act repeating the scientific experiment which establishes the contrary. Will it really be contended that the inconceivableness of the thing, in such circumstances, proves anything against the experimental origin of the conviction? Is it not clear that in whichever mode our belief in the proposition may have originated, the impossibility of our conceiving the negative of it must, on either hypothesis, be the same? As, then, Dr. Whewell exhorts those who have any difficulty in recognising the distinction held by him between necessary and contingent truths to study geometry,—a condition which I can assure him I have conscientiously fulfilled,—I, in return, with equal confidence, exhort those who agree with him, to study the general laws of association; being convinced that nothing more is requisite than a moderate familiarity with those laws to dispel the illusion which ascribes a peculiar necessity to our earliest inductions from experience, and measures the possibility of things in themselves by the human capacity of conceiving them.

INTUITION IN MATHEMATICS

*Henri Poincaré (1852-1912) has often been called the last of
the universal mathematicians. He did important work in
algebra, analysis, and mathematical astronomy. He also
wrote extensively on problems of scientific methodology.
This selection is taken from Chapter 1 of his* Science and
Hypothesis.*

I.

The very possibility of mathematical science seems an insoluble
contradiction. If this science is only deductive in appearance, from
whence is derived that perfect rigour which is challenged by none? If,
on the contrary, all the propositions which it enunciates may be derived in order by the rules of formal logic, how is it that mathematics
is not reduced to a gigantic tautology? The syllogism can teach us
nothing essentially new, and if everything must spring from the principle of identity, then everything should be capable of being reduced
to that principle. Are we then to admit that the enunciations of all the
theorems with which so many volumes are filled, are only indirect ways
of saying that A is A?

No doubt we may refer back to axioms which are at the source
of all these reasonings. If it is felt that they cannot be reduced to the
principle of contradiction, if we decline to see in them any more than
experimental facts which have no part or lot in mathematical necessity,
there is till one resource left to us: we may class them among *a priori*
synthetic views. But this is no solution of the difficulty—it is merely

*Translated by William John Greenstreet (The Walter Scott Publishing Co., 1905).

giving it a name; and even if the nature of the synthetic views had no longer for us any mystery, the contradiction would not have disappeared; it would have only been shirked. Syllogistic reasoning remains incapable of adding anything to the data that are given it; the data are reduced to axioms, and that is all we should find in the conclusions.

No theorem can be new unless a new axiom intervenes in its demonstration; reasoning can only give us immediately evident truths borrowed from direct intuition; it would only be an intermediary parasite. Should we not therefore have reason for asking if the syllogistic apparatus serves only to disguise what we have borrowed?

The contradiction will strike us the more if we open any book on mathematics; on every page the author announces his intention of generalising some proposition already known. Does the mathematical method proceed from the particular to the general, and, if so, how can it be called deductive?

Finally, if the science of number were merely analytical, or could be analytically derived from a few synthetic intuitions, it seems that a sufficiently powerful mind could with a single glance perceive all its truths; nay, one might even hope that some day a language would be invented simple enough for these truths to be made evident to any person of ordinary intelligence.

Even if these consequences are challenged, it must be granted that mathematical reasoning has of itself a kind of creative virtue, and is therefore to be distinguished from the syllogism. The difference must be profound. We shall not, for instance, find the key to the mystery in the frequent use of the rule by which the same uniform operation applied to two equal numbers will give identical results. All these modes of reasoning whether or not reducible to the syllogism, properly so called, retain the analytical character, and *ipso facto*, lose their power.

II.

The argument is an old one. Let us see how Leibnitz tried to show that two and two make four. I assume the number one to be defined, and also the operation $x+1$—*i.e.*, the adding of unity to a given number x. These definitions, whatever they may be, do not enter into the subsequent reasoning. I next define the numbers 2,3,4 by the equalities:—

(I) $1+1 = 2$; (2) $2+1 = 3$; (3) $3+1 = 4$, and in the same way I define the operation $x+2$ by the relation; (4) $x+2=(x+I)+I$.

Given this, we have:—

$2+2=(2+I)+I$; (def. 4).

$(2+I)+I=3+I$ (def. 2).

$3+I=4$ (def. 3).

whence $2+2=4$ Q.E.D.

It cannot be denied that this reasoning is purely analytical. But if we ask a mathematician, he will reply: "This is not a demonstration properly so called; it is a verification." We have confined ourselves to bringing together one or other of two purely conventional definitions, and we have verified their identity; nothing new has been learned. *Verification* differs from proof precisely because it is analytical, and because it leads to nothing. It leads to nothing because the conclusion is nothing but the premisses translated into another language. A real proof, on the other hand, is fruitful, because the conclusion is in a sense more general than the premisses. The equality $2+2=4$ can be verified because it is particular. Each individual enunciation in mathematics may be always verified in the same way. But if mathematics could be reduced to a series of such verifications it would not be a science. A chess-player, for instance, does not create a science by winning a piece. There is no science but the science of the general. It may even be said that the object of the exact sciences is to dispense with these direct verifications.

III.

Let us now see the geometer at work, and try to surmise some of his methods. The task is not without difficulty; it is not enough to open a book at random and to analyse any proof we may come across. First of all, geometry must be excluded, or the question becomes complicated by difficult problems relating to the role of the postulates, the nature and the origin of the idea of space. For analogous reasons we can not avail ourselves of the infinitesimal calculus. We must seek mathematical thought where it has remained pure—*i.e.,* in Arithmetic. But we still have to choose; in the higher parts of the theory of numbers the primitive mathematical ideas have already undergone so profound an elaboration that it becomes difficult to analyse them.

It is therefore at the beginning of Arithmetic that we must expect to find the explanation we seek; but it happens that it is precisely in the proofs of the most elementary theorems that the authors of classic treatises have displayed the least precision and rigour. We may not impute this to them as a crime; they have obeyed a necessity. Beginners are not prepared for real mathematical rigour; they would see in it nothing but empty, tedious subtleties. It would be a waste of time to try to make them more exacting; they have to pass rapidly and without stopping over the road which was trodden slowly by the founders of the science.

Why is so long a preparation necessary to habituate oneself to this perfect rigour, which it would seem should naturally be imposed on all minds? This is a logical and psychological problem which is well worthy of study. But we shall not dwell on it; it is foreign to our subject. All I wish to insist on is, that we shall fail in our purpose unless we reconstruct the proofs of the elementary theorems, and give them, not the rough form in which they are left so as not to weary the beginner, but the form which satisfy the skilled geometer.

DEFINITION OF ADDITION.

I assume that the operation $x+I$ has been defined; it consists in adding the number I to a given number x. Whatever may be said of this definition, it does not enter into the subsequent reasoning.

We now have to define the operation $x+a$, which consists in adding the number a to any given number x. Suppose that we have defined the operation $x+(a-I)$; the operation $x+a$ will be defined by the equality: $(I) x+a=[x+(a-I)]+I$. We shall know what $x+a$ is when we know what $x+(a-I)$ is, and as I have assumed that to start with we know what $x+I$ is, we can define successively and "by recurrence" the operations $x+2, x+3$, etc. This definition deserves a moment's attention; it is of a particular nature which distinguishes it even at this stage from the purely logical definition; the equality (I), in fact, contains an infinite number of distinct definitions, each having only one meaning when we know the meaning of its predecessor.

PROPERTIES OF ADDITION.

Associative.—I say that $a+(b+c)=(a+b)+c$; in fact, the theorem is true for $c=I$. It may then be written $a+(b+I)=(a+b)+I$; which remembering the difference of notation, is nothing but the equality (I) by which I have just defined addition. Assume the theorem true for $c=\gamma$, I say that it will be true for $c=\gamma+$I. Let $(a+b)+\gamma=a+(b+\gamma)$, it follows that $[(a+b)+\gamma]+$I$=[a+(b+\gamma)]+$I; or by def. (I)$-(a+b)+(\gamma+$I$)=a+(b+\gamma+$I$)=a+[b+(\gamma+$I$)]$, which shows by a series of purely analytical deductions that the theorem is true for $\gamma+$I. Being true for $c=$I, we see that it is successively true for $c=2$, $c=3$, etc.

Commutative.—(I) I say that $a+$I$=$I$+a$. The theorem is evidently true for $a=$I; we can *verify* by purely analytical reasoning that if it is true for $a=\gamma$ it will be true for $a=\gamma+$I.[1] Now, it is true for $a=$I, and therefore is true for $a=2$, $a=3$, and so on. This is what is meant by saying that the proof is demonstrated "by recurrence."

(2) I say that $a+b=b+a$. The theorem has just been shown to hold good for $b=$I, and it may be verified analytically that if it is true for $b=\beta$, it will be true for $b=\beta+$I. The proposition is thus established by recurrence.

DEFINITION OF MULTIPLICATION.

We shall define multiplication by the equalities: (I) $a\times$I$=a$. (2) $a\times b=[a\times(b-$I$)]+a$. Both of these include an infinite number of definitions; having defined $a\times$I, it enables us to define in succession $a\times2$, $a\times3$, and so on.

PROPERTIES OF MULTIPLICATION.

Distributive.—I say that $(a+b)\times c=(a\times c)+(b\times c)$. We can verify analyically that the theorem is true for $c=$I; then if it is true for $c=\gamma$, it will be true for $c=\gamma+$I. The proposition is then proved by recurrence.

Commutative.—(I) I say that $a\times$I$=$I$\times a$. The theorem is obvious for $a=$I. We can verify analytically that if it is true for $a=a$, it will be true for $a=a+$I.

(2) I say that $a\times b=b\times a$. The theorem has just been proved for $b=$I. We can verify analytically that if it be true for $b=\beta$ it will be true for $b=\beta+$I.

---

[1]For $(\gamma+$I$)+$I$=($I$+\gamma)+$I$=$I$+(\gamma+$I$)$.—[TR.]

IV.

This monotonous series of reasoning may now be laid aside; but their very monotony brings vividly to light the process, which is uniform, and is met again at every step. The process is proof by recurrence. We first show that a theorem is true for $n=1$; we then show that if it is true for $n-1$ it is true for n, and we conclude that it is true for all integers. We have now seen how it may be used for the proof of the rules of addition and multiplication—that is to say, for the rules of the algebraical calculus. This calculus is an instrument of transformation which lends itself to many more different combinations than the simple syllogism; but it is still a purely analytical instrument, and is incapable of teaching us anything new. If mathematics had no other instrument, it would immediately be arrested in its development; but it has recourse anew to the same process—*i.e.,* to reasoning by recurrence, and it can continue its forward march. Then if we look carefully, we find this mode of reasoning at every step, either under the simple form which we have just given to it, or under a more or less modified form. It is therefore mathematical reasoning *par excellence,* and we must examine it closer.

V.

The essential characteristic of reasoning by recurrence is that it contains, condensed, so to speak, in a single formula, an infinite number of syllogisms. We shall see this more clearly if we enunciate the syllogisms one after another. They follow one another, if one may use the expression, in a cascade. The following are the hypothetical syllogisms:— The theorem is true of the number I. Now, if it is true of I, it is true of 2; therefore it is true of 2. Now, if it is true of 2, it is true of 3; hence it is true of 3, and so on. We see that the conclusion of each syllogism serves as the minor of its successor. Further, the majors of all our syllogisms may be reduced to a single form. If the theorem is true of $n-1$, it is true of n.

We see, then, that in reasoning by recurrence we confine ourselves to the enunciation of the minor of the first syllogism, and the general formula which contains as particular cases all the majors. This unending series of syllogisms is thus reduced to a phrase of a few lines.

It is now easy to understand why every particular consequence of a theorem may, as I have above explained, be verified by purely analytical processes. If, instead of proving that our theorem is true for all numbers, we only wish to show that it is true for the number 6 for instance, it will be enough to establish the first five syllogisms in our cascade. We shall require 9 if we wish to prove it for the number 10; for a greater number we shall require more still; but however great the number may be we shall always reach it, and the analytical verification will always be possible. But however far we went we should never reach the general theorem applicable to all numbers, which alone is the object of science. To reach it we should require an infinite number of syllogisms, and we should have to cross an abyss which the patience of the analyst, restricted to the resources of formal logic, will never succeed in crossing.

I asked at the outset why we cannot conceive of a mind powerful enough to see at a glance the whole body of mathematical truth. The answer is now easy. A chess-player can combine for four or five moves ahead; but, however extraordinary a player he may be, he cannot prepare for more than a finite number of moves. If he applies his faculties to Arithmetic, he cannot conceive its general truths by direct intuition alone; to prove even the smallest theorem he must use reasoning by recurrence, for that is the only instrument which enables us to pass from the finite to the infinite. This instrument is always useful, for it enables us to leap over as many stages as we wish; it frees us from the necessity of long, tedious, and monotonous verifications which would rapidly become impracticable. Then when we take in hand the general theorem it becomes indispensable, for otherwise we should ever be approaching the analytical verification without ever actually reaching it. In this domain of Arithmetic we may think ourselves very far from the infinitesimal analysis, but the idea of mathematical infinity is already playing a preponderating part, and without it there would be no science at all, because there would be nothing general.

VI.

The views upon which reasoning by recurrence is based may be exhibited in other forms; we may say, for instance, that in any finite collection of different integers there is always one which is smaller than any other. We may readily pass from one enunciation to another, and thus give ourselves the illusion of having proved that reasoning by recurrence is legitimate. But we shall always be brought to a full stop— we shall always come to an indemonstrable axiom, which will at bottom be but the proposition we had to prove translated into another language. We cannot therefore escape the conclusion that the rule of reasoning by recurrence is irreducible to the principle of contradiction. Nor can the rule come to us from experiment. Experiment may teach us that the rule is true for the first ten or the first hundred numbers, for instance; it will not bring us to the indefinite series of numbers, but only to a more or less long, but always limited, portion of the series.

Now, if that were all that is in question, the principle of contradiction would be sufficient, it would always enable us to develop as many syllogisms as we wished. It is only when it is a question of a single formula to embrace an infinite number of syllogisms that this principle breaks down, and there, too, experiment is powerless to aid. This rule, inaccessible to analytical proof and to experiment, is the exact type of the *a priori* synthetic intuition. On the other hand, we cannot see in it a convention as in the case of the postulates of geometry.

Why then is this view imposed upon us with such an irresistible weight of evidence? It is because it is only the affirmation of the power of the mind which knows it can conceive of the indefinite repetition of the same act, when the act is once possible. The mind has a direct intuition of this power, and experiment can only be for it an opportunity of using it, and thereby of becoming conscious of it.

But it will be said, if the legitimacy of reasoning by recurrence cannot be established by experiment alone, is it so with experiment aided by induction? We see successively that a theorem is true of the number I, of the number 2, of the number 3, and so on—the law is manifest, we say, and it is so on the same ground that every physical law is true which is based on a very large but limited number of observations.

It cannot escape our notice that here is a striking analogy with the usual processes of induction. But an essential difference exists. Induction applied to the physical sciences is always uncertain, because it is based on the belief in a general order of the universe, an order which is external to us. Mathematical induction —*i.e.*, proof by recurrence—is, on the contrary, necessarily imposed on us, because it is only the affirmation of a property of the mind itself.

VII.

Mathematicians, as I have said before, always endeavour to generalise the propositions they have obtained. To seek no further example, we have just shown the equality, $a+I=I+a$, and we then used it to establish the equality, $a+b=b+a$, which is obviously more general. Mathematics may, therefore, like the other sciences, proceed from the particular to the general. This is a fact which might otherwise have appeared incomprehensible to us at the beginning of this study, but which has no longer anything mysterious about it, since we have ascertained the analogies between proof by recurrence and ordinary induction.

No doubt mathematical recurrent reasoning and physical inductive reasoning are based on different foundations, but they move in parallel lines and in the same direction—namely, from the particular to the general.

Let us examine the case a little more closely. To prove the equality $a+2=2+a$......(I), we need only apply the rule $a+I=I+a$, twice, and write $a+2=a+I+I=I+a+I=I+I+a=2+a$.......(2).

The equality thus deduced by purely analytical means is not, however, a simple particular case. It is something quite different. We may not therefore even say in the really analytical and deductive part of mathematical reasoning that we proceed from the general to the particular in the ordinary sense of the words. The two sides of the equality (2) are merely more complicated combinations than the two sides of the equality (I), and analysis only serves to separate the elements which enter into these combinations and to study their relations.

Mathematicians therefore proceed "by construction," they construct more complicated combinations. When they analyse these combinations, these aggregates, so to speak, into their primitive elements, they see the relations of the elements and deduce the relations of the aggregates themselves. The process is purely analytical, but it is not a passing from the general to the particular, for the aggregates obviously cannot be regarded as more particular than their elements.

Great importance has been rightly attached to this process of "construction," and some claim to see in it the necessary and sufficien condition of the progress of the exact sciences. Necessary, no doubt, but not sufficient! For a construction to be useful and not mere waste of mental effort, for it to serve as a stepping-stone to higher things, it must first of all possess a kind of unity enabling us to see something more than the juxtaposition of its elements. Or more accurately, there must be some advantage in considering the construction rather than the elements themselves. What can this advantage be? Why reason on a polygon, for instance, which is always decomposable into triangles, and not on elementary triangles? It is because there are properties of polygons of any number of sides, and they can be immediately applied to any particular kind of polygon. In most cases it is only after long efforts that those properties can be discovered, by directly studying the relations of elementary triangles. If the quadrilateral is anything more than the juxtaposition of two triangles, it is because it is of the polygon type.

A construction only becomes interesting when it can be placed side by side with other analogous constructions for forming species of the same genus. To do this we must necessarily go back from the particular to the general, ascending one or more steps. The analytical process "by construction" does not compel us to descend, but it leaves us at the same level. We can only ascend by mathematical induction, for from it alone can we learn something new. Without the aid of this induction, which in certain respects differs from, but is as fruitful as, physical induction, construction would be powerless to create science.

Let me observe, in conclusion, that this induction is only possible if the same operation can be repeated indefinitely. That is why the theory of chess can never become a science for the different moves of the same piece are limited and do not resemble each other.

ON THE NATURE OF MATHEMATICAL TRUTH

*C.G. Hempel (1905-   ) is one of the leading exponents
of logical empiricism. Many of his major articles have been
reprinted in* Aspects of Scientific Explanation. *The present
selection, entitled "On the Nature of Mathematical Truth,"
first appeared in the* American Mathematical Monthly, *Vol.
52 (1945).**

1. **The problem.** It is a basic principle of scientific inquiry that
no proposition and no theory is to be accepted without adequate
grounds. In empirical science, which includes both the natural and the
social sciences, the grounds for the acceptance of a theory consist in
the agreement of predictions based on the theory with empirical evidence obtained either by experiment or by systematic observation.
But what are the grounds which sanction the acceptance of mathematics? That is the question I propose to discuss in the present paper.
For reasons which will become clear subsequently, I shall use the term
"mathematics" here to refer to arithmetic, algebra, and analysis—to
the exclusion, in particular, of geometry [1].

2. **Are the propositions of mathematics self-evident truths?** One
of the several answers which have been given to our problem asserts
that the truths of mathematics, in contradistinction to the hypotheses
of empirical science, require neither factual evidence nor any other
justification because they are "self-evident." This view, however,
which ultimately relegates decisions as to mathematical truth to a
feeling of self-evidence, encounters various difficulties. First of all,

*Reprinted here by permission. Numbers in brackets refer to references given at the end
of this selection.

many mathematical theorems are so hard to establish that even to the specialist in the particular field they appear as anything but self-evident. Secondly, it is well known that some of the most interesting results of mathematics—especially in such fields as abstract set theory and topology—run counter to deeply ingrained intuitions and the customary kind of feeling of self evidence. Thirdly, the existence of mathematical conjectures such as those of A. Goldbach and of Fermat, which are quite elementary in content and yet undecided up to this day, certainly shows that not all mathematical truths can be self-evident. And finally, even if self-evidence were attributed only to the basic postulates of mathematics, from which all other mathematical propositions can be deduced, it would be pertinent to remark that judgments as to what may be considered as self-evident are subjective; they may vary from person to person and certainly cannot constitute an adequate basis for decisions as to the objective validity of mathematical propositions.

3. **Is mathematics the most general empirical science?** According to another view, advocated especially by John Stuart Mill, mathematics is itself an empirical science which differs from the other branches such as astronomy, physics, chemistry, *etc.*, mainly in two respects: its subject matter is more general than that of any other field of scientific research, and its propositions have been tested and confirmed to a greater extent than those of even the most firmly established sections of astronomy or physics. Indeed, according to this view, the degree to which the laws of mathematics have been borne out by the past experiences of mankind is so overwhelming that—unjustifiably—we have come to think of mathematical theorems as qualitatively different from the well-confirmed hypotheses or theories of other branches of science: we consider them as certain, while other theories are thought of as at best "very probable" or very highly confirmed.

But this view, too, is open to serious objections. From a hypothesis which is empirical in character—such as, for example, Newton's law of gravitation—it is possible to derive predictions to the effect that under certain specified conditions certain specified observable phenomena will occur. The actual occurrence of these phenomena constitutes confirming evidence, their non-occurrence disconfirming evidence for the hypothesis. It follows in particular that an empirical hypothesis is theoretically disconfirmable; *i.e.,* it is possible to indicate what kind of evidence, if actually encountered, would disconfirm the hypothesis. In the light of this remark, consider now a simply "hypothesis" from arithmetic: 3+2=5. If this is actually an empirical generalization of past experiences, then it must be possible to state what kind of evidence would oblige us to concede that the hypothesis was not generally true after all. If any disconfirming evidence for the given proposition can be thought of, the following illustration might well be typical of it: We place some microbes on a slide, putting down first three of them and then another two. Afterwards we count all the microbes to test whether in this instance 3 and 2 actually added up to 5. Suppose now that we counted 6 microbes altogether. Would we consider this an empirical disconfirmation of the given proposition, or at least as a proof that it does not apply to microbes? Clearly not; rather, we would assume we had made a mistake in counting or that one of the microbes had split in two between the first and the second count. But under no circumstances could the phenomenon just described invalidate the arithmetical proposition in question; for the latter asserts nothing whatever about the behavior of microbes; it merely states that any set consisting of 3+2 objects may also be said to consist of 5 objects. And this is so because the symbols "3+2" and "5" denote the same number: they are synonymous by virtue of the fact that the symbols "2," "3," "5," and "+" are *defined* (or tacitly understood) in such a way that the above identity holds as a consequence of the meaning attached to the concepts involved in it.

4. **The analytic character of mathematical propositions.** The statement that 3+2=5, then, is true for similar reasons as, say, the assertion that no sexagenarian is 45 years of age. Both are true simply by virtue of definitions or of similar stipulations which determine the meaning of the key terms involved. Statements of this kind share certain important characteristics: Their validation naturally requires no empirical evidence; they can be shown to be true by a mere analysis of the meaning attached to the terms which occur in them. In the language of logic sentences of this kind are called analytic or true a priori, which is to indicate that their truth is logically independent of, or logically prior to, any experimental evidence [2]. And while the statements of empirical science, which are synthetic and can be validated only a posteri are constantly subject to revision in the light of new evidence, the trut of an analytic statement can be established definitely, once and for all

However, this characteristic "theoretical certainty" of analytic propositions has to be paid for at a high price: An analytic statement conveys no factual information. Our statement about sexagenarians, for example, asserts nothing that could possibly conflict with any factual evidence: it has no factual implications, no empirical content; and it is precisely for this reason that the statement can be validated without recourse to empirical evidence.

Let us illustrate this view of the nature of mathematical propositions by reference to another, frequently cited, example of a mathematical—or rather logical—truth, namely the proposition that whenever $a=b$ and $b=c$ then $a=c$. On what grounds can this so-called "transitivity of identity" be asserted? Is it of an empirical nature and hence at least theoretically disconfirmable by empirical evidence? Suppose, for example, that $a,b,c,$ are certain shades of green, and that as far as we can see, $a=b$ and $b=c$, but clearly $a \neq c$. This phenomenon actually occurs under certain conditions; do we consider it as disconfirming evidence for the proposition under consideration? Undoubtedly not; we would argue that if $a \neq c$, it is impossible that $a=b$ and also $b=c$; between the terms of at least one of these latter pairs, there must obtain a difference, though perhaps only a subliminal one. And we would dismiss the possibility of empirical disconfirmation, and indeed the idea that an empirical test should be relevant here, on the grounds that identity is a transitive relation by virtue of its definition or by virtue of the basic postulates governing it [3]. Hence, the principle in question is true a priori.

5. **Mathematics as an axiomatized deductive system.** I have argued so far that the validity of mathematics rests neither on its alleged self-evidential character nor on any empirical basis, but derives from the stipulations which determine the meaning of the mathematical concepts, and that the propositions of mathematics are therefore essentially "true by definition." This latter statement, however, is obviously oversimplified and needs restatement and a more careful justification.

For the rigorous development of a mathematical theory proceeds not simply from a set of definitions but rather from a set of non-definitional propositions which are not proved within the theory; these are the postulates or axioms of the theory [4]. They are formulated in terms of certain basic or primitive concepts for which no definitions are provided within the theory. It is sometimes asserted that the postulates themselves represent "implicit definitions" of the primitive terms. Such a characterization of the postulates, however, is misleading. For while the postulates do limit, in a specific sense, the meanings that can possibly be ascribed to the primitives, any self-consistent postulate system admits, nevertheless, many different interpretations of the primitive terms (this will soon be illustrated), whereas a set of definitions in the strict sense of the word determines the meanings of the definienda in a unique fashion.

Once the primitive terms and the postulates have been laid down, the entire theory is completely determined; it is derivable from its postulational basis in the following sense: Every term of the theory is definable in terms of the primitives, and every proposition of the theory is logically deducible from the postulates. To be entirely precise, it is necessary also to specify the principles of logic which are to be used in the proof of the propositions, *i.e.* in their deduction from the postulates. These principles can be stated quite explicitly. They fall into two groups: Primitive sentences, or postulates, of logic (such as: if p and q is the case, then p is the case), and rules of deduction or inference (including, for example, the familiar modus ponens rule and the rules of substitution which make it possible to infer, from a general proposition, any one of its substitution instances). A more detailed discussion of the structure and content of logic would, however, lead too far afield in the context of this article.

6. **Peano's axiom system as a basis for mathematics.** Let us now consider a postulate system from which the entire arithmetic of the natural numbers can be derived. This system was devised by the Italian mathematician and logician G. Peano (1858-1932). The primitives of this system are the terms "0," "number," and "successor." While, of course, no definition of these terms is given within the theory, the symbol "0" is intended to designate the number 0 in its usual meaning while the term "number" is meant to refer to the natural numbers 0, 1,2,3. . .exclusively. By the successor of a natural number n, which will sometimes briefly be called n', is meant the natural number immediately following n in the natural order. Peano's system contains the following 5 postulates:

P1.   0 is a number
P2.   The successor of any number is a number
P3.   No two numbers have the same successor

P4.   0 is not the successor of any number
P5.   If P is a property such that (a) 0 has the property P, and (b)
      whenever a number n has the property P, then the successor of
      n also has the property P, then every number has the property P.

The last postulate embodies the principle of mathematical induction and illustrates in a very obvious manner the enforcement of a
mathematical "truth" by stipulation. The construction of elementary
arithmetic on this basis begins with the definition of the various natural
numbers. 1 is defined as the successor of 0, or briefly as $0'$; 2 as $1'$,
3 as $2'$, and so on. By virtue of P2, this process can be continued indefinitely; because of P3 (in combination with P5), it never leads back
to one of the numbers previously defined, and in view of P4, it does
not lead back to 0 either.

As the next step, we can set up a definition of addition which expresses in a precise form the idea that the addition of any natural number to some given number may be considered as a repeated addition
of 1; the latter operation is readily expressible by means of the successor
relation. This definition of addition runs as follows:
D1.   (a) $n + 0 = n;$ (b) $n + k' = (n+k)'$.

The two stipulations of this recursive definition completely determine the sum of any two integers. Consider, for example, the sum
3+2. According to the definitions of the numbers 2 and 1, we have
$3+2 = 3+1' = 3+(0')'$; by D1 (b), $3+(0')' = (3+0')' = ((3+0)')'$; but by
d1 (a), and by the definitions of the numbers 4 and 5, $((3+0)')' =$
$(3')' = 4' = 5$. This proof also renders more explicit and precise the
comments made earlier in this paper on the truth of the proposition
that 3+2 = 5: Within the Peano system of arithmetic, its truth flows
not merely from the definition of the concepts involved, but also
from the postulates that govern these various concepts. (In our specific
example, the postulates P1 and P2 are presupposed to guarantee that
1, 2, 3, 4, 5 are numbers in Peano's system; the general proof that D1
determines the sum of any two numbers also makes use of P5). If we
call the postulates and definitions of an axiomatized theory the "stipulations" concerning the concepts of that theory, then we may say now
that the propositions of the arithmetic of the natural numbers are true
by virtue of the stipulations which have been laid down initially for

the arithmetical concepts. (Note, incidentally, that our proof of the formula "3+2 = 5" repeatedly made use of the transitivity of identity; the latter is accepted here as one of the rules of logic which may be used in the proof of any arithmetical theorem; it is not, therefore, included among Peano's postulates no more than any other principle of logic.)

Now, the multiplication of natural numbers may be defined by means of the following recursive definition, which expresses in a rigorous form the idea that a product nk of two integers may be considered as the sum of k terms each of which equals n.

D2. (a) $n \cdot 0 = 0$;   (b) $n \cdot k' = n \cdot k + n$.

It now is possible to prove the familiar general laws governing addition and multiplication, such as the commutative, associative, and distributive laws $(n + k = k + n, \ n \cdot k = k \cdot n; \ n + (k+l) = (n+k) + l, \ n \cdot (k \cdot l) = (n \cdot k) \cdot l; \ n \cdot (k+l) = (n \cdot k) + (n \cdot l))$. —In terms of addition and multiplication, the inverse operations of subtraction and division can then be defined. But it turns out that these "cannot always be performed"; *i.e.,* in contradistinction to the sum and the product, the difference and the quotient are not defined for every couple of numbers; for example, $7-10$ and $7 \div 10$ are undefined. This situation suggests an enlargement of the number system by the introduction of negative and of rational numbers.

It is sometimes held that in order to effect this enlargemnt, we have to "assume" or else to "postulate" the existence of the desired additional kinds of numbers with properties that make them fit to fill the gaps of subtraction and division. This method of simply postulating what we want has its advantages; but, as Bertrand Russell [5] puts it, they are the same as the advantages of theft over honest toil; and it is a remarkable fact that the negative as well as the rational numbers can be obtained from Peano's primitives by the honest toil of constructing explicit definitions for them, without the introduction of any new postulates or assumptions whatsoever. Every positive and negative integer—in contradistinction to a natural number which has no sign—is definable as a certain set of ordered couples of natural numbers; thus, the integer +2 is definable as the set of all ordered couples (m, n) of natural numbers where $m=n+2$; the integer -2 is the set of all ordered couples (m,n) of natural numbers with $n=m+2$.—Similarly, rational numbers are defined as classes of ordered couples of integers.

—The various arithmetical operations can then be defined with reference to these new types of numbers, and the validity of all the arithmetical laws governing these operations can be proved by virtue of nothing more than Peano's postulates and the definitions of the various arithmetical concepts involved.

The much broader system thus obtained is still incomplete in the sense that not every number in it has a square root, and more generally, not every algebraic equation whose coefficients are all numbers of the system has a solution in the system. This suggests further expansions of the number system by the introduction of real and finally of complex numbers. Again, this enormous extension can be effected by mere definition, without the introduction of a single new postulate [6]. On the basis thus obtained, the various arithmetical and algebraic operations can be defined for the numbers of the new system, the concepts of function, of limit, of derivative and integral can be introduced, and the familiar theorems pertaining to these concepts can be proved, so that finally the huge system of mathematics as here delimited rests on the narrow basis of Peano's system: Every concept of mathematics can be defined by means of Peano's three primitives, and every proposition of mathematics can be deduced from the five postulates enriched by the definitions of the non-primitive terms [6a]. These deductions can be carried out, in most cases, by means of nothing more than the principles of formal logic; the proof of some theorems concerning real numbers, however, requires one assumption which is not usually included among the latter. This is the so-called axiom of choice. It asserts that given a class of mutually exclusive classes, none of which is empty, there exists at least one class which has exactly one element in common with each of the given classes. By virtue of this principle and the rules of formal logic, the content of all of mathematics can thus be derived from Peano's modest system—a remarkable achievement in systematizing the content of mathematics and clarifying the foundations of its validity.

7. **Interpretations of Peano's primitives.** As a consequence of this result, the whole system of mathematics might be said to be true by virtue of mere definitions (namely, of the non-primitive mathematical terms) provided that the five Peano postulates are true. However, strictly speaking, we cannot, at this juncture, refer to the Peano postulates as propositions which are either true or false, for they contain

three primitive terms which have not been assigned any specific meaning. All we can assert so far is that any specific interpretation of the primitives which satisfies the five postulates—i.e., turns them into true statements— will also satisfy all the theorems deduced from them. But for Peano's system, there are several—indeed infinitely many—interpretations which will do this. For example, let us understand by 0 the origin of a half-line, by the successor of a point on that half-line the point 1 cm. behind it, counting from the origin, and by a number any point which is either the origin or can be reached from it by a finite succession of steps each of which leads from one point to its successor. It can then readily be seen that all the Peano postulates as well as the ensuing theorems turn into true propositions, although the interpretation given to the primitives is certainly not the customary one, which was mentioned earlier. More generally, it can be shown that every progression of elements of any kind provides a true interpretation, or a "model," of the Peano system. This example illustrates our earlier observation that a postulate system cannot be regarded as a set of "implicit definitions" for the primitive terms: The Peano system permits of many different interpretations, whereas in everyday as well as in scientific language, we attach one specific meaning to the concepts of arithmetic. Thus, *e.g.,* in scientific and in everyday discourse, the concept 2 is understood in such a way that from the statement "Mr. Brown as well as Mr. Cope, but no one else is in the office, and Mr. Brown is not the same person as Mr. Cope," the conclusion "Exactly two persons are in the office" may be validly inferred. But the stipulations laid down in Peano's system for the natural numbers, and for the number 2 in particular, do not enable us to draw this conclusion; they do not "implicitly determine" the customary meaning of the concept 2 or of the other arithmetical concepts. And the mathematician cannot acquiesce at this deficiency by arguing that he is not concerned with the customary meaning of the mathematical concepts; for in proving, say, that every positive real number has exactly two real square roots, he is himself using the concept 2 in its customary meaning, and his very theorem cannot be proved unless we presuppose more about the number 2 than is stipulated in the Peano system.

If therefore mathematics is to be a correct theory of the mathematical concepts in their intended meaning, it is not sufficient for its validation to have shown that the entire system is derivable from the

Peano postulates plus suitable definitions; rather, we have to inquire further whether the Peano postulates are actually true when the primitives are understood in their customary meaning. This question, of course, can be answered only after the customary meaning of the terms "0", "natural number," and "successor" has been clearly defined. To this task we now turn.

8. **Definition of the customary meaning of the concepts of arithmetic in purely logical terms.** At first blush, it might seem a hopeless undertaking to try to define these basic arithmetical concepts without presupposing other terms of arithmetic, which would involve us in a circular procedure. However, quite rigorous definitions of the desired kind can indeed be formulated, and it can be shown that for the concepts so defined, all Peano postulates turn into true statements. This important result is due to the research of the German logician G. Frege (1848-1925) and to the subsequent systematic and detailed work of the contemporary English logicians and philosophers B. Russell and A.N. Whitehead. Let us consider briefly the basic ideas underlying these definitions [7].

A natural number—or, in Peano's term, a number—in its customary meaning can be considered as a characteristic of certain *classes* of objects. Thus, *e.g.,* the class of the apostles has the number 12, the class of the Dionne quintuplets the number 5, any couple the number 2, and so on. Let us now express precisely the meaning of the assertion that a certain class C has the number 2, or briefly, than $n(C) = 2$. Brief reflection will show that the following definiens is adequate in the sense of the customary meaning of the concept 2: There is some object x and some object y such that (1) $x \epsilon C$ *(i.e.,* x is an element of $C)$ and $y \epsilon C$, (2) $x \neq y$, and (3) if z is any object such that $z \epsilon C$, then either $z=x$ or $z=y$. (Note that on the basis of this definition it becomes indeed possible to infer the statement "The number of persons in the office is 2" from "Mr. Brown as well as Mr. Cope, but no one else is in the office, and Mr. Brown is not identical with Mr. Cope"; C is here the class of persons in the office.) Analogously, the meaning of the statement that $n(C) = 1$ can be defined thus: There is some x such that $x \epsilon C$, and any object y such that $y \epsilon C$, is identical with x. Similarly, the customary meaning of the statement that $n(C)=0$ is this: There is no object such that $x \epsilon C$.

The general pattern of these definitions clearly lends itself to the

definition of any natural number. Let us note especially that in the
definitions thus obtained, the definiens never contains any arithmetical
term, but merely expressions taken from the field of formal logic, including the signs of identity and difference. So far, we have defined
only the meaning of such phrases as "$n(C)$=2," but we have given no
definition for the numbers 0, 1, 2, . . . apart from this context. This
desideratum can be met on the basis of the consideration that 2 is that
property which is common to all couples, $i.e.,$ to all classes C such
that $n(C)$=2. This common property may be conceptually represented
by the class of all those classes which share this property. Thus we arrive at the definition: 2 is the class of all couples, $i.e.,$ the class of all
C for which $n(C) = 2$. —This definition is by no means circular because
the concept of couple—in other words, the meaning of "$n(C)$ =2—has
been previously defined without any reference to the number 2. Analogously, 1 is the class of all unit classes, $i.e.,$ the class of all classes for which
$n(C)$=1. Finally, 0 is the class of all null classes, $i.e.,$ the class of all classes
without elements. And as there is only one such class, 0 is simply the class
whose only element is the null class. Clearly, the customary meaning of
any given natural number can be defined in this fashion [8]. In order to
characterize the intended interpretation of Peano's primitives, we
actually need, of all the definitions here referred to, only that of the
number 0. It remains to define the terms "successor" and "integer."

The definition of "successor," whose precise formulation involves
too many niceties to be stated here, is a careful expression of a simple
idea which is illustrated by the following example: Consider the number
5, $i.e.,$ the class of all quintuplets. Let us select an arbitrary one of these
quintuplets and add to it an object which is not yet one of its members.
5′, the successor of 5, may then be defined as the number applying to
the set thus obtained (which, of course, is a sextuplet). Finally, it is
possible to formulate a definition of the customary meaning of the
concept of natural number; this definition, which again cannot be given
here, expresses, in a rigorous form, the idea that the class of the natural
numbers consists of the number 0, its successor, the successor of that
successor, and so on.

If the definitions here characterized are carefully written out—
this is one of the cases where the techniques of symbolic, or mathematical, logic prove indispensable—it is seen that the definiens of every one
of them contains exclusively terms from the field of pure logic. In fact,
it is possible to state the customary interpretation of Peano's primitives

and thus also the meaning of every concept definable by means of them—and that includes every concept of mathematics—in terms of the following 7 expressions, in addition to variables such as *"x"* and *"C"*: *not, and, if—then; for every object x* it is the case that. . . ; *there is some object x such that.* . . ; *x* is an *element* of class C; *the class of all things x such that* . . . .And it is even possible to reduce the number of logical concepts needed to a mere four: The first three of the concepts just mentioned are all definable in terms of *"neither—nor,"* and the fifth is definable by means of the fourth and *"neither—nor"* Thus, all the concepts of mathematics prove definable in terms of four concepts of pure logic. (The definition of one of the more complex concepts of mathematics in terms of the four primitives just mentioned may well fill hundreds or even thousands of pages; but clearly this affects in no way the theoretical importance of the result just obtained; it does, however, show the great convenience and indeed practical indispensability for mathematics of having a large system of highly complex defined concepts available.)

9. The truth of Peano's postulates in their customary interpretation. The definitions characterized in the preceding section may be said to render precise and explicit the customary meaning of the concepts of arithmetic. Moreover—and this is crucial for the question of the validity of mathematics—it can be shown that the Peano postulates all turn into true propositions if the primitives are construed in accordance with the definitions just considered.

Thus, P1 (0 is a number) is true because the class of all numbers—*i.e.,* natural numbers—was defined as consisting of 0 and all its successors. The truth of P2 (The successor of any number is a number) follows from the same definition. This is true also of P5, the principle of mathematical induction. To prove this, however, we would have to resort to the precise definition of "integer" rather than the loose description given of that definition above. P4 (0 is not the successor of any number) is seen to be true as follows: By virtue of the definition of "successor," a number which is a successor of some number can apply only to classes which contain at least one element; but the number 0, by definition, applies to a class if and only if that class is empty.—While the truth of P1, P2, P4, P5 can be inferred from the above definitions simply by means of the principles of logic, the proof of P3 (No two numbers have the same successor) presents a certain

difficulty. As was mentioned in the preceding section, the definition
of the successor of a number n is based on the process of adding, to
a class of n elements, one element not yet contained in that class. Now
if there should exist only a finite number of things altogether then
this process could not be continued indefinitely, and P3, which (in
conjunction with P1 and P2) implies that the integers form an infinite
set, would be false. Russell's way of meeting this difficulty [9] was to
introduce a special "axiom of infinity," which stipulates, in effect,
the existence of infinitely many objects and thus makes P3 demonstrable. The axiom of infinity can be formulated in purely logical
terms and may therefore be considered as a postulate of logic; however, it certainly does not belong to the generally recognized principles
of logic; and it thus introduces a foreign element into the otherwise
unexceptionable derivation of the Peano postulates from pure logic.
Recently, however, it has been shown [10] that a suitable system of
logical principles can be set up which is even less comprehensive than
the rules of logic which are commonly used [11], and in which the
existence of infinitely many objects can be proved without the need
for a special axiom.

   10. **Mathematics as a branch of logic.** As was pointed out earlier,
all the theorems of arithmetic, algebra, and analysis can be deduced
from the Peano postulates and the definitions of those mathematical
terms which are not primitives in Peano's system. This deduction requires only the principles of logic plus, in certain cases, the axiom of
choice. By combining this result with what has just been said about
the Peano system, the following conclusion is obtained, which is also
known as *the thesis of logicism concerning the nature of mathematics:*

   Mathematics is a branch of logic. It can be derived from logic in
the following sense:

   a. All the concepts of mathematics, *i.e.* of arithmetic, algebra,
and analysis, can be defined in terms of four concepts of pure logic.

   b. All the theorems of mathematics can be deduced from those
definitions by means of the principles of logic (including the axiom
of choice).

   In this sense it can be said that the propositions of the system of
mathematics as here delimited are true by virtue of the definitions of
the mathematical concepts involved, or that they make explicit certain
characteristics with which we have endowed our mathematical concep-

by definition. The propositions of mathematics have, therefore, the same unquestionable certainty which is typical of such propositions as "All bachelors are unmarried," but they also share the complete lack of empirical content which is associated with that certainty: The propositions of mathematics are devoid of all factual content; they convey no information whatever on any empirical subject matter.

11. **On the applicability of mathematics to empirical subject matter**. This result seems to be irreconcilable with the fact that after all mathematics has proved to be eminently applicable to empirical subject matter, and that indeed the greater part of present-day scientific knowledge has been reached only through continual reliance on and application of the propositions of mathematics.—Let us try to clarify this apparent paradox by reference to some examples.

Suppose that we are examining a certain amount of some gas, whose volume v, at a certain fixed temperature, is found to be 9 cubic feet when the pressure p is 4 atmospheres. And let us assume further that the volume of the gas for the same temperature and $p=6$ *at.*, is predicted by means of Boyle's law. Using elementary arithmetic we reason thus: For corresponding values of v and p, $vp=c$, and $v=9$ when $p=4$; hence $c=36$; Therefore, when $p=6$, then $v=6$. Suppose that this prediction is borne out by subsequent test. Does that show that the arithmetic used has a predictive power of its own, that its propositions have factual implications? Certainly not. All the predictive power here deployed, all the empirical content exhibited items from the initial data and from Boyle's law, which asserts that $vp=c$ for *any* two corresponding values of v and p, hence also for $v=9$, $p=4$, and for $p=6$ and the corresponding value of v [12]. The function of the mathematics here applied is not predictive at all; rather, it is analytic or explicative: it renders explicit certain assumptions or assertions which are included in the content of the premises of the argument (in our case, these consist of Boyle's law plus the additional data); mathematical reasoning reveals that those premises contain—hidden in them, as it were,—an assertion about the case as yet unobserved. In accepting our premises—so arithmetic reveals—we have—knowingly or unknowingly—already accepted the implication that the p-value in question is 6. Mathematical as well as logical reasoning is a conceptual technique of making explicit what is implicitly contained in a set of premises. The conclusions to which this technique leads assert nothing that is *theoretically new* in the sense of not being contained in the content of the premises. But the results obtained may well be *psychologically new:* we may not have been aware, before using the techniques of logic and mathematics, what we commited ourselves to in accepting a certain set of assumptions or assertions.

A similar analysis is possible in all other cases of applied mathematics, including those involving, say, the calculus. Consider, for example, the hypothesis that a certain object, moving in a specified electric field, will undergo a constant acceleration of 5 feet/sec^2. For the purpose of testing this hypothesis, we might derive from it, by means of two successive integrations, the prediction that if the object is at rest at the beginning of the motion, then the distance covered by it at any time t is $\frac{5}{2}t^2$ feet. This conclusion may clearly be psychologically new to a person not acquainted with the subject, but it is not theoretically new; the content of the conclusion is already contained in that of the hypothesis about the constant accleration. And indeed, here as well as in the case of the compression of a gas, a failure of the prediction to come true would be considered as indicative of the factual incorrectness of at least one of the premises involved (*f.ex.*, of Boyle's law in its application to the particular gas), but never as a sign that the logical and mathematical principles involved might be unsound.

Thus, in the establishment of empirical knowledge, mathematics (as well as logic) has, so to speak, the function of a theoretical juice extractor: the techniques of mathematical and logical theory can produce no more juice of factual information than is contained in the assumptions to which they are applied; but they may produce a great deal more juice of this kind than might have been anticipated upon a first intuitive inspection of those assumptions which form the raw material for the extractor.

At this point, it may be well to consider briefly the status of those mathematical disciplines which are not outgrowths of arithmetic and thus of logic; these include in particular topology, geometry, and the various branches of abstract algebra, such as the theory of groups, lattices, fields, etc. Each of these disciplines can be developed as a purely deductive system on the basis of a suitable set of postulates. If P be the conjunction of the postulates for a given theory, than the proof of a proposition T of that theory consists in deducing T from P by means of the principles of formal logic. What is established by the proof is therefore not the truth of T, but rather the fact that T is true provided that the postulates are. But since both P and T contain certain primitive terms of the theory, to which no specific meaning is assigned, it is not strictly possible to speak of the truth of either P or T; it is therefore more adequate to state the point as follows: If a proposition T is logically deduced from P, then every specific interpretation of the primitives which turns all the postulates of P into true statements, will also render T a true statement.—Up to this point, the analysis is exactly analogous to that of arithmetic as based on Peano's set of postulates. In the case of arithmetic, however, it proved possible to go a step further, namely to define the customary meanings of the primitives in terms of purely logical concepts and to show that the postulates—and therefore also the theorems—of arithmetic are unconditionally true by virtue of these definitions. An analogous procedure is not applicable to those disciplines which are not outgrowths of arithmetic: The primitives of the various branches of abstract algebra have no specific "customary meaning"; and if geometry in its customary interpretation is thought of as a theory of the structure of physical space, then its primitives have to be construed as referring to certain types of physical entities, and the question of the truth of a geometrical theory in this interpretation turns into an *empirical* problem [13]. For the purpose of applying any one of these non-arithmetical disciplines to some specific field of mathematics or empirical science, it is therefore necessary first to assign to the primitives some specific meaning and then to ascertain whether in this interpretation the postulates turn into true statements. If this is the case, then we can be sure that all the theorems are true statements too, because they are logically derived from the postulates and thus simply explicate the content of the latter in the given interpretation.—In their application to empirical subject matter, therefore, these mathematical theories no less than those which grow out of arithmetic and ultimately out of pure logic, have the function of an analytic tool, which brings to light the implications of a given set of assumptions but adds nothing to their content.

But while mathematics in no case contributes anything to the content of our knowledge of empirical matters, it is entirely indispensable as an instrument for the validation and even for the linguistic expression of such knowledge: The majority of the more far-reaching theories in empirical science—including those which lend themselves most eminently to prediction or to practical application—are stated with the help of mathematical concepts; the formulation of these theories make use, in particular, of the number system, and of functional relationships among different metrical variables. Furthermore, the scientific test of these theories, the establishment of predictions by means of them, and finally their practical application, all require the deduction, from the general theory, of certain specific consequences; and such deduction would be entirely impossible without the techniques of mathematics which reveal what the given general theory implicitly asserts about a certain special case.

Thus, the analysis outlined on these pages exhibits the system of mathematics as a vast and ingenious conceptual structure without empirical content and yet an indispensable and powerful theoretical instrument for the scientific understanding and mastery of the world of our experience.

References

1. A discussion of the status of geometry is given in my article, Geometry and Empirical Science, American Mathematical Monthly, vol. 52, pp. 7-17, 1945.

2. The objection is sometimes raised that without certain types of experience, such as encountering several objects of the same kind, the integers and the arithmetical operations with them would never have been invented, and that therefore the propositions of arithmetic do have an empirical basis. This type of argument, however, involves a confusion of the logical and the psychological meaning of the term "basis." It may very well be the case that certain experiences occasion psychologically the formation of arithmetical ideas and in this sense form an empirical "basis" for them; but this point is entirely irrelevant for the logical questions as to the grounds on which the propositions of arithmetic may be accepted as true. The point made above is that no empirical "basis" or evidence whatever is needed to establish the truth of the propositions of arithmetic.

3. A precise account of the definition and the essential characteristics of the identity relation may be found in A. Tarski, Introduction to Logic, New York, 1941, Ch. III.

4. For a lucid and concise account of the axiomatic method, see A. Tarski, l.c., Ch. VI.

5. Bertrand Russell, Introduction to Mathematical Philosophy, New York and London, 1919, p. 71.

6. For a more detailed account of the construction of the number system on Peano's basis cf. Bertrand Russell, l.c., esp. Chs. I and VII.—A rigorous and concise presentation of that construction, beginning, however, with the set of all integers rather than that of the natural numbers, may be found in G. Birkhoff and S. MacLane, A Survey of Modern Algebra. New York 1941, Chs. I, II, III, V.—For a general survey of the construction of the number system, c.f. also J.W. Young, Lectures on the Fundamental Concepts of Algebra and Geometry New York, 1911, esp. lectures X, XI, XII.

6a. As a result of very deep-reaching investigations carried out by K. Godel it is known that arithmetic, and a fortiori mathematics, is an incomplete theory in the following sense: While all those propositions which belong to the classical systems of arithmetic, algebra, and analysis can indeed be derived, in the sense characterized above, from the Peano postulates, there exist nevertheless other propositions which can be expressed in purely arithmetical terms, and which are true, but which cannot be derived from the Peano system. And more generally: For any postulate system of arithmetic (or of mathematics for that matter) which is not self-contradictory, there exist propositions which are true, and which can be stated in purely arithmetical terms, but which cannot be derived from that postulate system. In other words, it is impossible to construct a postulate system which is not self-contradictory, and which contains among its consequences all true propositions which can be formulated within the language of arithmetic.

This fact does not, however, affect the result outlined above, namely, that it is possible to deduce, from the Peano postulates and the additional definitions of non-primitive terms, all those propositions which constitute the classical theory of arithmetic, algebra, and analysis; and it is to these propositions that I refer above and subsequently as the propositions of mathematics.

7. For a more detailed discussion, c.f. Russel, l.c., Chs. II, III, IV. A complete technical development of the idea can be found in the great standard work in mathematical logic, A.N. Whitehead and B. Russell, Principia Mathematica, Cambridge, England, 1910-1913.– For a very precise recent development of the theory, see W.V.O. Quine, Mathematical Logic, New York 1940.–A specific discussion of the Peano system and its interpretations from the viewpoint of semantics is included in R. Carnap, Foundations of Logic and Mathematics, International Encyclopedia of Unified Science, vol. I, no. 3, Chicago, 1939; especially sections 14, 17, 18.

8. The assertion that the definitions given above state the "customary" meaning of the arithmetical terms involved is to be understood in the logical, not the psychological sense of the term "meaning." It would obviously be absurd to claim that the above definitions express "what everybody has in mind" when talking about numbers and the various operations that can be performed with them. What is achieved by those definitions is rather a "logical reconstruction" of the concepts of arithmetic in the sense that if the definitions are accepted, then those statements in science and everyday discourse which involve arithmetical terms can be interpreted coherently and systematically in such a manner that they are capable of objective validation. The statement about the two persons in the office provides a very elementary illustration of what is meant here.

9. C.f. Bertrand Russell, l.c., p. 24 and Ch. XIII.

10. This result has been obtained by W.V.O. Quine; cf. his Mathematical Logic, New York, 1940.

11. The principles of logic developed in Quine's work and in similar modern systems of formal logic embody certain restrictions as compared with those logical rules which had been rather generally accepted as sound until about the turn of the 20th century. At that time, the discovery of the famous paradoxes of logic, especially of Russell's paradox (cf. Russell, l.c., Ch. XIII) revealed the fact that the logical principles implicit in customary mathematical reasoning involved contradictions and therefore had to be curtailed in one manner or another.

12. Note that we may say "hence" by virtue of the rule of substitution, which is one of the rules of logical inference.

13. For a more detailed discussion of this point, cf. the article mentioned in reference I.

GEOMETRY

GEOMETRY AS THE *A PRIORI* SCIENCE OF SPACE

Immanuel Kant (1725-1804) is one of the most important figures in the history of western philosophy. His main works are his three critiques, The Critique of Pure Reason, The Critique of Practical Reason, *and* The Critique of Judgment. *The present selection is taken from the Introduction and the Transcendental Aesthetic in his* Critique of Pure Reason *(translated by F. Max Müller in 1881 and reprinted from the Anchor Books edition).*

INTRODUCTION [B1–B18]

I

Of the Difference between *Pure and Empirical Knowledge*

That all our knowledge begins with experience there can be no doubt. For how should the faculty of knowledge be called into activity if not by objects which affect our senses, and which either produce representations by themselves, or rouse the activity of our understanding to compare, to connect, or to separate them; and thus to convert the raw material of our sensuous impressions into a knowledge of objects, which we call experience? In respect of time, therefore, no knowledge within us is antecedent to experience, but all knowledge begins with it.

But although all our knowledge begins with experience, it does not follow that it arises from experience. For it is quite possible that even our empirical experience is a compound of that which we receive through impressions, and of that which our own faculty of knowledge (incited only by sensuous impressions), supplies from itself, a supplement which we do not distinguish from that raw material, until long practice has roused our attention and rendered us capable of separating one from the other.

It is therefore a question which deserves at least closer investigation, and cannot be disposed of at first sight, whether there exists a knowledge independent of experience, and even of all impressions of the senses? Such *knowledge* is called *a priori,* and distinguished from *empirical* knowledge, which has its sources a *posteriori,* that is, in experience.

This term *a priori,* however, is not yet definite enough to indicate the full meaning of our question. For people are wont to say, even with regard to knowledge derived from experience, that we have it, or might have it, *a priori,* because we derive it from experience, not *immediately,* but from a general rule, which, however, has itself been derived from experience. Thus one would say of a person who undermines the foundations of his house, that he might have known *a priori* that it would tumble down, that is, that he need not wait for the experience of its really tumbling down. But still he could not know this entirely *a priori,* because he had first to learn from experience that bodies are heavy, and will fall when their supports are taken away.

We shall therefore, in what follows, understand by knowledge *a priori* knowledge which is *absolutely* independent of all experience, and not of this or that experience only. Opposed to this is empirical knowledge, or such as is possible *a posteriori* only, that is, by experience. Knowledge *a priori,* if mixed up with nothing empirical, is called *pure.* Thus the proposition, for example, that every change has its cause, is a proposition *a priori,* but not pure: because change is a concept which can only be derived from experience.

II

We are in Possession of Certain Cognitions a priori, *and even the Ordinary Understanding is never without them*

All depends here on a criterion, by which we may safely distinguish between pure and empirical knowledge. Now experience teaches us, no doubt, that something is so or so, but not that it cannot be different. *First,* then, if we have a proposition, which is thought, together with its necessity, we have a judgment *a priori;* and if, besides, it is not derived from any proposition, except such as is itself again considered as necessary, we have an absolutely *a priori* judgment. *Secondly,* experience never imparts to its judgments true or strict, but only assumed or relative universality (by means of induction), so that we ought always to say, so far as we have observed hitherto, there is no exception to this or that rule. If, therefore, a judgment is thought with strict universality, so that no exception is admitted as possible, it is not derived from experience, but valid absolutely *a priori.* Empirical universality, therefore, is only an arbitrary extension of a validity which applies to most cases, to one that applies to all: as, for instance, in the proposition, all bodies are heavy. If, on the contrary, strict universality is essential to a judgment, this always points to a special source of knowledge, namely, a faculty of knowledge *a priori.* Necessity, therefore, and strict universality are safe criteria of knowledge *a priori,* and are inseparable one from the other. As, however, in the use of these criteria, it is sometimes easier to show the contingency than the empirical limitation[1] of judgments, and as it is sometimes more convincing to prove the unlimited universality which we attribute to a judgment than its necessity, it is advisable to use both criteria separately, each being by itself infallible.

That there really exist in our knowledge such necessary, and in the strictest sense universal, and therefore pure judgments *a priori,* is easy to show. If we want a scientific example, we have only to look to any of the propositions of mathematics; if we want one from the sphere of the ordinary understanding, such a proposition as that each change must have a cause, will answer the purpose; nay, in the latter case, even the concept of cause contains so clearly the concept of the necessity of its connection with an effect, and of the strict universality of the rule, that it would be destroyed altogether if we attempted to derive it, as Hume does, from the frequent concomitancy of that which happens with that which precedes, and from a habit arising thence (therefore from a purely subjective necessity), of connecting representations. It is possible even, without having recourse to such examples in proof of the reality of pure propositions *a priori* within

---

[1] According to an emendation adopted both by Vaihinger and Adickes.

our knowledge, to prove their indispensability for the possibility of experience itself, thus proving it *a priori*. For whence should experience take its certainty, if all the rules which it follows were always again and again empirical, and therefore contingent and hardly fit to serve as first principles? For the present, however, we may be satisfied for having shown the pure employment of the faculty of our knowledge as a matter of fact, with the criteria of it.

Not only in judgments, however, but even in certain concepts, can we show their origin *a priori*. Take away, for example, from the concept of a body, as supplied by experience, everything that is empirical, one by one; such as colour, hardness or softness, weight, and even impenetrability, and there still remains the space which the body (now entirely vanished) occupied: that you cannot take away. And in the same manner, if you remove from your empirical concept of any object, corporeal or incorporeal, all properties which experience has taught you, you cannot take away from it that property by which you conceive it as a substance, or inherent in a substance (although such a concept contains more determinations than that of an object in general). Convinced, therefore, by the necessity with which that concept forces itself upon you, you will have to admit that it has its seat in your faculty of knowledge *a priori*.

III

Philosophy requires a science to determine the possibility, the principles, and the extent of all cognitions a priori

But what is still more extraordinary is this, that certain kinds of knowledge leave the field of all possible experience, and seem to enlarge the sphere of our judgments beyond the limits of experience by means of concepts to which experience can never supply any corresponding objects.

And it is in this very kind of knowledge which transcends the world of the senses, and where experience can neither guide nor correct us, that reason prosecutes its investigations, which by their importance we consider far more excellent and by their tendency far more elevated than anything the understanding can find in the sphere of phenomena. Nay, we risk rather anything, even at the peril of error, than that we

should surrender such investigations, either on the ground of their
uncertainty, or from any feeling of indifference or contempt. These
inevitable problems of pure reason itself are, *God, Freedom,* and
Immortality. The science which with all its apparatus is really intended
for the solution of these problems, is called *Metaphysic.* Its procedure
is at first *dogmatic, i.e.* unchecked by a previous examination of what
reason can and cannot do, before it engages confidently in so arduous
an undertaking.

Now it might seem natural that, after we have left the solid ground
of experience, we should not at once proceed to erect an edifice with
knowledge which we possess without knowing whence it came, and
trust to principles the origin of which is unknown, without having
made sure of the safety of the foundations by means of careful examination. It would seem natural, I say, that philosophers should first of
all have asked the question how the mere understanding could arrive
at all this knowledge *a priori,* and what extent, what truth, and what
value it could possess. If we take natural to mean what is just and
reasonable, then indeed nothing could be more natural. But if we understand by natural what takes place ordinarily, then, on the contrary,
nothing is more natural and more intelligible than that this examination should have been neglected for so long a time. For one part of
this knowledge, namely, the mathematical, has always been in possession of perfect trustworthiness; and thus produces a favourable presumption with regard to other parts also, although these may be of a
totally different nature. Besides, once beyond the precincts of experience, and we are certain that experience can never contradict us, while
the charm of enlarging our knowledge is so great that nothing will
stop our progress until we encounter a clear contradiction. This can
be avoided if only we are cautious in our imaginations, which nevertheless remain what they are, imaginations only. How far we can advance independent of all experience in *a priori* knowledge is shown by
the brilliant example of mathematics, It is true they deal with objects
and knowledge so far only as they can be represented in intuition. But
this is easily overlooked, because that intuition itself may be given *a
priori,* and be difficult to distinguish from a pure concept. Thus in-
spirited by a splendid proof of the power of reason, the desire of
enlarging our knowledge sees no limits. The light dove, piercing in her
easy flight the air and perceiving its resistance, imagines that flight

would be easier still in empty space. It was thus that Plato left the world of sense, as opposing so many hindrances to our understanding and ventured beyond on the wings of his ideas into the empty space of pure understanding. He did not perceive that he was making no progress by these endeavours, because he had no resistance as a fulcrum on which to rest or to apply his powers, in order to cause the understanding to advance. It is indeed a very common fate of human reason first of all to finish its speculative edifice as soon as possible, and then only to enquire whether the foundation be sure. Then all sorts of excuses are made in order to assure us as to its solidity, or to decline altogether such a late and dangerous enquiry. The reason why during the time of building we feel free from all anxiety and suspicion and believe in the apparent solidity of our foundation, is this:—A great, perhaps the greatest portion of what our reason finds to do consists in the analysis of our concepts of objects. This gives us a great deal of knowledge which, though it consists in no more than in simplifications and explanations of what is comprehended in our concepts (though in a confused manner), is yet considered as equal, at least in form, to new knowledge. It only separates and arranges our concepts, it does not enlarge them in matter or contents. As by this process we gain a kind of real knowledge *a priori,* which progresses safely and usefully, it happens that our reason, without being aware of it, appropriates under that pretence propositions of a totally different character, adding to given concepts new and strange ones *a priori,* without knowing whence they come, nay without even thinking of such a question. I shall therefore at the very outset treat of the distinction between these two kinds of knowledge.

IV

Of the Distinction between Analytical and Synthetical Judgments

In all judgments in which there is a relation between subject and predicate (I speak of affirmative judgments only, the application to negative ones being easy), that relation can be of two kinds. Either the predicate B belongs to the subject A as something contained (though covertly) in the concept A; or B lies outside the sphere of the

concept A, though somehow connected with it. In the former case I
call the judgment analytical, in the latter synthetical. Analytical judgments (affirmative) are therefore those in which the connection of the
predicate with the subject is conceived through identity, while others
in which that connection is conceived without identity, may be called
synthetical. The former might be called illustrating, the latter expanding
judgments, because in the former nothing is added by the predicate to the
concept of the subject, but the concept is only divided into its constituent concepts which were always conceived as existing within it,
though confusedly; while the latter add to the concept of the subject
a predicate not conceived as existing within it, and not to be extracted
from it by any process of mere analysis. If I say, for instance, All bodies
are extended, this is an analytical judgment. I need not go beyond the
concept connected with it. I have only to analyse that concept and
become conscious of the manifold elements always contained in it, in
order to find that predicate. This is therefore an analytical judgment.
But if I say, All bodies are heavy, the predicate is something quite
different from what I think as the mere concept of body. The addition
of such a predicate gives us a synthetical judgment.

Empirical judgments, as such, are all synthetical; for it would be
absurd to found an analytical judgment on experience, because in order
to form such a judgment, I need not at all step out of my concept, or
appeal to the testimony of experience. That a body is extended, is a
proposition perfectly certain *a priori,* and not an empirical judgment.
For, before I call in experience, I am already in possession of all the
conditions of my judgment in the concept of body itself. I have only
to draw out from it, according to the principle of contradiction, the
required predicate, and I thus become conscious, at the same time, of
the necessity of the judgment, which experience could never teach me.
But, though I do not include the predicate of gravity in the general
concept of body, that concept, nevertheless, indicates an object of
experience through one of its parts: so that I may add other parts also
of the same experience, besides those which belonged to the former
concept. I may, first, by an analytical process, realise the concept of
body, through the predicates of extension, impermeability, form, etc.
all of which are contained in it. Afterwards I expand my knowledge,
and looking back to the experience from which my concept of body
was abstracted, I find gravity always connected with the before-

mentioned predicates, and therefore I add it synthetically to that concept as a predicate. It is, therefore, experience on which the possibility of the synthesis of the predicate of gravity with the concept of body is founded: because both concepts, though neither of them is contained in the other, belong to each other, though accidentally only, as parts of a whole, namely, of experience, which is itself a synthetical connection of intuitions.

In synthetical judgments *a priori,* however, that help is entirely wanting. If I want to go beyond the concept A in order to find another concept B connected with it, where is there anything on which I may rest and through which a synthesis might become possible, considering that I cannot have the advantage of looking about in the field of experience? Take the proposition that all which happens has its cause. In the concept of something that happens I no doubt conceive of something existing preceded by time, and from this certain analytical judgments may be deduced. But the concept of cause is entirely outside that concept, and indicates something different from that which happens, and is by no means contained in that representation. How can I venture then to predicate of that which happens something totally different from it, and to represent the concept of cause, though not contained in it, as belonging to it, and belonging to it by necessity? What is here the unknown x, on which the understanding may rest in order to find beyond the concept A a foreign predicate B, which nevertheless is believed to be connected with it? It cannot be experience, because the proposition that all which happens has its cause represents this second predicate as added to the subject not only with greater generality than experience can ever supply, but also with a character of necessity, and therefore purely *a priori,* and based on concepts. All our speculative knowledge *a priori* aims at and rests on such synthetical, i.e. expanding propositions, for the analytical are no doubt very important and necessary, yet only in order to arrive at that cleaness of concepts which is requisite for a safe and wide synthesis, serving as a really new addition to what we possess already.

V

In all Theoretical Sciences of Reason Synthetical Judgments a priori *are contained as Principles*

1. All mathematical judgments are synthetical. This proposition,

though incontestably certain, and very important to us for the future, seems to have hitherto escaped the observation of those who are engaged in the anatomy of human reason; nay, to be directly opposed to all their conjectures. For as it was found that all mathematical conclusions proceed according to the principle of contradiction (which is required by the nature of all apodictic certainty), it was supposed that the fundamental principles of mathematics also rested on the authority of the same principle of contradiction. This, however, was a mistake: for though a synthetical proposition may be understood according to the principle of contradiction, this can only be if another synthetical proposition is presupposed, from which the latter is deduced, but never by itself. First of all, we ought to observe, that mathematical propositions, properly so called, are always judgments *a priori,* and not empirical, because they carry along with them necessity, which can never be deduced from experience. If people should object to this, I am quite willing to confine my statement to pure mathematics, the very concept of which implies that it does not contain empirical, but only pure knowledge *a priori.*

At first sight one might suppose indeed that the proposition $7 + 5 = 12$ is merely analytical, following, according to the principle of contradiction, from the concept of a sum of 7 and 5. But, if we look more closely, we shall find that the concept of the sum of 7 and 5 contains nothing beyond the union of both sums into one, whereby nothing is told us as to what this single number may be which combines both. We by no means arrive at a concept of Twelve, by thinking that union of Seven and Five; and we may analyse our concept of such a possible sum as long as we will, still we shall never discover in it the concept of Twelve. We must go beyond these concepts, and call in the assistance of the intuition corresponding to one of the two, for instance, our five fingers, or, as Segner does in his arithmetic, five points, and so by degrees add the units of the Five, given in intuition, to the concept of the Seven. For I first take the number 7, and taking the intuition of the fingers of my hand, in order to form with it the concept of the 5, I gradually add the units, which I before took together, to make up the number 5, by means of the image of my hand, to the number 7, and I thus see the number 12 arising before me. That 5 should be added to 7 was no doubt implied in my concept of a sum $7 + 5$, but not that the sum should be equal to 12. An

arithmetical proposition is, therefore, always synthetical, which is
seen more easily still by taking larger numbers, where we clearly perceive that, turn and twist our conceptions as we may, we could never
by means of the mere analysis of our concepts and without the help
of intuition, arrive at the sum that is wanted.

Nor is any proposition of pure geometry analytical. That the
straight line between two points is the shortest, is a synthetical proposition. For my concept of *straight* contains nothing of magnitude
(quantity), but a quality only. The concept of the *shortest* is, therefore, purely adventitious, and cannot be deduced from the concept of
the straight line by any analysis whatsoever. The aid of intuition,
therefore, must be called in, by which alone the synthesis is possible.

[It is true that some few propositions, presupposed by the geometrician, are really analytical, and depend on the principle of contradiction: but then they serve only, like identical propositions, to form
the chain of the method, and not as principles. Such are the propositions, $a = a$, the whole is equal to itself, or $(a + b) > a$, that the whole
is greater than its part. And even these, though they are valid according
to mere concepts, are only admitted in mathematics, because they
can be represented in intuition.[1]] What often makes us believe that the
predicate of such apodictic judgments is contained in our concept, and
the judgment therefore analytical, is merely the ambiguous character
of the expression. We are told that we *ought* to join in thought a certain predicate to a given concept, and this necessity is inherent in the
concepts themselves. But the question is not what we *ought* to join to
the given concept, but what we *really think* in it, though confusedly
only, and then it becomes clear that the predicate is no doubt inherent
in those concepts by necessity, not, however, as thought in the concept itself, but by means of an intuition, which must be added to the
concept.

2. *Natural science (physica) contains synthetical judgments*
a priori *as principles.* I shall adduce, as examples, a few propositions
only, such as, that in all changes of the material world the quantity
of matter always remains unchanged: or that in all communication of
motion, action and reaction must always equal each other. It is clear
not only that both convey necessity, and that, therefore, their origin
is *a priori,* but also that they are synthetical propositions. For in the

---

[1]This paragraph from It is true to intuition seems to have been a marginal note, as shown by
Dr. Vaihinger.

concept of matter I do not conceive its permanency, but only its presence in the space which it fills. I therefore go beyond the concept of matter in order to join something to it *a priori,* which I did not be-fore conceive *in it.* The proposition is, therefore, not analytical, but synthetical, and yet *a priori,* and the same applies to the other propo-sitions of the pure part of natural science.

3. Metaphysic, even if we look upon it as hitherto a tentative science only, which, however, is indispensable to us, owing to the very nature of human reason, is meant to *contain synthetical knowledge a priori.* Its object is not at all merely to analyse such concepts as we make to ourselves of things *a priori,* and thus to explain them analytic-ally, but to expand our knowledge *a priori.* This we can only do by means of concepts which add something to a given concept that was not contained in it; nay, we even attempt, by means of synthetical judgments *a priori,* to go so far beyond a given concept that experience itself cannot follow us: as, for instance, in the proposition that the world must have a first beginning. Thus, according at least to its in-tentions, metaphysic consists merely of synthetical propositions *a priori.*

FIRST SECTION OF THE TRANSCENDENTAL ÆSTHETIC
[B37-B46]

Of Space

§ *Metaphysical Exposition of This Concept*

By means of our external sense, a property of our mind (Gemüth), we represent to ourselves objects as external or outside ourselves, and all of these in space. It is within space that their form, size, and rela-tive position are fixed or can be fixed. The internal sense by means of which the mind perceives itself or its internal state, does not give an intuition (Anschauung) of the soul (Seele) itself, as an object, but it is nevertheless a fixed form under which alone an intuition of its in-ternal state is possible, so that whatever belongs to its internal deter-minations (Bestimmungen) must be represented in relations of time. Time cannot be perceived (angeschaut) externally, as little as space can be perceived as something within us.

What then are space and time? Are they real beings? Or, if not that, are they determinations or relations of things, but such as would belong to them even if they were not perceived? Or lastly, are they determinations and relations which are inherent in the form of intuition only, and therefore in the subjective nature of our mind, without which such predicates as space and time would never be ascribed to anything?

In order to understand this more clearly, let us first consider space.

1. Space is not an empirical concept which has been derived from external experience. For in order that certain sensations should be referred to something outside myself, i.e. to something in a different part of space from that where I am; again, in order that I may be able to represent them (vorstellen) as side by side, that is, not only as different, but as in different places, the representation (Vorstellung) of space must already be there. Therefore the representation of space cannot be borrowed through experience from relations of external phenomena, but, on the contrary, this external experience becomes possible only by means of the representation of space.

2. Space is a necessary representation *a priori,* forming the very foundation of all external intuitions. It is impossible to imagine that there should be no space, though one might very well imagine that there should be space without objects to fill it. Space is therefore regarded as a condition of the possibility of phenomena, not as a determination produced by them; it is a representation *a priori* which necessarily precedes all external phenomena.

3. Space is not a discursive or so-called general concept of the relations of things in general, but a pure intuition. For, first of all, we can imagine one space only and if we speak of many spaces, we mean parts only of one and the same space. Nor can these parts be considered as antecedent to the one and all-embracing space and, as it were, its component parts out of which an aggregate is formed, but they can be thought of as existing within it only. Space is essentially one; its multiplicity, and therefore the general concept of spaces in general, arises entirely from limitations. Hence it follows that, with respect to space, an intuition *a priori,* which is not empirical, must form the foundation of all conceptions of space. In the same manner all geometrical principles, e.g. 'that in every triangle two sides together are greater than the third,' are never to be derived from the general concepts of side and triangle, but from an intuition, and that *a priori,*

with apodictic certainty.

4. Space is represented as an infinte given quantity. Now it is quite true that every concept is to be thought as a representation, which is contained in an infinte number of different possible representations (as their common characteristic), and therefore comprehends them: but no concept, as such, can be thought as if it contained in itself an infinite number of representations. Nevertheless, space is so thought (for all parts of infinite space exist simultaneously). Consequently, the original representation of space is an *intuition a priori,* and not a concept.

§ 3

Transcendental Exposition of the Concept of Space

I understand by transcendental *exposition (Erörterung),* the explanation of a concept, as of a principle by which the possibility of other synthetical cognitions *a priori* can be understood. For this purpose it is necessary, 1. That such cognitions really do flow from the given concept. 2. That they are possible only under the presupposition of a given mode of explanation of such concept.

Geometry is a science which determines the properties of space synthetically, and yet *a priori.* What then must be the representation of space, to render such a knowledge of it possible? It must be originally intuitive; for it is impossible from a mere concept to deduce propositions which go beyond that concept, as we do in geometry (Introduction V.). That intuition, however, must be *a priori,* that is, it must exist within us before any perception of the object, and must therefore be pure, not empirical intuition. For all geometrical propositions are apodictic, that is, connected with the consciousness of their necessity, as for instance the proposition, that space has only three dimensions; and such propositions cannot be empirical judgments, nor conclusions from them (Introduction II.).

How then can an external intuition dwell in the mind anterior to the objects themselves, and in which the concept of objects can be determined *a priori*? Evidently not otherwise than so far as it has its seat in the subject only, as the formal condition under which the subject is affected by the objects and thereby is receiving an *immediate representation,* that is, *intuition* of them; therefore as a form of the external *sense* in general.

It is therefore by our explanation only that the *possibility* of *geometry* as a synthetical science *a priori* becomes intelligible. Every other explanation, which fails to account for this possibility, can best be distinguished from our own by that criterion, although it may seem to have some similarity with it.

Conclusions from the Foregoing Concepts.

a. Space does not represent any quality of objects by themselves, or objects in their relation to one another; i.e. space does not represent any determination which is inherent in the objects themselves, and would remain, even if all subjective conditions of intuition were removed. For no determinations of objects, whether belonging to them absolutely or in relation to others, can enter into our intuition before the actual existence of the objects themselves, that is to say, they can never be intuitions *a priori.*

b. Space is nothing but the form of all phenomena of the external senses; it is the subjective condition of our sensibility, without which no external intuition is possible for us. If then we consider that the receptivity of the subject, its capacity of being affected by objects, must necessarily precede all intuition of objects, we shall understand how the form of all phenomena may be given before all real perceptions, may be, in fact, *a priori* in the soul, and may, as a pure intuition, by which all objects must be determined, contain, prior to all experience, principles regulating their relations.

It is therefore from the human standpoint only that we can speak of space, extended objects, etc. If we drop the subjective condition under which alone we can gain external intuition, that is, so far as we ourselves may be affected by objects, the representation of space means nothing. For this predicate is applied to objects only in so far as they appear to us, and are objects of our senses. The constant form of this receptivity, which we call sensibility, is a necessary condition of all relations in which objects, as without us, can be perceived; and, when abstraction is made of these objects, what remains is that pure intuition which we call space. As the peculiar conditions of our sensibility cannot be looked upon as conditions of the possibility of the objects themselves, but only of their appearance as phenomena to us, we may say indeed that space comprehends all things which may appear to us externally, but not all things by themselves, whether perceived by us or not, or by any subject whatsoever. We cannot judge whether the intuitions of other thinking beings are subject to the same conditions which determine our intuition, and which for us are generally binding. If we add the limitation of a judgment to a subjective concept, the judgment gains absolute validity. The proposition 'all things are beside each other in space,' is valid only under the limitation that things are taken as objects of our sensuous intuition (Anschauung). If I add that limitation to the concept and say 'all things, as external phenomena, are beside each other in space,' the rule obtains universal and unlimited validity. Our discussions teach therefore the reality, i.e. the objective validity, of space with regard to all that can come to us externally as an object, but likewise the *ideality* of space with regard to things, when they are considered in themselves by our reason, and independent of the nature of our senses. We maintain the empirical reality of space, so far as every possible external experience is concerned, but at the same time its transcendental ideality; that is to say, we maintain that space is nothing, if we leave out of consideration the condition of a possible experience, and accept it as something on which things by themselves are in any way dependent.

With the exception of space there is no other subjective representation (Vorstellung) referring to something external, that would be called *a priori* objective. For from none of them can we derive synthetical propositions *a priori,* as we can from the intuition in space §3. Strictly speaking, therefore, they can claim no ideality at all, though they agree with the representation of space in this, that they belong only to the subjective nature of sensibility, for instance, of sight, of hearing, and feeling, through the sensations of colours, sounds, and heat. All these, however, being sensations only, and not intuitions, do not help us by themselves to know any object, least of all *a priori.*

My object in what I have said just now is only to prevent people from imagining that they can elucidate the ideality of space by illustrations which are altogether insufficient, such as colour, taste, etc., which should never be considered as qualities of things, but as modi-

fications of the subject, and which therefore may be different with
different people. For in this case that which originally is itself a phenomenon only, as for instance, a rose, is taken by the empirical understanding for a thing by itself, which nevertheless, with regard to colour,
may appear different to every eye. The transcendental conception, on
the contrary, of all phenomena in space, is a critical warning that
nothing which is seen in space is a thing by itself, nor space a form of
things supposed to belong to them by themselves, but that objects by
themselves are not known to us at all, and that what we call external
objects are nothing but representations of our senses, the form of
which is space, and the true correlative of which, that is the thing by
itself, is not known, nor can be known by these representations, nor
do we care to know anything about it in our daily experience.

CONVENTIONALISM IN GEOMETRY

This second selection from Poincaré's work is taken from Chapters 3 and 5 of his Science and Hypothesis *(1905).* *

Every conclusion presumes premisses. These premisses are either self-evident and need no demonstration, or can be established only if based on other propositions; and, as we cannot go back in this way to infinity, every deductive science, and geometry in particular, must rest upon a certain number of indemonstrable axioms. All treatises of geometry begin therefore with the enunciation of these axioms. But there is a distinction to be drawn between them. Some of these, for example, "Things which are equal to the same thing are equal to one another," are not propositions in geometry but propositions in analysis. I look upon them as analytical *a priori* intuitions, and they concern me no further. But I must insist on other axioms which are special to geometry. Of these most treatises explicitly enunciate three: —(1) Only one line can pass through two points; (2) a straight line is the shortest distance between two points; (3) through one point only one parallel can be drawn to a given straight line. Although we generally dispense with proving the second of these axioms, it would be possible to deduce it from the other two, and from those much more numerous axioms which are implicitly admitted without enunciation, as I shall explain further on. For a long time a proof of the third axiom known as Euclid's postulate was sought in vain. It is impossible to imagine the efforts that have been spent in pursuit of this chimera. Finally, at the beginning of the nineteenth century, and almost simultaneously, two scientists, a Russian and a Bulgarian, Lobatschewsky and Bolyai, showed irrefutably that this proof is impossible. They have nearly rid

*Translated by William John Greenstreet (The Walter Scott Publishing Co., 1905).

us of inventors of geometries without a postulate, and ever since the
Académie des Sciences receives only about one or two new demonstrations a year. But the question was not exhausted, and it was not long
before a great step was taken by the celebrated memoir of Riemann,
entitled: *Ueber die Hypothesen welche der Geometrie zum Grunde
liegen.* This little work has inspired most of the recent treatises to
which I shall later on refer, and among which I may mention those of
Beltrami and Helmholtz.

The Geometry of Lobatschewsky.—If it were possible to deduce
Euclid's postulate from the several axioms, it is evident that by rejecting the postulate and retaining the other axioms we should be led to
contradictory consequences. It would be, therefore, impossible to
found on those premises a coherent geometry. Now, this is precisely
what Lobatschewsky has done. He assumes at the outset that several
parallels may be drawn through a point to a given straight line, and
he retains all the other axioms of Euclid. From these hypotheses he
deduces a series of theorems between which it is impossible to find
any contradiction, and he constructs a geometry as impeccable in its
logic as Euclidean geometry. The theorems are very different, however,
from those to which we are accustomed, and at first will be found a
little disconcerting. For instance, the sum of the angles of a triangle
is always less than two right angles, and the difference between that
sum and two right angles is proportional to the area of the triangle.
It is impossible to construct a figure similar to a given figure but of
different dimensions. If the circumference of a circle be divided into
n equal parts, and tangents be drawn at the points of intersection, the
n tangents will form a polygon if the radius of the circle is small
enough, but if the radius is large enough they will never meet. We need
not multiply these examples. Lobatschewsky's propositions have no
relation to those of Euclid, but they are none the less logically inter-
connected.

Riemann's Geometry.—Let us imagine to ourselves a world only
peopled with beings of no thickness, and suppose these "infinitely
flat" animals are all in one and the same plane, from which they cannot emerge. Let us further admit that this world is sufficiently distant
from other worlds to be withdrawn from their influence, and while we
are making these hypotheses it will not cost us much to endow these
beings with reasoning power, and to believe them capable of making

a geometry. In that case they will certainly attribute to space only
two dimensions. But now suppose that these imaginary animals, while
remaining without thickness, have the form of a spherical, and not of
a plane figure, and are all on the same sphere, from which they cannot
escape. What kind of a geometry will they construct? In the first
place, it is clear that they will attribute to space only two dimensions.
The straight line to them will be the shortest distance from one point
on the sphere to another—that is to say, an arc of a great circle. In a
word, their geometry will be spherical geometry. What they will call
space will be the sphere on which they are confined, and on which
take place all the phenomena with which they are acquainted. Their
space will therefore be *unbounded,* since on a sphere one may always
walk forward without ever being brought to a stop, and yet it will be
finite; the end will never be found, but the complete tour can be made.
Well, Riemann's geometry is spherical geometry extended to three
dimensions. To construct it, the German mathematician had first of
all to throw overboard, not only Euclid's postulate, but also the first
axiom that *only one line can pass through two points.* On a sphere,
through two given points, we can *in general* draw only one great
circle which, as we have just seen, would be to our imaginary beings
a straight line. But there was one exception. If the two given points
are at the ends of a diameter, an infinite number of great circles can
be drawn through them. In the same way, in Riemann's geometry—at
least in one of its forms—through two points only one straight line
can in general be drawn, but there are exceptional cases in which
through two points an infinite number of straight lines can be drawn.
So there is a kind of opposition between the geometries of Riemann
and Lobatschewsky. For instance, the sum of the angles of a triangle
is equal to two right angles in Euclid's geometry, less than two right
angles in that of Lobatschewsky, and greater than two right angles in
that of Riemann. The number of parallel lines that can be drawn
through a given point to a given line is one in Euclid's geometry, none
in Riemann's, and an infinite number in the geometry of Lobatschewsky.
Let us add that Riemann's space is finite, although unbounded in the
sense which we have above attached to these words.

   Surfaces with Constant Curvature.—One objection however, remains possible. There is no contradiction between the theorems of
Lobatschewsky and Riemann; but however numerous are the other

consequences that these geometers have deduced from their hypotheses, they had to arrest their course before they exhausted them all, for the number would be infinite; and who can say that if they had carried their deductions further they would not have eventually reached some contradiction? This difficulty does not exist for Riemann's geometry, provided it is limited to two dimensions. As we have seen, the two-dimensional geometry of Riemann, in fact, does not differ from spherical geometry, which is only a branch of ordinary geometry, and is therefore outside all contradiction. Beltrami, by showing that Lobatschewsky's two-dimensional geometry was only a branch of ordinary geometry, has equally refuted the objection as far as it is concerned. This is the course of his argument: Let us consider any figure whatever on a surface. Imagine this figure to be traced on a flexible and inextensible canvas applied to the surface, in such a way that when the canvas is displaced and deformed the different lines of the figure change their form without changing their length. As a rule, this flexible and inextensible figure cannot be displaced without leaving the surface. But there are certain surfaces for which such a movement would be possible. They are surfaces of constant curvature. If we resume the comparison that we made just now, and imagine beings without thickness living on one of these surfaces, they will regard as possible the motion of a figure all the lines of which remain of a constant length. Such a movement would appear absurd, on the other hand, to animals without thickness living on a surface of variable curvature. These surfaces of constant curvature are of two kinds. The curvature of some is *positive,* and they may be deformed so as to be applied to a sphere. The geometry of these surfaces is therefore reduced to spherical geometry—namely, Riemann's. The curvature of others is *negative.* Beltrami has shown that the geometry of these surfaces is identical with that of Lobatschewsky. Thus the two dimensional geometries of Riemann and Lobatschewsky are connected with Euclidean geometry.

   Interpretation of Non-Euclidean Geometries.—Thus vanishes the objection so far as two-dimensional geometries are concerned. It would be easy to extend Beltrami's reasoning to three dimensional geometries, and minds which do not recoil before space of four dimensions will see no difficulty in it; but such minds are few in number. I prefer, then, to proceed otherwise. Let us consider a certain plane, which I shall call the fundamental plane, and let us construct a kind of dictionary by making a double series of terms written in two columns, and corresponding each to each, just as in ordinary dictionaries the words in two languages which have the same signification correspond to one another:—

Space	The portion of space situated above the fundamental plane.
Plane	Sphere cutting orthogonally the fundamental plane.
Line	Circle cutting orthogonally the fundamental plane.
Sphere	Sphere.
Circle	Circle.
Angle	Angle.
Distance between two points ...	Logarithm of the anharmonic ratio of these two points and of the intersection of the fundamental plane with the circle passing through these two points and cutting it orthogonally.
Etc.	Etc.

Let us now take Lobatschewsky's theorems and translate them by the aid of this dictionary, as we would translate a German text with the aid of a German-French dictionary. *We shall then obtain the theorems of ordinary geometry.* For instance, Lobatschewsky's theorem: "The sum of the angles of a triangle is less than two right angles," may be translated thus: "If a curvilinear triangle has for its sides arcs of circles which if produced would cut orthogonally the fundamental plane, the sum of the angles of this curvilinear triangle will be less than two right angles." Thus, however far the consequences of Lobatschewsky's hypotheses are carried, they will never lead to a contradiction; in fact, if two of Lobatschewsky's theorems were contradictory, the translations of these two theorems made by the aid of our dictionary would be contradictory also. But these translations are theorems of ordinary geometry, and no one doubts that ordinary geometry is exempt from contradiction. Whence is the certainty derived, and how far is it justified? That is a question upon which I cannot enter here, but it is a very interesting question, and I think not insoluble. Nothing, therefore, is left of the objection I formulated above. But this is not all. Lobatschewsky's geometry being susceptible of a concrete interpretation, ceases to be a useless logical exercise, and may be applied. I have no time here to deal with these applications, nor with what Herr Klein and myself have done by using them in the integration of linear equations. Further, this interpretation is not unique, and several dictionaries may be constructed analogous to that above, which will enable us by a simple translation to convert Lobatschewsky's theorems into the theorems of ordinary geometry.

Implicit Axioms.—Are the axioms implicitly enunciated in our text-books the only foundation of geometry? We may be assured of the contrary when we see that, when they are abandoned one after another, there are still left standing some propositions which are common to the geometries of Euclid, Lobatschewsky, and Riemann. These propositions must be based on premises that geometers admit without enunciation. It is interesting to try and extract them from the classical proofs.

John Stuart Mill asserted[1] that every definition contains an axiom, because by defining we implicitly affirm the existence of the object defined. That is going rather too far. It is but rarely in mathematics that a definition is given without following it up by the proof of the existence of the object defined, and when this is not done it is generally because the reader can easily supply it; and it must not be forgotten that the word "existence" has not the same meaning when it refers to a mathematical entity as when it refers to a material object.

A mathematical entity exists provided there is no contradiction implied in its definition, either in itself, or with the propositions previously admitted. But if the observation of John Stuart Mill cannot be applied to all definitions, it is none the less true for some of them. A plane is sometimes defined in the following manner:—The plane is a surface such that the line which joins any two points upon it lies wholly on that surface. Now, there is obviously a new axiom concealed in this definition. It is true we might change it, and that would be preferable, but then we should have to enunciate the axiom explicitly. Other definitions may give rise to no less important reflections, such as, for example, that of the equality of two figures. Two figures are equal when they can be superposed. To superpose them, one of them must be displaced until it coincides with the other. But how must it

---

[1]Logic, c. viii, cf. Definitions, § 5-6.—Tr.

be displaced? If we asked that question, no doubt we should be
told that it ought to be done without deforming it, and as an invariable solid is displaced. The vicious circle would then be evident.
As a matter of fact, this definition defines nothing. It has no meaning to a being living in a world in which there are only fluids. If it
seems clear to us, it is because we are accustomed to the properties
of natural solids which do not much differ from those of the ideal
solids, all of whose dimensions are invariable. However, imperfect
as it may be, this definition implies an axiom. The possibility of the
motion of an invariable figure is not a self-evident truth. At least
it is only so in the application to Euclid's postulate, and not as an
analytical *a priori* intuition would be. Moreover, when we study
the definitions and the proofs of geometry, we see that we are compelled to admit without proof not only the possibility of this motion, but also some of its properties. This first arises in the definition
of the straight line. Many defective definitions have been given, but
the true one is that which is understood in all the proofs in which
the straight line intervenes. "It may happen that the motion of an
invariable figure may be such that all the points of a line belonging
to the figure are motionless, while all the points situated outside that
line are in motion. Such a line would be called a straight line." We
have deliberately in this enunciation separated the definition from
the axiom which it implies. Many proofs such as those of the cases
of the equality of triangles, of the possibility of drawing a perpendicular from a point to a straight line, assume propositions the
enunciations of which are dispensed with, for they necessarily imply
that it is possible to move a figure in space in a certain way.

   The Fourth Geometry.—Among these explicit axioms there is
one which seems to me to deserve some attention, because when we
abandon it we can construct a fourth geometry as coherent as those
of Euclid, Lobatschewsky, and Riemann. To prove that we can
always draw a perpendicular at a point A to a straight line A B, we
consider a straight line A C movable about the point A, and initially
identical with the fixed straight line A B. We then can make it turn
about the point A until it lies in A B produced. Thus we assume two
propositions—first, that such a rotation is possible, and then that it
may continue until the two lines lie the one in the other produced.
If the first point is conceded and the second rejected, we are led to

a series of theorems even stranger than those of Lobatschewsky and Riemann, but equally free from contradiction. I shall give only one of these theorems, and I shall not choose the least remarkable of them. *A real straight line may be perpendicular to itself.*

Lie's Theorem. —The number of axioms implicitly introduced into classical proofs is greater than necessary, and it would be interesting to reduce them to a minimum. It may be asked, in the first place, if this reduction is possible—if the number of necessary axioms and that of imaginable geometries is not infinite? A theorem due to Sophus Lie is of weighty importance in this discussion. It may be enunciated in the following manner:—Suppose the following premises are admitted: (I) space has n dimensions; (2) the movement of an invariable figure is possible; (3) p conditions are necessary to determine the position of this figure in space.

The number of geometries compatible with these premises will be limited. I may even add that if n is given, a superior limit can be assigned to p. If, therefore, the possibility of the movement is granted, we can only invent a finite and even a rather restricted number of three-dimensional geometries.

Riemann's Geometries. —However, this result seems contradicted by Riemann, for that scientist constructs an infinite number of geometries, and that to which his name is usually attached is only a particular case of them. All depends, he says, on the manner in which the length of a curve is defined. Now, there is an infinite number of ways of defining this length, and each of them may be the starting point of a new geometry. That is perfectly true, but most of these definitions are incompatible with the movement of a variable figure such as we assume to be possible in Lie's theorem. These geometries of Riemann, so interesting on various grounds, can never be, therefore, purely analytical, and would not lend themselves to proofs analogous to those of Euclid.

On the Nature of Axioms. —Most mathematicians regard Lobatschewsky's geometry as a mere logical curiosity. Some of them have however, gone further. If several geometries are possible, they say, is it certain that our geometry is the one that is true? Experiment no doubt teaches us that the sum of the angles of a triangle is equal to two right angles, but this is because the triangles we deal with are too small. According to Lobatschewsky, the difference is propor-

tional to the area of the triangle, and will not this become sensible
when we operate on much larger triangles, and when our measurements become more accurate? Euclid's geometry would thus be a
provisory geometry. Now, to discuss this view we must first of all
ask ourselves, what is the nature of geometrical axioms? Are they
synthetic *a priori* intuitions, as Kant affirmed? They would then be
imposed upon us with such a force that we could not conceive of
the contrary proposition, nor could we build upon it a theoretical
edifice. There would be no non-Euclidean geometry. To convince
ourselves of this, let us take a true synthetic *a priori* intuition—the
following, for instance, which played an important part in the first
chapter:—If a theorem is true for the number I, and if it has been
proved that it is true of $n + I$, provided it is true of n, it will be
true for all positive integers. Let us next try to get rid of this, and
while rejecting this proposition let us construct a false arithmetic
analogous to non-Euclidean geometry. We shall not be able to do it.
We shall be even tempted at the outset to look upon these intuitions
as analytical. Besides, to take up again our fiction of animals without
thickness, we can scarcely admit that these beings, if their minds are
like ours, would adopt the Euclidean geometry, which would be contradicted by all their experience. Ought we, then, to conclude that
the axioms of geometry are experimental truths? But we do not
make experiments on ideal lines or ideal circles; we can only make
them on material objects. On what, therefore, would experiments
serving as a foundation for geometry be based? The answer is easy.
We have seen above that we constantly reason as if the geometrical
figures behaved like solids. What geometry would borrow from experiment would be therefore the properties of these bodies. The
properties of light and its propagation in a straight line have also
given rise to some of the propositions of geometry, and in particular
to those of projective geometry, so that from that point of view
one would be tempted to say that metrical geometry is the study of
solids, and projective geometry that of light. But a difficulty remains,
and is unsurmountable. If geometry were an experimental science,
it would not be an exact science. It would be subjected to continual
revision. Nay, it would from that day forth be proved to be erroneous,
for we know that no rigorously invariable solid exists. *The geometrical
axioms are therefore neither synthetic a priori intuitions nor experi-*

mental facts. They are conventions. Our choice among all possible conventions is *guided* by experimental facts; but it remains *free,* and is limited by the necessity of avoiding every contradiction, and thus it is that postulates may remain rigorously true even when the experimental laws which have determined their adoption are only approximate. In other words, *the axioms of geometry* (I do not speak of those of arithmetic) *are only definitions in disguise.* What then, are we to think of the question: Is Euclidean geometry true? It has no meaning. We might as well ask if the metric system is true, and if the old weights and measures are false; if Cartesian co-ordinates are true and polar coordinates false. One geometry cannot be more true than another; it can only be more convenient. Now, Euclidean geometry is, and will remain, the most convenient: Ist, because it is the simplest, and it is not so only because of our mental habits or because of the kind of direct intuition that we have of Euclidean space; it is the simplest in itself, just as a polynomial of the first degree is simpler than a polynomial of the second degree; 2nd, because it sufficiently agrees with the properties of natural solids, those bodies which we can compare and measure by means of our senses.

CHAPTER V.

EXPERIMENT AND GEOMETRY

I. I have on several occasions in the preceding pages tried to show how the principles of geometry are not experimental facts, and that in particular Euclid's postulate cannot be proved by experiment. However convincing the reasons already given may appear to me, I feel I must dwell upon them, because there is a profoundly false conception deeply rooted in many minds.

2. Think of a material circle, measure its radius and circumference, and see if the ratio of the two lengths is equal to π. What have we done? We have made an experiment on the properties of the matter with which this *roundness* has been realised, and of which the measure we used is made.

3. *Geometry and Astronomy.* —The same question may also be asked in another way. If Lobatschewsky's geometry is true, the parallax of a very distant star will be finite. If Riemann's is true, it will

be negative. These are the results which seem within the reach of experiment, and it is hoped that astronomical observations may enable us to decide between the two geometries. But what we call a straight line in astronomy is simply the path of a ray of light. If, therefore, we were to discover negative parallaxes, or to prove that all parallaxes are higher than a certain limit, we should have a choice between two conclusions: we could give up Euclidean geometry, or modify the laws of optics, and suppose that light is not rigorously propagated in a straight line. It is needless to add that every one would look upon this solution as the more advantageous. Euclidean geometry, therefore, has nothing to fear from fresh experiments.

4. Can we maintain that certain phenomena which are possible in Euclidean space would be impossible in non-Euclidean space, so that experiment in establishing these phenomena would directly contradict the non-Euclidean hypothesis? I think that such a question cannot be seriously asked. To me it is exactly equivalent to the following, the absurdity of which is obvious:—There are lengths which can be expressed in metres and centimetres, but cannot be measured in toises, feet, and inches; so that experiment, by ascertaining the existence of these lengths, would directly contradict this hypothesis, that there are toises divided into six feet. Let us look at the question a little more closely. I assume that the straight line in Euclidean space possesses any two properties, which I shall call A and B; that in non-Euclidean space it still possesses the property A, but no longer possesses the property B; and, finally, I assume that in both Euclidean and non-Euclidean space the straight line is the only line that possesses the property A. If this were so, experiment would be able to decide between the hypotheses of Euclid and Lobatschewsky. It would be found that some concrete object, upon which we can experiment—for example, a pencil of rays of light— possesses the property A. We should conclude that it is rectilinear, and we should then endeavour to find out if it does not, possess, the property B. But *it is not so.* There exists no property which can, like this property A, be an absolute criterion enabling us to recognise the straight line, and to distinguish it from every other line. Shall we say, for instance, "This property will be the following: the straight line is a line such that a figure of which this line is a part can move without the mutual distances of its points varying, and in

such a way that all the points in this straight line remain fixed"?
Now, this is a property which in either Euclidean or non-Euclidean
space belongs to the straight line, and belongs to it alone. But how
can we ascertain by experiment if it belongs to any particular concrete object? Distances must be measured, and how shall we know
that any concrete magnitude which I have measured with my material instrument really represents the abstract distance? We have only
removed the difficulty a little farther off. In reality, the property
that I have just enunciated is not a property of the straight line
alone; it is a property of the straight line and of distance. For it to
serve as an absolute criterion, we must be able to show, not only
that it does not belong to any other line than the straight line but also
that it does not belong to any other magnitude than distance. Now,
that is not true, and if we are not convinced by these considerations,
I challenge any one to give me a concrete experiment which can be interpreted in the Euclidean system, and which cannot be interpreted in
the system of Lobatschewsky. As I am well aware that this challenge
will never be accepted, I may conclude that no experiment will ever be
in contradiction with Euclid's postulate; but, on the other hand, no
experiment will ever be in contradiction with Lobatschewsky's postulate.

REICHENBACH

THE NATURE OF GEOMETRY

H. Reichenbach (1891-1953) was one of the most important logical positivists. His main works include The Philosophy of Space and Time, The Theory of Probability, Philosophic Foundations of Quantum Mechanics, Experience and Prediction, *and* The Rise of Scientific Philosophy, *from which the present selection is taken.* *

Ever since the death of Kant in 1804 science has gone through a development, gradual at first and rapidly increasing in tempo, in which it abandoned all absolute truths and preconceived ideas. The principles which Kant had considered to be indispensable to science and nonanalytic in their nature have been recognized as holding only to a limited degree. Important laws of classical physics were found to apply only to phenomena occurring in our ordinary environment. For astronomical and for submicroscopic dimensions they had to be replaced by laws of the new physics, and this fact alone makes it obvious that they were empirical laws and not laws forced on us by reason itself. Let me illustrate this *disintegration of the synthetic a priori* by tracing the development of geometry.

The historical origin of geometry, which goes back to the Egyptians, supplies one of the many instances in which intellectual discoveries have grown from material needs. The annual floods of the Nile which fertilized the soil of Egypt brought trouble to landowners: the borderlines of their estates were destroyed every year and had to be reestablished by means of geometrical measurements. The geographical

---

*Chapter 8 (Berkeley: University of California Press, 1968); used by permission.

and social conditions of their country, therefore, compelled the
Egyptians to invent the art of surveying. Geometry thus arose as an
empirical science, whose laws were the results of observations. For
instance, the Egyptians knew from practical experience that if they
made a triangle the sides of which were respectively 3, 4, and 5 units
long it would be a right triangle. The deductive proof for this result
was provided much later by Pythagoras, whose famous theorem explai
the Egyptian findings by the fact that the sum of the squares of 3 and
4 is equal to the square of 5.

Pythagoras' theorem illustrates the contribution which the Greek
made to geometry: the discovery that geometry can be built up as a
deductive system, in which every theorem is strictly derivable from the
set of axioms (see p. 96). The construction of geometry in the form of
an axiomatic system is forever connected with the name of Euclid. His
logically ordered presentation of geometry has remained the program
of every course in geometry and was used until recently as a text in
our schools.

The axioms of Euclid's system appeared so natural and obvious
that their truth seemed unquestionable. In this respect, Euclid's system confirmed earlier conceptions, developed before the principles of
geometry acquired the form of an ordered system. Plato, who lived in t
generation before Euclid, was led by the apparent self-evidence of
geometrical principles to his theory of ideas; and it was explained in
Chapter 2 that the axioms of geometry were regarded by him as revealed to us through an act of vision, which showed geometrical relations as properties of ideal objects. The long line of development
beginning with Plato, which did not essentially change this conception
germinated in the more precise though less poetical theory of Kant,
according to which the axioms were synthetic a priori. Mathematicians
more or less shared these views, but they were not so much interested
in the philosophical discussion of the axioms as in the analysis of the
mathematical relations holding between them. They tried to reduce
the axioms to a minimum by showing some of them to be derivable
from the others.

There was in particular one axiom, the axiom of parallels, which
they disliked and attempted to eliminate. The axiom states that throug
a given point one and only one parallel can be drawn with respect to
a given line; that is, there is one and only one line that does not ulti-

mately intersect with a given line and yet lies in the same plane. We do not know why the mathematicians disliked this axiom, but we know of many attempts, dating back to antiquity, that were made with the intention of transofrming this axiom into a theorem, that is, of deriving it from the other axioms. Mathematicians repeatedly believed that they had found a way of deriving the proposition about parallels from the other axioms. Invariably, however, these proofs have later been demonstrated to be fallacious. The mathematicians had unknowingly introduced some assumption which was not included in the other axioms but was of equal efficacy as the axiom of the parallels. The result of this development was, then, that there are equivalents of this axiom. But the mathematician had no more reason to accept these equivalents than to accept Euclid's axiom. For instance, an equivalent of the axiom of the parallels is the principle that the sum of the angles of a triangle is equal to two right angles. Euclid had derived this principle from his axiom, but it was shown that conversely the principle of the parallels is derivable when the principle of the angular sum is assumed as an axiom. What is an axiom in one system, thus becomes a theorem in another system, and vice versa.

The problem of parallels had occupied mathematicians for more than two thousand years before it found its solution. About twenty years after the death of Kant, a young Hungarian mathematician, John Bolyai (1802-1860), discovered that the axiom of parallels is not a necessary constituent of a geometry. He constructed a geometry in which the axiom of parallels was abandoned and replaced by the novel assumption that there exists more than one parallel to a given line through a given point. The same discovery was made about the same time by the Russian mathematician N.I. Lobachevski (1793-1856) and by the German mathematician K.F. Gauss (1777-1855). The geometries so constructed were called *non-Euclidean geometries*. A more general form of a non-Euclidean geometry, which includes systems in which there exist no parallel lines at all, was later developed by the German mathematician B. Riemann (1826-1866).

A non-Euclidean geometry contradicts Euclidean geometry—for instance, in a non-Euclidean triangle the sum of the angles is different from 180 degrees. Still, each non-Euclidean geometry is free from internal contradictions; it is a consistent system in the same sense that

Euclid's geometry is consistent. A plurality of geometries thus replaces
the unique system of Euclid. It is true that the Euclidean geometry is
distinguished from all others by the fact that it is easily accesible to
a visual presentation, whereas it seems impossible to visualize a geometry
in which there is more than one parallel to a given line through a given
point. But the mathematicians were not very much concerned about
questions of visualization and regarded various geometrical systems
as being of equal mathematical validity. In keeping with this somewhat
detached attitude of the mathematician, I shall postpone the discussion
of visualization until I have discussed some other problems.

The existence of a plurality of geometries demanded a new approach to the problem of the geometry of the physical world. As long
as there was only one geometry, the Euclidean geometry, there was no
question of the geometry of physical space. In the absence of an alternative, Euclid's geometry was naturally assumed to apply to physical
reality. It was Kant's merit to emphasize more than others that the
coincidence of mathematical and physical geometry calls for an explanation, and his theory of the synthetic a priori must be regarded as
the great attempt of a philosopher to account for this coincidence.
With the discovery of a plurality of geometries the situation changed
completely. If the mathematician was offered a choice between geometries, there arose the question which of them was the geometry of
the physical world. It was obvious that reason could not answer this
question, that its answer was left to empirical observation.

The first to draw this conclusion was Gauss. After his discovery
of non–Euclidean geometry he attempted to carry through an empirical test by means of which the geometry of the physical world was to
be ascertained. For this purpose, Gauss measured the angles of a
triangle the corners of which were marked by three mountain tops. The
result of his measurements was carefully worded: it said that within the
errors of observation the Euclidean principle was true, or in other word
that if there was a deviation of the angular sum from 180 degrees, the
inevitable errors of the observation made it impossible to prove its
existence. If the world was non-Euclidean, it was controlled by a non-
Euclidean geometry so slightly different from the Euclidean that dis-
crimination between the two was impossible.

But Gauss's measurement requires some discussion. The problem
of the geometry of physical space is more complicated than Gauss

assumed and cannot be answered in so simple a way.

Assume for a moment that Gauss' result had been positive and that the angular sum of the triangle he measured had been different from 180 degrees. Would it follow that the geometry of the world is non-Euclidean?

There is a way to evade this consequence. Measuring angles between two distant objects is done by sighting the objects through lenses attached to a sextant or a similar instrument. Thus the light rays traveling from the objects to the sight device are used as defining the sides of the triangle. How do we know that the light rays move along straight lines? It would be possible to maintain that they do not, that their path is curved, and that Gauss' measurement did not refer to a triangle whose sides were straight lines. On this assumption the measurement was not conclusive.

Is there a way to test the new assumption? A straight line is the shortest distance between two points. If the path of the light ray is curved, it must be possible to connect the starting point with the end point by another line, which is shorter than the path of the light ray. Such a measurement could be made, in principle at least, with the help of measuring rods. The rods would have to be carried along the path of the light ray and then along several other lines of connection. If there is a shorter line of connection, it would thus be found by repeated trials.

Suppose that the test was carried through and it was negative, that is, we found the path of the light ray to be the shortest connection between the two points. Would this result, in combination with the previous measurement of the angular sum, prove the geometry to be Euclidean?

It is easily seen that the situation is as inconclusive as before. We questioned the behavior of light rays and checked it through measurements with solid rods. We now can question the behavior of the solid rods. The measurement of a distance is reliable only if the rod does not change its length while it is transported. We might assume that the rod transported along the path of the light ray was expanded by some unknown force; then the number of rods that can be deposited along the path is made smaller, and the numerical value found for the distance would be too small. We thus would believe the path of the light ray to be shorter than other paths, whereas in reality it is longer.

Testing whether a line is the shortest distance thus depends on the behavior of measuring rods. How can we test whether a solid rod is really solid, that is does not expand or contract?

We transport a solid rod from one place to a distant point. Is it still as long as before? In order to test its length we would have to employ a second rod. Assume that at the first place the two rods have equal length when one is put on top of the other; then one is transported to a different place. Do the two rods still have equal length? We cannot answer this question. In order to compare the rods, we should have either to transport the one rod back to the first place, or the other rod to the second place, since a comparison of length is possible only when one rod is on top of the other. In such a way we would find that they have equal length, too, when they are both at the second place. But there is no way of knowing whether two rods are equal when they are in different places.

The objection might be raised that there are other means of comparison. For instance, if a rod changes its length on transportation, we should discover the change if we compared the rod with the length of our arms. To eliminate this objection let us assume that the forces contracting or expanding transported bodies are universal, that is, that all physical objects, including human bodies, change their length in the same way. It is obvious that then no change would be observable.

The problem under consideration is the problem of congruence. It must be realized that there is no means of testing congruence. Suppose that during the night all physical objects, including our own bodies, became ten times as large. On awakening this morning we should be in no condition to test this assumption. In fact, we shall never be able to find it out. The consequences of such change are, in accordance with the conditions laid down, unobservable, and hence we can collect no evidence either for or against it. Perhaps we all are ten times as tall today as we were yesterday.

There is only one way to escape such ambiguities: to regard the question of congruence not as a matter of observation, but of definition. We must not say "the two rods located at different places *are* equal", but we must say that we *call* these two rods equal. The transportation of solid rods defines congruence. This interpretation eliminates the unreasonable problems mentioned. It no longer makes sense to ask whether today we are ten times as tall as we were yesterday;

we call our height of today equal to that of yesterday, and it has no meaning to ask whether it really is the same height. Definitions of this kind are called *coördinative definitions.* They coördinate a physical object, a solid rod, to the concept "equal length" and thus specify its denotation; this peculiarity explains the name.

Statements about the geometry of the physical world, therefore, have a meaning only after a coördinative definition of congruence is set up. If we change the coördinative definition of congruence, a different geometry will result. This fact is called the *relativity of geometry.* To illustrate the meaning of this result, assume again that Gauss' measurement had proved a deviation of the angular sum from 180 degrees and that measurements with solid rods had confirmed light rays to be the shortest distance: still there would be nothing to prevent us from regarding the geometry of our space as Euclidean. We then would say that the light rays are curved and the rods expanded; and we could figure out the amount of these distortions in such a way that the "corrected" congruence leads to a Euclidean geometry. The distortions may be regarded as the effect of forces which vary from place to place, but are alike for all bodies and light rays and thus are *universal forces.* The assumption of such forces means merely a change in the coördinative definition of congruence. This consideration shows that there is not just one geometrical description of the physical world, but that there exists a class of *equivalent descriptions;* each of these descriptions is true, and apparent differences between them concern, not their content, but only the languages in which they are formulated.

On first sight this result looks like a confirmation of Kant's theory of space. If every geometry can be applied to the physical world, it seems as though geometry does not express a property of the physical world and is merely a subjective addition by the human observer, who in this way establishes an order among the objects of his perception. Neo-Kantians have used this argument in defense of their philosophy; and it was used in a philosophical conception called *conventionalism,* introduced by the French mathematician Henri Poincaré, according to whom geometry is a matter of convention and there is no meaning in a statement which purports to describe the geometry of the physical world.

Closer investigation shows the argument to be untenable. Although every geometrical system can be used to describe the structure of the physical world, the geometrical system taken alone does not describe the structure completely. The description will be complete only if it includes a statement about the behavior of solid bodies and light rays. When we call two descriptions equivalent, or equally true, we refer to complete descriptions, in this sense. Among the equivalent descriptions there will be one, and only one, in which solid bodies and light rays are not called "deformed" through universal forces. For this description I shall employ the name *normal system*. The question can now be asked which geometry leads to the normal system; and this geometry may be called the *natural geometry*. Obviously, the question as to the natural geometry, that is, the geometry for which solid bodies and light rays are not deformed, can be answered only through empirical investigation. In this sense the question of the geometry of physical space is an empirical question.

The empirical meaning of geometry can be illustrated by reference to other relative concepts. If a New Yorker says "Fifth Avenue is to the left of Fourth Avenue", this statement is neither true nor false unless he specifies the direction from which he looks at these streets. Only the complete statement "Fifth Avenue is to the left of Fourth Avenue seen from the South" is verifiable; and it is equivalent to the statement "Fifth Avenue is to the right of Fourth Avenue seen from the North". Relative concepts like "to the left of" or "to the right of" thus can very well be used in the formulation of empirical knowledge but care must be taken that the formulation includes the point of reference. In the same sense, geometry is a relative concept. We can speak about the geometry of the physical world only after a coördinative definition of congruence has been given. But on that condition an empirical statement about the geometry of the physical world can be made. When we speak about the physical geometry, it is therefore understood that some coördinative definition of congruence has been laid down.

Poincaré was right if he wanted to say that the choice of one from the class of equivalent descriptions is a matter of convention. But he was mistaken if he believed that the determination of natural geometry, in the sense defined, is a matter of convention. This geometry can only be ascertained empirically. It seems Poincaré believed erroneously that the "solid" rod and thus congruence can be defined only by the requirement that the resulting geometry must be Euclidean. Thus he argued that if measurements on triangles should lead to an angular sum different from 180 degrees, the physicist *must* introduce corrections for the paths of light rays and the lengths of solid rods because otherwise he could not say what he meant by equal length. But Poincaré overlooked the fact that such a requirement might compel the physicist to assume universal forces,* and that vice versa the definition of congruence can be given by the requirement that universal forces are to be excluded. By the use of this definition of congruence an empirical statement about geometry can be made.

I should like to explain my criticism of Poincaré more fully, because recently Professor Einstein has undertaken a witty defense of conventionalism by depicting an imaginary conversation between Poincaré and me.† Since I believe that there can be no differences of opinion between mathematical philosophers if only opinions are clearly stated, I wish to state my conception in such a way that it might convince, if not Poincaré, yet Professor Einstein, for whose scientific work I certainly have as much admiration as he has so charmingly expressed for the work of Poincaré.

Assume that empirical observations are compatible with the following two descriptions:

CLASS I

(a) The geometry is Euclidean, but there are universal forces distorting light rays and measuring rods.

(b) The geometry is non-Euclidean, and there are no universal forces.

Poincaré is right when he argues that each of these descriptions can be assumed as true, and that it would be erroneous to discriminate between them. They are merely different languages describing the same state of affairs.

Now assume that in a different world, or in a different part of our world, empirical observations were made which are compatible

---

*The rule always to use Euclidean geometry for the ordering of geometrical observations can lead to further complications, namely, to certain violations of the principle of causality. This will be the case if the space of physics is topologically different from Euclid's space, for instance, if it is finite. In such cases, at least one of Kant's a priori principles, either Euclidean geometry or causality, has to be abandoned. See the author's Philosophie der Raum-Zeit-Lehre (Berlin, 1928), p. 82.

†In P.A. Schlipp, Albert Einstein, Philosopher-Scientist, Evanston, 1949, pp. 677-679.

with the following two descriptions:

CLASS II

(a) The geometry is Euclidean, and there are no universal forces.

(b) The geometry is non-Euclidean, but there are universal forces distorting light rays and measuring rods.

Once more Poincaré is right when he argues that these two descriptions are both true; they are equivalent descriptions.

But Poincaré would be mistaken if he were to argue that the two worlds I and II were the same. They are objectively different. Although for each world there is a class of equivalent descriptions, the different *classes* are not of equal truth value. Only one class can be true for a given kind of world; which class it is, only empirical observation can tell. Conventionalism sees only the equivalence of the descriptions within one class, but stops short of recognizing the differences between the classes. The theory of equivalent descriptions, however, enables us to describe the world objectively by assigning empirical truth to only one class of descriptions, although within each class all descriptions are of equal truth value.

Instead of using classes of descriptions, it is convenient to single out, in each class, one description as the *normal system* and use it as a representative of the whole class. In this sense, we can select the description for which universal forces vanish as the normal system, calling it *natural geometry*. Incidentally, we cannot even prove that there must be a normal system; that in our world there is one, and only one, must be regarded as an empirical fact. (For instance, it might happen that the geometry of light rays differs from that of solid bodies.

The theory of equivalent descriptions thus does not rule out an empirical meaning of geometry; it merely demands that we state the geometrical structure of the physical world by the addition of certain qualifications, namely, in the form of a statement about the natural geometry. In this sense Gauss' experiment presents important empirical evidence. The natural geometry of the space of our environment, within the exactness accessible to us, is Euclidean; or in other words, the solid bodies and light rays of our environment behave according to the laws of Euclid. If Gauss' experiment had led to a different result, if it had revealed a measurable deviation from Euclidean relations, the natural geometry of our terrestrial environment would be different. In order to carry through a Euclidean geometry we then would have had to resort to the assumption of universal forces that distort light rays and transported bodies in a peculiar way. That the natural geometry of the world of our environment is Euclidean must be regarded as a fortunate empirical fact.

These formulations allow us to state the additions which Einstein made with respect to the problem of space. From his general theory of relativity he derived the conclusion that in astronomic dimensions the natural geometry of space is non-Euclidean. This result does not contradict Gauss' measurement according to which the geometry of terrestrial dimensions is Euclidean, because it is a general property of a non-Euclidean geometry that for small areas it is practically identical with the Euclidean geometry. Terrestrial dimensions are small as compared with astronomic dimensions. We are unable to observe the deviations from Euclidean geometry through terrestrial observations, because within these dimensions the deviations are too small. Gauss' measurement would have to be made with an exactness many thousands of times greater, in order to prove a deviation of the angular sum from 180 degrees. But such exactness is far beyond our reach and will presumably forever remain so. Only for larger triangles would the non-Euclidean character become measurable, since the angular deviation from 180 degrees grows with the size of the triangle. If we could measure the angles of a triangle whose corners were represented by three fixed stars, or better, by three galaxies, we would actually observe that the angular sum is more than 180 degrees. We shall have to wait for the establishment of cosmic travel before such a direct test can be made, since we would have to visit each of the three stars separately in order to be able to measure the three angles. So we have to be satisfied by the use of indirect methods of inference, which even in the present status of our knowledge indicate that stellar geometry is non-Euclidean.

There is a further addition made by Einstein. According to his conception the cause of the deviation from Euclidean geometry is to be found in the gravitational forces originating from the masses of the stars. In the neighborhood of a star the deviations are stronger than in interstellar space. Einstein has thus established a relation between geometry and gravitation. This amazing discovery, which was confirmed by measurements made during an eclipse of the sun and which had never before been anticipated, demonstrates anew the empirical character of physical space.

Space is not a form of order by means of which the human observer constructs his world—it is a system formulating the relations of order holding between transported solid bodies and light rays and thus expressing a very general feature of the physical world, which constitutes the basis for all other physical measurements. Space is not subjective, but real—that is the outcome of the development of modern mathematics and physics. Strangely enough, this long historical line leads ultimately back to the position held at its beginning: geometry began as an empirical science with the Egyptians, was made a deductive science by the Greeks, and finally was turned back into an empirical science after logical analysis of the highest perfection had uncovered a plurality of geometries, one and only one of which is the geometry of the physical world.

This consideration shows that we have to distinguish between mathematical and physical geometry. Mathematically speaking, there exist many geometrical systems. Each of them is logically consistent and that is all a mathematician can ask. He is interested not in the truth of the axioms, but in the implications between axioms and theorems: "if the axioms are true, then the theorem is true"—of this form are the geometrical statements made by the mathematician. But these implications are analytic; they are validated by deductive logic. The geometry of the mathematician is therefore of an analytic nature. Only when the implications are broken up, and axioms and theorems are asserted separately, does geometry lead to synthetic statements. The axioms then require an interpretation through coördinative definitions and thus become statements about physical objects; and geometry is thus made a system which is descriptive of the physical world. In that meaning, however, it is not a priori, but of an empirical nature. There is no synthetic a priori science of geoemtry: either geometry is a pri and then it is mathematical geometry and analytic—or geometry is synthetic, and then it is physical geometry and empirical. The evolution of geometry culminates in the disintegration of the synthetic a priori.

One question remains to be answered, the question of visualizatio: How can we ever visualize non-Euclidean relations in the way we can see the Euclidean relations? It may be true that by means of mathematical formulas we are able to deal with non-Euclidean geometries;

but will they ever be as presentative as the Euclidean geometry, that is, will we be able to see their rules in our imagination in the way we see the Euclidean rules?

The foregoing analysis enables us to answer this question satisfactorily. Euclidean geometry is the geometry of our physical environment; no wonder that our visual conceptions have become adjusted to this environment and thus follow Euclidean rules. Should we ever live in an environment whose geometrical structure is noticeably different from Euclidean geometry, we would get adjusted to the new environment and learn to see non-Euclidean triangles and laws in the same way that we now see Euclidean structures. We would find it natural that the angles in a triangle add up to more than 180 degrees and would learn to estimate distances in terms of the congruence defined by the solid bodies of that world. To imagine geometrical relations visually means to imagine the experiences which we would have if we lived in a world where those relations hold. It was the physicist Helmholtz who gave this explanation of visualization. The philosopher had committed the mistake of regarding as a vision of ideas, or as laws of reason, what is actually the product of habit. It took more than two thousand years to uncover this fact; without the work of the mathematician and all its technicalities we would never have been able to break away from established habits and free our minds from alleged laws of reason.

The historical development of the problem of geometry is a striking illustration of the philosophical potentialities contained in the development of science. The philosopher who claimed to have uncovered the laws of reason rendered a bad service to the theory of knowledge: what he regarded as laws of reason was actually a conditioning of human imagination by the physical structure of the environment in which human beings live. The power of reason must be sought not in rules that reason dictates to our imagination, but in the ability to free ourselves from any kind of rules to which we have been conditioned through experience and tradition. It would never have been possible to overcome the compulsion of established habits by philosophical reflection alone. The versatility of the human mind could not become manifest before the scientist had shown ways of handling structures different from those for which an age-old tradition had trained our minds. On the path to philosophical insight the scientist is the trail blazer.

The philosophical aspect of geometry has at all times reflected itself in the basic trend of philosophy, and thus philosophy has been strongly influenced in its historical development by that of geometry. Philosophic rationalism, from Plato to Kant, had insisted that all knowledge should be constructed after the pattern of geometry. The rationalist philosopher had built up his argument on an interpretation of geometry which, for more than two thousand years, had remained unquestioned: on the conception that geometry is both a product of reason and descriptive of the physical world. Empiricist philosophers had fought in vain against this argument; the rationalist had the mathematician on his side, and the battle against his logic appeared hopeless. With the discovery of non-Euclidean geometries the situation was reversed. The mathematician discovered that what he could prove was merely the system of mathematical implications, of *if-then* relations leading from the axioms of geometry to its theorems. He no longer felt entitled to assert the axioms as true, and he left this assertion to the physicist. Mathematical geometry was thus reduced to analytic truth, and the synthetic part of geometry was surrendered to empirical science. The rationalist philosopher had lost his most powerful ally, and the path was free for empiricism.

Had these mathematical developments begun some two thousand years earlier, the history of philosophy would present a different picture. In fact, one of Euclid's disciples might very well have been a Bolyai and might have discovered the non-Euclidean geometry; the elements of this geometry can be developed with rather simple means of the kind available in Euclid's era. After all, the heliocentric system was discovered in that time, and Greek-Roman civilization had developed forms of abstract thought that rank with those of modern times. Such a mathematical development would have greatly changed the systems of the philosophers. Plato's doctrine of ideas would have been abandoned as lacking its basis in geometrical knowledge. The skeptics would have had no inducement to be more skeptical toward empirical knowledge than toward geometry and might have found the courage to teach a positive empiricism. The Middle Ages would have found no consistent rationalism which could be incorporated into theology. Spinoza would not have written his *Ethics Presented after the Geometrical Method,* and Kant would not have written his *Critique of Pure Reason.*

Or am I too optimistic? Can error be weeded out by teaching the truth? The psychological motives which led to philosophic rationalism are so strong that one might well assume they would have found other forms of expression. They might have pounced upon other productions of the mathematician and turned them into alleged evidence for a rationalist interpretation of the world. In fact, since Bolyai's discovery, more than a hundred years have passed and rationalism has not died out. Truth is not a sufficient weapon to outlaw error— or rather, the intellectual recognition of truth does not always endow the human mind with the strength to resist the deep-rooted emotional appeal of the search for certainty.

But truth is a powerful weapon, and it has at all times collected followers among the best. There is good evidence that the circle of its followers is growing larger and larger. And perhaps that is all that can be hoped for.

SUGGESTIONS FOR FURTHER READING

This bibliography is intended to serve as an introduction to, rather than a comprehensive survey of, the literature on the problems of scientific methodology. For further bibliographical information, consult the bibliographies of the books mentioned below.

Theories of Scientific Method by R. Blake, C.J. Ducasse, and E. Madden (University of Washington Press, 1960) is the best introduction to the history of theories of scientific methodology. It lacks, however, a discussion of ancient and medieval theories and of work done in this area in the present century.

The best general surveys of recent ideas on scientific methodology are found in the following texts (listed according to the level of difficulty of the material presented): C.G. Hempel, *Philosophy of Natural Science* (Prentice-Hall, 1966); E. Nagel, *The Structure of Science* (Harcourt, Brace and World, 1961); I. Scheffler, *The Anatomy of Inquiry* (Alfred A. Knopf, 1963); and A. Pap, *An Introduction to the Philosophy of Science* (Free Press, 1962). In connection with these texts, it would be useful to consult some of the articles collected in A. Danto and S. Morgenbesser's *Philosophy of Science* (Meridian Books,) 1960) and E. Madden's *The Structure of Scientific Thought* (Houghton, Mifflin & Co., 1960).

The problem of the status of scientific theories has been widely discussed in recent years. Reductionism and instrumentalism are critically evaluated in Chapters 1–4 of R.B. Braithwaite's *Scientific Explanation* (Harper Torchbooks, 1960), Chapter 8 of C.G. Hempel's *Aspects of Scientific Explanation* (Free Press, 1965), and Chapter 4 of S. Toulmin's *The Philosophy of Science: An Introduction* (Harper Torchbooks, 1960).

In the last few years, there has been a growing tendency to defend some version of realism. The following works contain (from various points of view) a favorable discussion of realism: Chapter 4 of R. Harre's *An Introduction to the Logic of the Sciences* (Macmillan,

1960), Chapter 1 of M.B. Hesse's *Forces and Fields* (Nelson and Sons, 1961), W. Sellar's "Theoretical Explanation" in W.L. Reese, *Philosophy of Science: The Delaware Seminar,* Vol. 2 (John Wiley, 1963), and H. Putnam's "What Theories are Not" in E. Nagel, P. Suppes, and A. Tarski, *Logic, Methodology, and Philosophy of Science* (Stanford University Press, 1962).

A very introductory discussion of the problem of the discovery and confirmation of scientific hypotheses is found in B. Skyrm's *Choice and Chance* (Dickenson Publishing Co., 1966); many of the important recent articles on this topic are collected in M.H. Foster and M.L. Martin's *Probability, Confirmation, and Simplicity* (Odyssey Press, 1966). The following are two of the most important attempts to formalize, in quite different ways, the classical conception of confirmation Chapter 1 of C.G. Hempel, *Aspects of Scientific Explanation* (Free Press, 1965) and R. Carnap, *Logical Foundations of Probability* (University of Chicago Press, 1950). Popper's alternative to the classical conception is elaborated in his book *The Logic of Scientific Discovery* (Science Editions, 1961). T. Kuhn's *The Structure of Scientific Revolutions* (University of Chicago Press, 1962) offers various historical and philosophical considerations that tend to indicate that the classical conception is far too simple-minded. Finally, N.R. Hanson's *Patterns of Discovery* (Cambridge University Press, 1961) contains a detailed treatment of his views about the discovery of scientific hypotheses, while his article "Is There a Logic of Discovery" in H. Feigl and G. Maxwell, *Current Issues in the Philosophy of Science* (Holt, Rinehart and Winston, 1961) argues for the necessity of such an enterprise.

A general introduction to the philosophy of mathematics is offered in S.F. Barker's *Philosophy of Mathematics* (Prentice-Hall, 1964), and many of the major articles in this area are collected in P. Benacerraf and H. Putnam's *Philosophy of Mathematics* (Prentice-Hall, 1964). Neither of these works deals extensively with problems about the measurement process. These problems are discussed in B. Ellis, *Basic Concepts of Measurement* (Cambridge University Press, 1966) and in the various articles in C.W. Churchman and P. Ratoosh, *Measurement: Definitions and Theories* (John Wiley, 1959). The various views on the nature of geometrical truths are discussed, from an empiricist point of view, in Part I of H. Reichenbach's *The Philos*